BRITISH WEATHER IN MAPS

BRITISH WEATHER IN MAPS

BY

JAMES A. TAYLOR, M.A.
F. R. Met. Soc.

AND

R. A. YATES, M.Sc.
LECTURERS IN GEOGRAPHY,
UNIVERSITY COLLEGE OF WALES, ABERYSTWYTH

LONDON
MACMILLAN & CO LTD
NEW YORK · ST MARTIN'S PRESS
1958

MACMILLAN AND COMPANY LIMITED
London Bombay Calcutta Madras Melbourne

THE MACMILLAN COMPANY OF CANADA LIMITED
Toronto

ST MARTIN'S PRESS INC
New York

PRINTED IN GREAT BRITAIN

PREFACE

This book presents a method of geographical analysis and interpretation of the " primary documents " of British weather, viz. the British Daily Weather Reports. These provide an historical record of complex and baffling sequences of weather types and phases which defy rigid classification and systematic interpretation. Within the chaos of these weather variations, however, it has become possible to recognise certain recurring patterns, which present bases for classifications. Inevitably, however, such classifications involve an arbitrary element since they try to express the intricate complexities of the atmosphere in terms of simple categories. The major problem is often to reconcile anomalies with the basic patterns of the classifications. Even so, examples to illustrate each standard category of a given classification may be sought out and identified, for they are the keys by which the complexities can be simplified, the norms from which the deviations may be assessed, the lessons by which the subject of the weather may be learned.

The succession of theories which have evolved to explain and classify the weather are described herein as a background to an appreciation of the present format and function of the British Daily Weather Report. Recent issues of the Report have been selected for times and dates when each standard weather type was well developed over the British Isles. Each of these " text book " examples is then analysed and interpreted. The method of analysis proceeds firstly, by the separate plotting of each weather element from the Report concerned and secondly, by examining the distribution of each element as revealed by its pattern of *isopleths*, which is the general term for lines joining points of equal value in a given distribution field, for example, *isotherms* for *temperature*. Areas of relative *continuity*, indicated by widely spaced, irregular isopleths, and zones of *discontinuity*, indicated by closely bunched, regular isopleths, are noted and labelled. Thirdly, a study of the various isopleth distributions in relation to each other enables a composite picture to be built up, thus revealing the type of weather situation, the nature of any discontinuities present and their relationship to the adjacent areas of continuity. A collection of other examples relating to each standard weather type has been included at the end of the book in Appendix 1; these may be analysed, and the weather situations identified, by the same method.

This work does not claim to be a text book of meteorology. It is intended primarily for geographers and is in fact based on part of the First Year Course in Practical Climatology which the authors have conducted in recent years at the University College of Wales, Aberystwyth. It is also anticipated that much of the material herein would be intelligible to the VIth Form Geography student. The work is amenable to use as a class book with a variety of test exercises available from which the teacher may select the particular example required (Appendix 1).

Throughout the work the weather codes used are those given in the publication "Instructions for the Preparation of Weather Maps" M.O. 515. 1954, H.M.S.O. Some of the symbols more frequently used are given in Appendix 2, but the "code book", M.O. 515, is an essential reference for the fullest interpretation of the examples analysed here.

We should like to acknowledge the kind co-operation of the Meteorological Office in the preparation of this work, and in granting permission to use many maps and diagrams included herein. Permission to publish this material was kindly granted by the Controller of Her Majesty's Stationery Office. Acknowledgement to these Authorities is made beneath the Figures concerned.

We wish to record our appreciation to our colleagues for advice and encouragement and particularly to Professor E. G. Bowen, M.A., F.S.A. for placing at our disposal the Departmental equipment and resources required. All the illustrations in this work were compiled by the authors and were reproduced by Mr. Gerald Roberts, Departmental Cartographer.

We are specially indebted to Dr. R. C. Sutcliffe, the Director of Research at the Meteorological Office, for his advice and encouragement, and to R. W. Gloyne Esq., and W. H. Hogg Esq.

who read through the manuscript at the typescript stage and offered valuable, constructive criticism.

Finally, our special thanks are due to our publishers, Messrs Macmillan & Co. Ltd. for their willing co-operation at all times.

JAMES A. TAYLOR
R. A. YATES

Department of Geography and Anthropology
University College of Wales, Aberystwyth
July 1957

CONTENTS

LIST OF ILLUSTRATIONS

CHAPTER 5

CHAPTER 6

Chapter 1

(A) GENERAL CONSIDERATIONS

The Position of the British Isles

The British Isles being situated in the Middle Latitudes (50°–60° N.) have an equable climate normally free from the extremes of temperature experienced in the Polar regions to the north and in the Tropical regions to the south. Unusually cold weather for the time of year in Britain is often due to the southward penetration of Polar air. Similarly, very warm weather for the time of year is often caused by the northward penetration of Tropical air.

In the North Atlantic there is a drift of warm water, initially the Gulf Stream which later becomes the North Atlantic or West Wind Drift, which moves generally east-north-east towards the seas around the British Isles. Thus Maritime air from the west persistently modifies British weather producing relatively high winter temperatures and relatively low summer temperatures, and often being responsible for cloud and rain. To the east of the British Isles lies the continent of Europe which is merely a projection from the vast landmass of Asia. This large land area is relatively cold in winter and relatively warm in summer. Continental air then comes from the east, tending to raise temperatures over Britain in summer and to lower them in winter ; it has therefore, an effect directly opposite to that of the Maritime air. Moreover, the Continental air, as it comes from the land, is associated with drier conditions though a certain amount of moisture may be acquired during the crossing of the North Sea or English Channel.

Thus, in the most simple and general terms, the British Isles are located in a region where Polar, Tropical, Maritime and Continental types of air may meet (Fig. 1), and the constantly changing relationships among them largely determine the character of the general weather situation over the British Isles at any particular time. The significance and interpretation of these relationships and the framework within which they develop require systematic explanation.

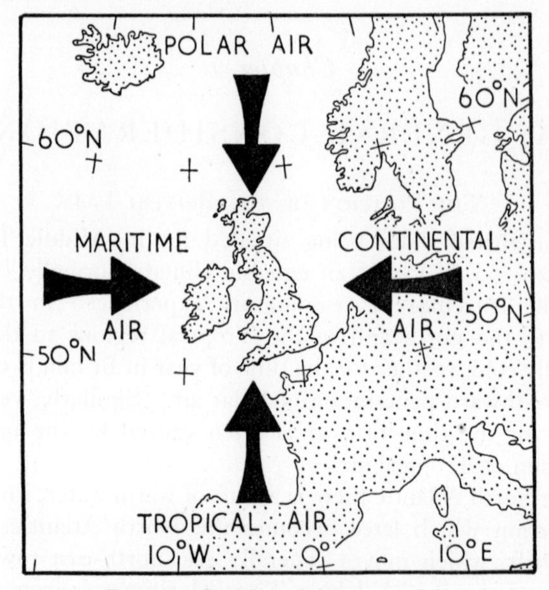

FIG. 1. — Position of the British Isles

Seasonal Pressure Distributions

The first essential to be appreciated is the seasonal distribution of the chief atmospheric pressure systems for it is the balance between the major " highs " and " lows " which strongly affects the pattern of British weather at different seasons. The systems involved are three in number, the " Icelandic " centre of low pressure, the " Azores " centre of high pressure and the " European " centre which is of low pressure in summer and of high pressure in winter.

In July (Fig. 2) the Azores " high " is intense and widespread and reaches a relatively northerly position not far from the Western Approaches. To the north, the Icelandic " low " is weak and restricted to the Greenland area. Much more powerful is the " low " over the continent of Europe which draws the main airflow eastwards from the Azores " high ". In January (Fig. 2) the Azores " high " is less prominent and lies further to the south. The Icelandic " low ", on the other hand, is now a dominating in-

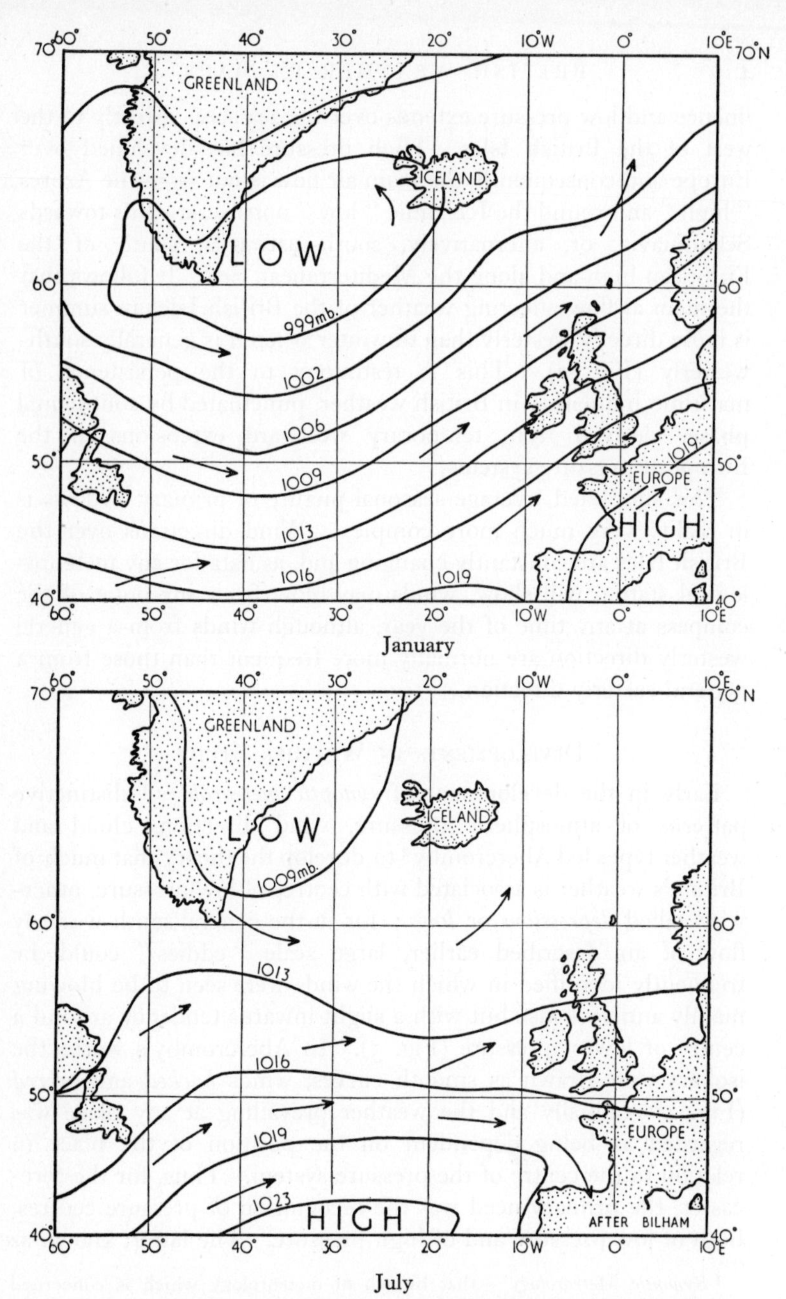

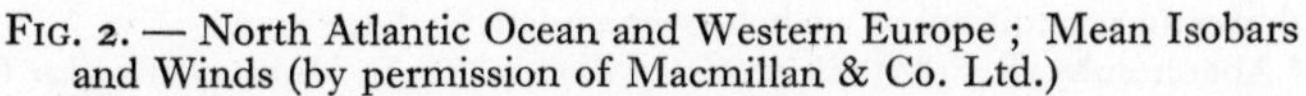

FIG. 2. — North Atlantic Ocean and Western Europe ; Mean Isobars and Winds (by permission of Macmillan & Co. Ltd.)

Note : The isobar interval on the maps above is not constant. This is explained by the fact that in the original maps pressure values were expressed in " inches of mercury ". These have been converted to millibars and are given *correct to the nearest whole millibar.*

fluence and low pressure extends over the sea areas directly to the west of the British Isles. High pressure has developed over Europe and consequently the main air flow is out from the Azores " high " and round the Icelandic " low " north-eastwards towards Scandinavia, or, alternatively, south-eastwards, south of the European high and along the Mediterranean Sea. It follows that the main airflow affecting weather of the British Isles in summer is more directly westerly than in winter when it is generally south-westerly (Fig. 2). This is testimony to the persistence of maritime influences in British weather, punctuated by continental phases derived from temporary westward extensions of the European pressure systems.

This simplified, average seasonal picture of primary airflows is in reality very much more complex. Wind directions over the British Isles are constantly changing and, as data for any meteorological station will show, winds may blow from any point of the compass at any time of the year, although winds from a general westerly direction are normally more frequent than those from a general easterly direction.

Developments in Weather Study

Early in the development of *synoptic meteorology* [1] distinctive patterns of atmospheric pressure, wind direction, cloud and weather types led Abercromby [2] to develop the theory that much of Britain's weather is associated with centres of low pressure, otherwise called *depressions* or *lows* ; for in the general south-westerly flow of air described earlier, large scale " eddies " could be frequently identified in which the winds were seen to be blowing mainly anticlockwise but with a slight inwards tendency around a centre of lowest pressure (Fig. 3). In Abercromby's works the isobars were drawn as smooth curves, winds *backed* and *veered* (Fig. 4) gradually and the weather prevailing at any place was regarded as being dependent on the position of the place in relation to the centre of the pressure system. Thus, for the forecaster, the primary need was the recognition of pressure centres, both of low pressure and of high pressure. The latter, known as

[1] *Synoptic Meteorology* — that branch of meteorology which is concerned with weather conditions as a whole over a relatively large area.

[2] Abercromby, R., 1883, *Principles of Forecasting by Means of Weather Charts.*

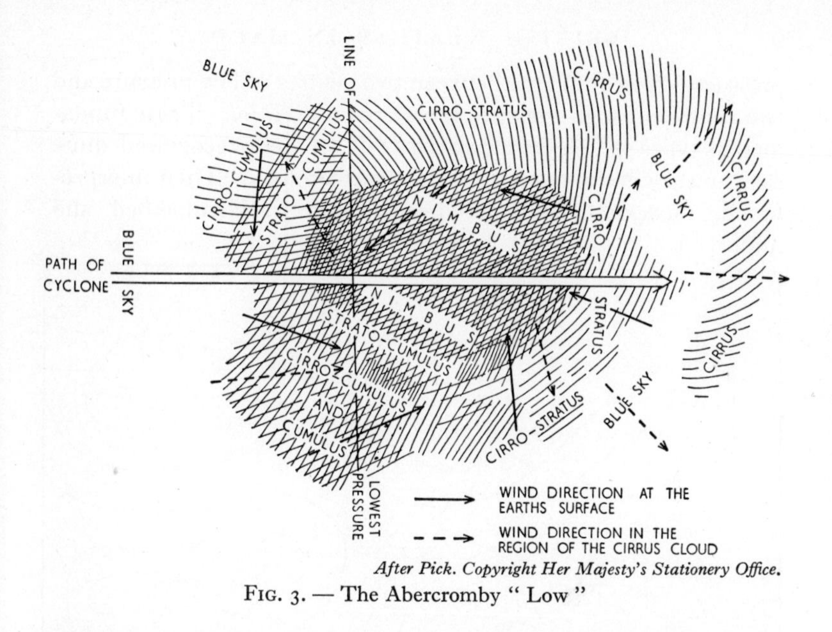

After Pick. Copyright Her Majesty's Stationery Office.

FIG. 3. — The Abercromby " Low "

anticyclones, are in many ways the complete antithesis of the former. They occupy large areas as a rule and have a clockwise, slightly outward circulation of winds which are generally light in strength except perhaps on the edges of the anticyclone. The weather associated with these high pressure areas is usually quiet, persistent and often fair and fine in summer but cloud and fog may typify the winter varieties. An extension from an anticyclone centre is referred to as a *wedge* or *ridge* of high pressure. Any extension from a depression centre is referred to as a *trough* of low

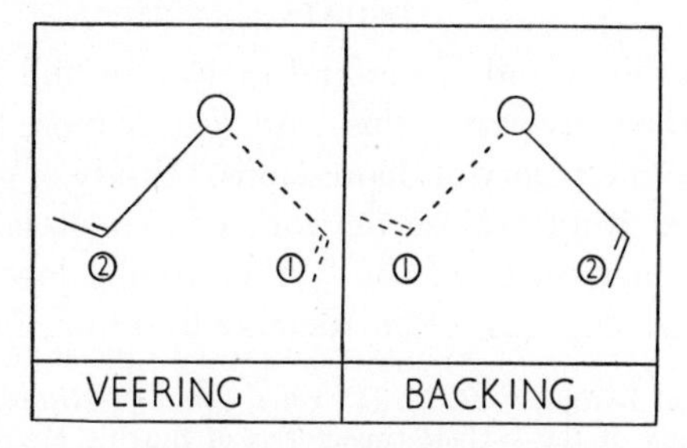

FIG. 4. — " Backing " and " Veering " of the Wind

Note : The change in wind direction from position 1 to position 2 when clockwise is termed *veering* and when anticlockwise, *backing*.

pressure. A neutral area between two centres of low pressure and two centres of high pressure is referred to as a *col*. These fundamental types of pressure pattern (Fig. 5) were recognised quite early in the development of modern meteorology. Their interpretation, however, has since been progressively modified and improved.

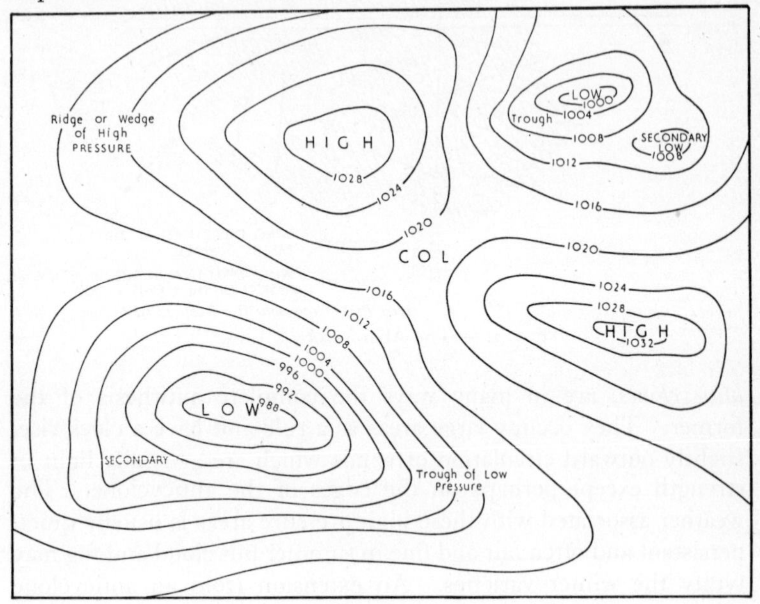

FIG. 5. — Types of Pressure Distribution

FRONTS

Research by Shaw and Lempfert[1] in Britain and by Bjerknes[2] in Norway in the early part of this century gave more satisfying and fuller details to the theory of depressions. Study of great amounts of data derived from a close network of meteorological stations revealed that the passage of the " Abercromby lows " was often accompanied by changes, often remarkedly rapid, in wind direc-

[1] Shaw, N., and Lempfert, R. G. K., 1906, *The Life History of Surface Air Currents*. A study of the surface trajectories of moving air. Meteorological Office M.O. 174.

[2] Bjerknes, J., and Solberg, H., 1922, *Life Cycle of Cyclones and the Polar Front Theory of Atmospheric Circulation*, Geofysiske Publikationer, Vol. 3, No. 1.

tion and in air temperature. Furthermore, most of the rapid changes or " discontinuities " could be clearly discerned along lines which stretched for considerable distances, 300 to 500 miles or more, and also, they could be traced progressively in time from one synoptic chart to the next. These lines of discontinuity, termed *fronts*, were recognised as boundary zones between air of different origins and characteristics; for example, relatively high temperatures indicated air of Tropical origin and relatively low temperatures air of Polar origin. Again, relatively high humidities indicated air originating over the sea and relatively low humidities air originating over the land. The depression was recognised as possessing *warm* and *cold sectors*, separated by *warm* and *cold fronts*. This pattern was identified as the *mature* stage of the development of the depression, the initial formation of which was associated with two adjacent currents of air of different temperature, flowing in opposite directions or in the same direction but at different speeds, and separated by a nearly straight boundary. This zone of transition, idealised as a simple linear boundary between air of Polar and Tropical origins was called the *Polar Front* along which the majority of depressions of temperate latitudes develop.

From the initial stage a wave develops in the Polar Front towards the cold side due to the interaction of the moving airflows of different densities. A tongue of warm air is projected over the colder air and at its tip an area of low pressure forms the centre of the new depression (Figs. 6*a* and 6*b*). This tongue of warm air constitutes the *warm sector*; the cold air on either side of the warm sector is referred to as the *cold sector*. The depression moves generally in an easterly direction across the British Isles and the amplitude of the wave increases in a horizontal north-south extent (Fig. 6*c*). The line along which there is contact between the forward edge of the warm sector and the cold air in advance of it is known as the *warm front*. The cold air flows round the warm sector and arrives as a cold north-westerly current behind the depression; the line along which this cold air contacts the rear edge of the warm sector is known as the *cold front*. Simultaneously, with further increase in the amplitude of the wave the warm tongue narrows laterally because the cold front normally moves faster than the warm front and eventually overtakes it. The warm sector undercut by the cold air thus becomes elevated gradually, a pro-

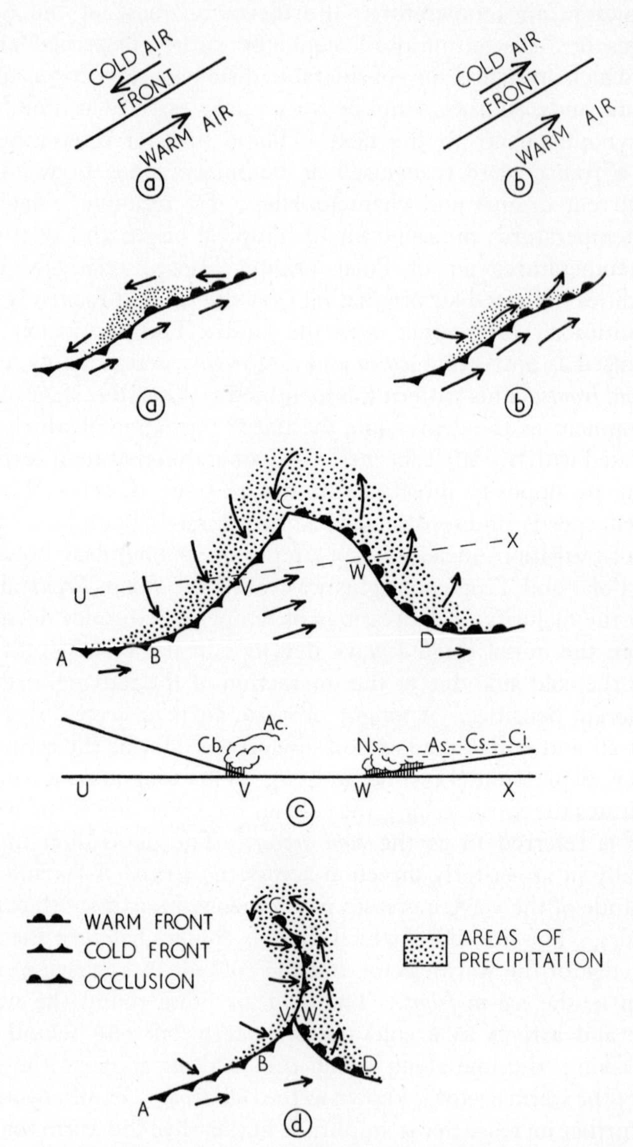

After " The Weather Map " 1941. Copyright Her Majesty's Stationery Office.

FIG. 6. — Formation of a Warm Sector Depression : Northern Hemisphere

cess which starts from the centre of the depression. When the warm sector is no longer in contact with the ground the depression is said to be *occluded* (Fig. 6*d*). Below the elevated warm sector a boundary line still exists at the surface for a time between the two cold air masses now in contact. This is the line of the *occluded front* or, more simply, of an *occlusion* (Fig. 6*d*). Eventually, the two air masses lose their identity by intermixture, and a vortex of cold air remains at the surface whilst the warm sector aloft is ultimately assimilated into the general circulation of the atmosphere. At this final stage there are no discontinuities of temperature at the ground.

From the foregoing it will be seen that temperature has become a basic criterion for the recognition of fronts ; other criteria include humidity, wind direction and force, weather characteristics, e.g. precipitation zones and cloud forms. They have tended to replace atmospheric pressure as the first consideration in weather analysis. Nevertheless, atmospheric pressure is still an essential aid in assessing, and forecasting from, synoptic situations.

Air Masses

More recently, increasing recognition has been made of the existence of extensive areas of the atmosphere which are so adequately uniform in air temperature and humidity as to constitute particular types of *air mass*. The concept of air masses was introduced into meteorological literature by Bergeron,[1] and the concepts of fronts and air masses seen in their proper perspective, can hardly be separated. Air which remains stationary for a long period over a large area of uniform geographical character, such as the Arctic ice-cap, the Atlantic Ocean, the Sahara Desert, gradually acquires properties of temperature and humidity typical of the area. Should the air now move away from the area where it originated, that is, the *source region*, it takes with it the properties acquired at the source. During transit changes almost invariably take place, especially if the direction of movement is northwards or southwards, the rate of movement slow and the route different in character from the source region. Many air masses reaching Britain have been modified considerably in transit, some to such an extent

[1] Bergeron, T., 1928, *Geophys. Publikasjoner*, Norske Videnskaps — Akad., Oslo, Vol. v, No. 6.

that they are difficult to recognise on arrival. The following list gives the major types of air mass which have been recognised as affecting Britain's weather:

(1) Polar-Maritime.
(2) Polar-Continental.
(3) Tropical-Maritime.
(4) Tropical-Continental.

Tables and diagrams (Figs. 28, 29 and 30) show the nature and general provenance to Britain of each type of air mass. Within this relatively complex air mass classification is discernable the simple pattern which was noted at the outset of four types of air converging on the British Isles, namely, Polar, Tropical, Maritime and Continental (Fig. 1), the Tropical-Maritime and the Polar-Maritime combinations being far more frequent than the Polar-Continental and the Tropical-Continental combinations (Fig. 31).

(B) SOME FUNDAMENTAL PROPERTIES OF THE ATMOSPHERE

Air masses by their very nature, are differentiated in terms of their vertical as well as their horizontal profiles of temperature and humidity and also by secondary characteristics such as cloudiness, visibility, etc. Modifications of air masses in general take place from the base upwards as the air moves from its source region. Consequently, accurate diagnosis is possible only by reference to conditions in the *Upper Air*.[1] It may be possible sometimes to recognise air masses by reference only to the surface data for temperature, humidity, and wind direction but such data are liable to be completely misleading. Indeed, modifications which occur during transit and the effects of the local weather factors in the lower atmosphere make it necessary to examine conditions in the upper layers of an air mass to secure accurate identification.

[1] *Upper Air* — that part of the atmosphere which is not in close proximity to the earth's surface — say above 2,000 feet. The observations are obtained by the use of aeroplanes, pilot balloons and by radio-sondes. In the latter small wireless transmitters are attached to balloons and signals are sent back to the ground concerning pressure, temperature and humidity. The balloon can be tracked by theodolite or radar so that information concerning winds can be obtained. This information is published in the Daily Aerological Record (Meteorological Office, London).

Lapse Rates

To understand the significance of Upper Air data some fundamental properties of the atmosphere must be explained at this stage. Many weather phenomena depend on whether air is *stable* or *unstable*, two complementary terms which require careful elucidation.

The *lapse rate* of air temperature is the rate at which the temperature in a column of air decreases with unit height. For example, if an imaginary sample of *unsaturated air*[1] moves upwards through the surrounding atmosphere it comes under lower pressure and expands. The heat energy used up in expanding against the external pressure results in lower temperature. It is important to stress that no heat is transferred from inside to outside the sample of air ; the cooling is due simply to the expansion. Such temperature changes are said to be *adiabatic*[2] ; they are measurable and amount to 5·4° F. per 1,000 feet of ascent. This figure is termed the *dry adiabatic lapse rate* (D.A.L.R.) and it is a constant. However, if the sample of air is *saturated*[1] with moisture the results are somewhat different. If it ascends adiabatically then, due to the expansion of the air alone, the rate of loss of heat will be 5·4° F. per 1,000 feet. Cooling of *saturated air*, however, produces condensation during which *latent heat*[3] is liberated and taken in by the air. The heat loss due to the expansion, however, is greater than the latent heat gain so that saturated air, like unsaturated air, also cools as it ascends, but at a *slower* rate. This rate of cooling of saturated air is known as the *saturated adiabatic lapse rate* (S.A.L.R.). Its value varies with the amount of water vapour in the saturated air which in turn varies with the temperature. The S.A.L.R. is about 3° F. per 1,000 feet for air at

[1] A body of air at a given temperature and pressure can hold up to a certain limited amount of water vapour. When this limit is reached the air is said to be *saturated.* Before the limit is reached the air is said to be *unsaturated. vide infra* p. 30.

[2] *Adiabatic* — the cooling due to expansion when a bicycle tyre is suddenly deflated and the more familiar heating due to compression when the tyre is inflated are both adiabatic processes.

[3] *Latent Heat* — When a unit mass of water vapour is converted to water at the same temperature the heat given out in the process is known as the *latent heat of condensation.* Conversely, whenever a unit mass of water is converted to vapour an amount of heat is absorbed which is known as the *latent heat of evaporation.*

50° F. whilst at 85° F. it is less than 2° F. per 1,000 feet. At very low temperatures (–20° F.) the amount of water vapour is so small that the S.A.L.R. is virtually the same as the D.A.L.R.

The curves[1] which represent the D.A.L.R. and the S.A.L.R. on temperature/height diagrams are called *dry adiabatics* and *saturated adiabatics* respectively. The curve which shows the lapse rates of rising air is called the *path curve*; it is composed of the dry adiabatic and/or the saturated adiabatic. The curve which represents the *actual variation of temperature* with height in a given atmosphere, at a given moment of time at a given station, as obtained by aircraft ascent or radio-sonde, is known as the *environment curve*; it shows the *environment lapse rate* (E.L.R.) and its inclination and form will obviously vary with time and place.

In Fig. 7, *ABCD* is the environment curve for the air in the surface layer. *AXCY* is the path curve, consisting of the dry adiabatic, *AX*, below the condensation level, and the saturation adiabatic, *XCY*, above the condensation level. In this example, below point *C* the path curve lies to the right of the environment curve, and the air at *A*, if disturbed, would ascend spontaneously to that level. If it penetrated beyond C, to point *Y*, for example, it would be in an environment warmer than itself, its upward movement would be arrested and it would sink to point *C*.

The stability or instability of air at a particular place and instant depends on the relationship between the environment curve and the path curve as will be shown below.

The Stability of Unsaturated Air

Suppose that measurements of air temperature up to 4,000 feet are taken. When plotted on graph paper they give the line *AB* (Fig. 8) which is the environment curve for that particular instant. It will be seen that the E.L.R. is 3° F. per 1,000 feet. If a sample at the surface, where the temperature is 68° F., is lifted to 1,000 feet then it will cool adiabatically at 5·4° F. per 1,000 feet so that its temperature will be 62·6° F. This temperature is 2·4° F. lower than that of the surrounding air, cf. lines *AB* and *AC* at 1,000 feet.

[1] The D.A.L.R. and the S.A.L.R. when plotted on linear graph paper are so very slightly curved that they appear to be straight lines when only the lowest portion of the atmosphere is represented on a diagram.

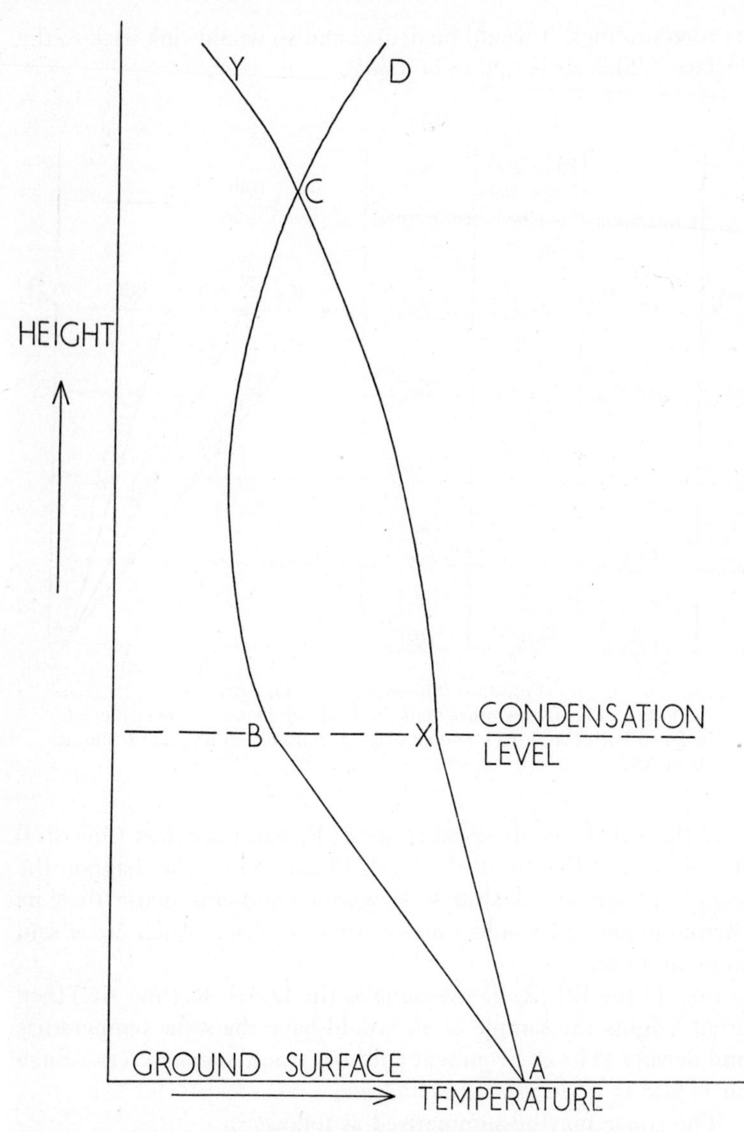

FIG. 7. — The Path Curve and the Environment Curve.

The sample is thus colder and denser than its environment, so that it will sink back to the surface. Should it be raised to 2,000 feet or 3,000 feet, on each occasion it would be at a lower temperature than its surroundings, it would be denser and so would sink back to the surface. This air is said to be *stable*.

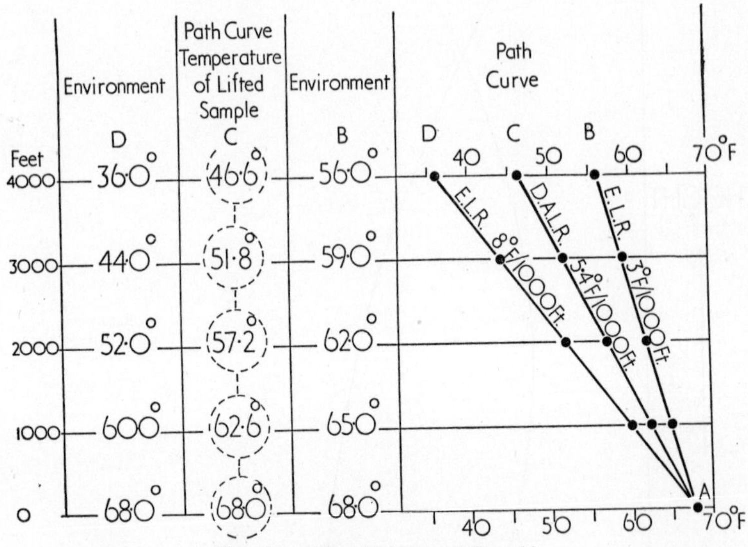

FIG. 8. — The Stability of Dry Air

Note : The temperature data in Column D on the extreme left refer to Path Curve AD, and similarly Column C to AC, and Column B to AB.

If the E.L.R. is observed to be 8° F. per 1,000 feet (line *AD*) it will be seen that at all the levels illustrated on the diagram the sample of air would always be warmer and less dense than its surroundings and would thus continue to rise. Such air is said to be *unstable*.

Should the E.L.R. be the same as the D.A.L.R. (line *AC*) then at all heights the sample of air would have the same temperature and density as its environment and so it would come to rest. Such air is said to be in *neutral equilibrium*.

The above may be summarised as follows :

(*a*) Dry air is always stable if its observed lapse rate (E.L.R.) is less than the D.A.L.R.

(*b*) Dry air is always unstable if its E.L.R. is greater than the D.A.L.R.

The Stability of Saturated Air

By similar reasoning it can be shown that:

(*a*) Saturated air will be stable if its E.L.R. (line *SB*) is less than the S.A.L.R. (Fig. 9).

(*b*) Saturated air will be unstable if its E.L.R. (line *SD*) is greater than the S.A.L.R. (Fig. 9).

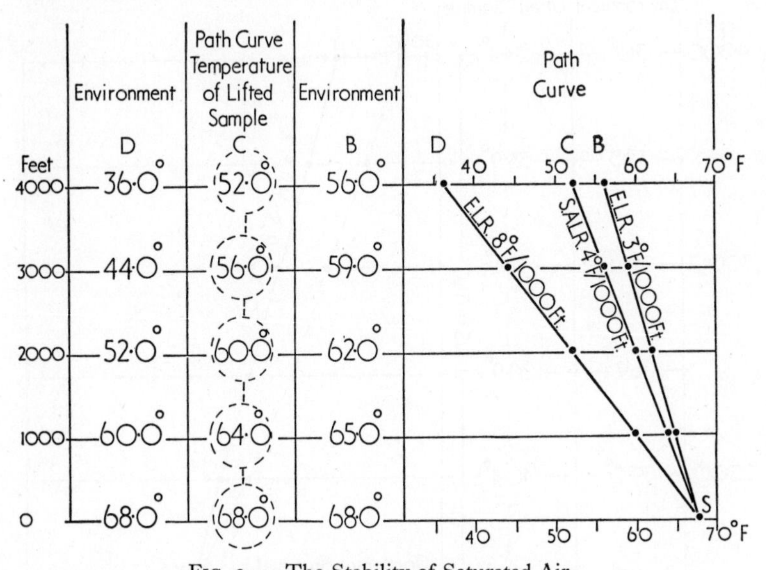

Fig. 9. — The Stability of Saturated Air

Note: The temperature data in Column D on the extreme left refer to Path Curve SD, and similarly Column C to SC, and Column B to SB.

Seldom does the path curve consist solely of the D.A.L.R. for adiabatic cooling of 5·4° F. for every 1,000 feet of ascent may reduce the temperature of the rising air to its *dew point*,[1] at which stage the air becomes saturated. Further ascent of the now saturated air will be at the S.A.L.R. and cooling will produce condensation. Thus the path curve is usually compound — the portion below *condensation level* being the D.A.L.R. and that above being the S.A.L.R. For example, in Fig. 10 *ABXC* is the environment curve and *AXY* is the path curve which consists of

[1] *vide infra* p. 31.

the dry adiabatic below *X* and the saturation adiabatic above *X*. At the surface at *A*, let the temperature be 50° F. and the dew point be 41·9° F. It will be seen that at 1,500 feet the air temperature is 41·9° F. which equals its dew point; thus 1,500 feet is the

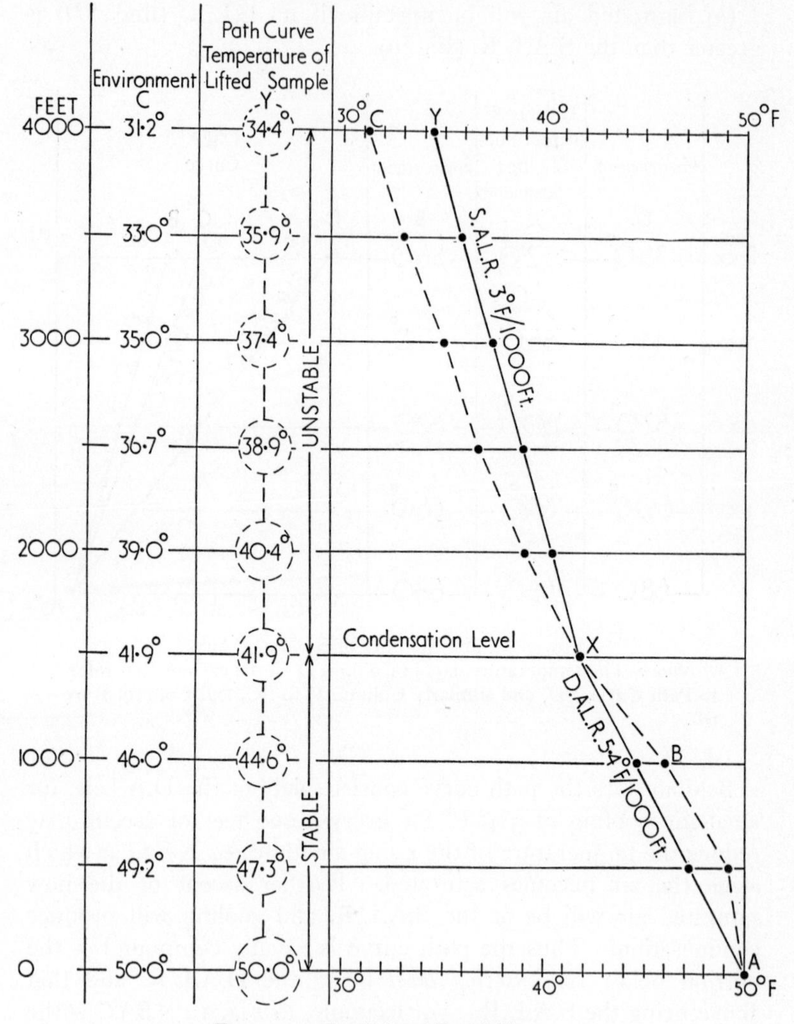

FIG. 10. — Conditional Instability

Note: The temperature data in Column C on the extreme left refer to line ABXC; those in Column Y refer to Line AXY.

condensation level. Thus from *A* to 1,500 feet a sample of air when lifted would cool at the D.A.L.R. but as it would become saturated at 1,500 feet any cooling due to further ascent would be at the S.A.L.R. It may be noted also that air may be stable when unsaturated and unstable when condensation is occurring. Such air is said to be in a state of *conditional instability* ; it occurs often in nature and the nearer such air is to its dew point before it is lifted from the surface[1] the more likely is it to become unstable.

Instability in a conditionally unstable atmosphere may be initiated by a number of processes collectively known as " *trigger action* ". They are the heating of the surface air, the increase of water vapour content of the surface air and the mechanical lifting of the surface air.

Inversions

Temperature normally falls with increasing height from ground level. There are many occasions, however, when this is reversed and temperature increases with height, thus creating an *inversion*

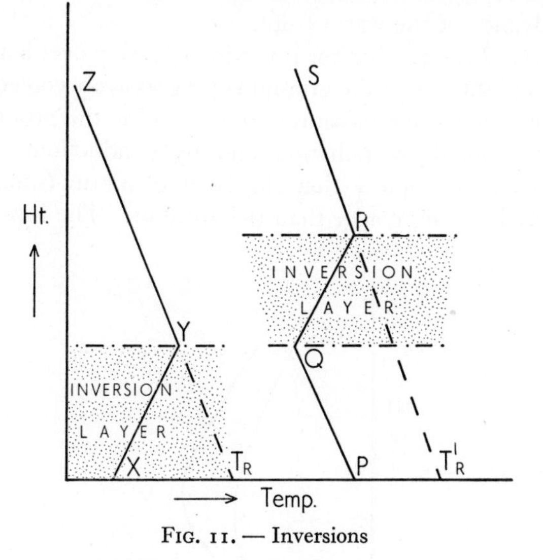

FIG. 11. — Inversions

[1] In nature air may be forced to ascend in three ways, namely, due to relief (orographic uplift) ; in a depression (cyclonic uplift) ; due to convectional heating (convectional uplift).

of temperature, or more simply, an *inversion*. Such a situation may develop in atmospheric layers of limited thickness, for example, a few hundred feet, or, less frequently, in layers of greater thickness, e.g. a few thousand feet. Inversions may develop in the lowest layers of the atmosphere in contact with the ground or at higher elevations within the atmosphere away from contact with the ground. These two types of inversion are illustrated in Fig. 11, the first by the environment curve sloping upwards to the right from the ground (*XY*) and the second by the environment curve sloping upwards to the right from the base (*Q*) of the inversion layer (*QR*) above the earth's surface with normal environment curves (i.e. sloping to the left) above and below it.

Inversions may be formed in any one of three ways, though it is possible to have two inversions developed from different causes on the same graph relating to one station :

(1) By cooling of the lower layers of the atmosphere ;
(2) By the heating of the upper layers of the atmosphere ;
(3) By the presence of a warm air mass aloft (i.e. the warm sector) above a cold air mass at the ground ; for example, in advance of the warm front.

Inversion Type 1. Surface inversions develop over land on calm, cloudless nights when the ground is progressively cooled by rapid, out-going, long-wave radiation. The air near the ground is subsequently cooled by radiation and by conduction. The land surface cools so rapidly that the layer of air in contact with it ultimately becomes colder than the air aloft. The lowest layer of

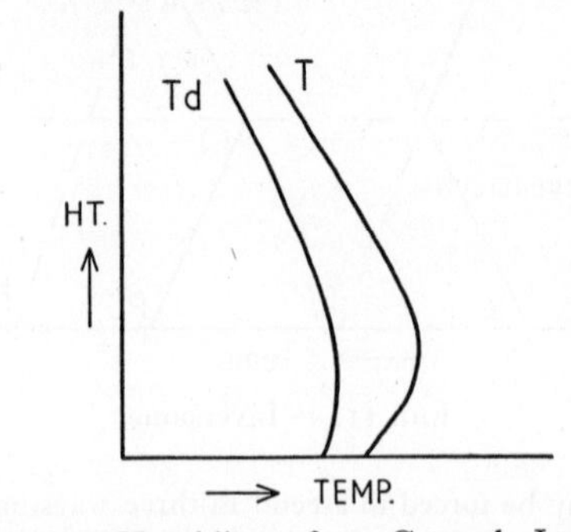

Fig. 12. — Humidity of a Ground Inversion
Td — Dew Point Temperature ; T — Dry Bulb Temperature

the atmosphere is also more liable to be cooled to its dew point than the air aloft (Fig. 12); its relative humidity therefore is higher, a characteristic which differentiates this type of inversion from the second type considered below which is normally associated with dry air. As the ground heats up during the course of

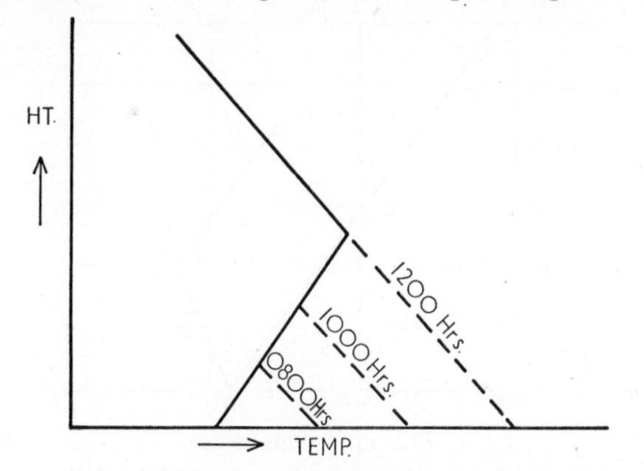

FIG. 13. — Effect of Daytime Insolation in the Dispersion of an Inversion formed the Previous Night

the day the inversion may be dispersed (Fig. 13). The dispersion may also be due to strong or moderate winds which cause mixing of the air. This type of inversion is typical of Polar-Continental anticyclones in winter and of cold Polar-Maritime air all the year round.

Valley inversions may also be noted. These are inversions occurring at ground level in hollows or troughs and their development is conditioned by topography.

Inversion Type 2. Inversions caused by heating in the upper layers of the atmosphere rarely develop down to ground level. They are characterised by their dryness. They form due to the process of *subsidence* in the free atmosphere. *Subsidence* is the gradual sinking of a large body of air over a wide area, such as occurs in an anticyclone, due perhaps to its being relatively cold. The rate of settling may be in the order of 1,000–1,500 feet per day. Sometimes, however, when there is a rapid rise in surface atmospheric pressure a localised form of subsidence may have a settling rate as high as 200 feet per hour. The sinking of the air causes adiabatic heating (compare adiabatic cooling when air is lifted from the surface, see page 11), and should it occur at high and middle levels of the atmosphere then the temperature of the subsiding air becomes greater than that of the air below it, thus forming an inversion (Fig. 14). These temperature changes

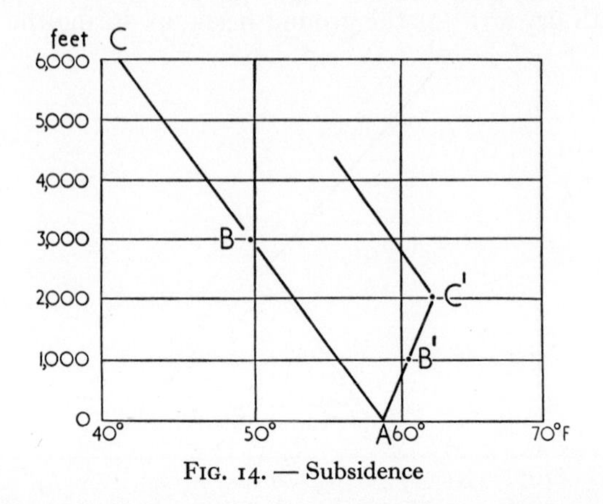

FIG. 14. — Subsidence

are usually so great that they can occur despite such influences as strong winds causing mixing, which might conceivably prevent, delay the development of, or eliminate, the inversion. Let *ABC* in Fig. 14 represent the normal distribution of temperature in the lowest 6,000 feet layer of the atmosphere, and let the lapse rate be constant at 3° F. per 1,000 feet. Let *BC* be the distribution of temperature from 3,000 to 6,000 feet, the temperature at *B* being 50° F. that at *C* being 41° F. Now let layer *BC* subside until its base is at 1,000 feet. Due to the increased pressure the thickness of the layer will diminish, and as it is approaching the earth's surface, which is immovable, the air will spread out and so diminish the thickness. Assume that the air in its new position is 1,000 feet thick. The temperature at the base and at the top may now be calculated by adding, to the respective original temperatures, 5·4° F. for each 1,000 feet of descent (i.e. the D.A.L.R., see page 11)

Final temperature at base $= 50 + (2 \times 5{\cdot}4) = 60{\cdot}8°$ F.
Final temperature at top $= 41 + (4 \times 5{\cdot}4) = 62{\cdot}6°$ F.

These temperatures when plotted give points *B′* and *C′* respectively and it will be seen that there is now an inversion in that layer. As the relative humidity decreases in proportion to the adiabatic heating, so the subsiding air is characterised by its extreme dryness (Figs. 15, 16 and 17).

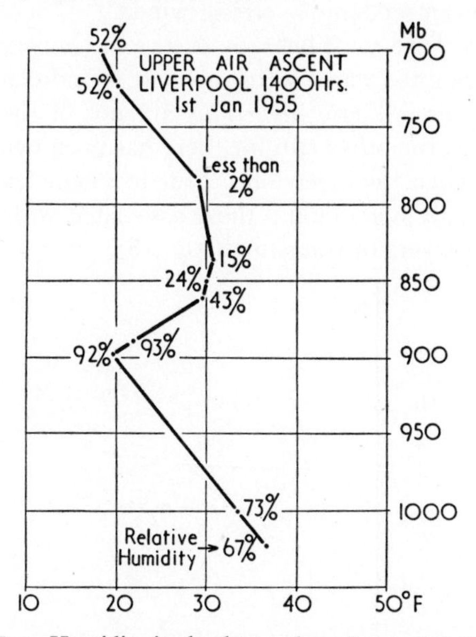

FIG. 15. — Low Humidity in the Atmosphere due to Subsidence
Note : Compare the relative humidities below the inversion zone (e.g. 67%, 73%, 92%) with those just above it (e.g. 43%, 24%, 15%, <2%).

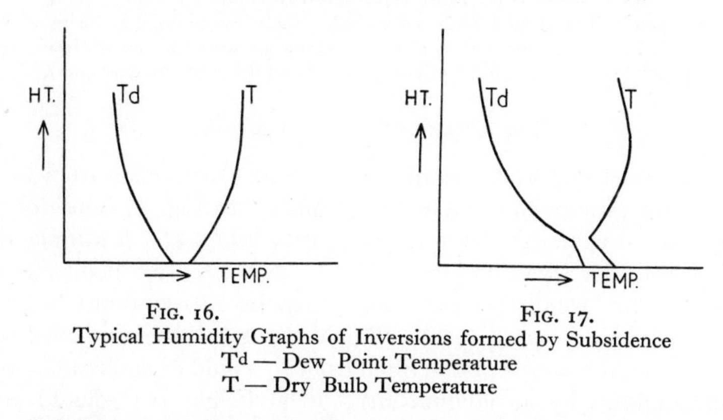

FIG. 16. FIG. 17.
Typical Humidity Graphs of Inversions formed by Subsidence
Td — Dew Point Temperature
T — Dry Bulb Temperature

Subsidence in the atmosphere occurs most frequently in anticyclones, ridges of high pressure, under cold front surfaces and, more locally, in any area where the barometric pressure is increasing rapidly.

Unlike ground inversions (Type 1), this type may develop and persist in even moderately strong winds.

Inversion Type 3. This type occurs in connection with frontal surfaces when the warm sector up aloft is underlain by a wedge of cold Polar air. These inversions are not of the same mode of formation as the other two for there has been neither heating nor cooling to cause the inversion. True inversion layers (types 1 and 2) are virtually horizontal; those associated with frontal surfaces are sloping layers of transition (Fig. 18).

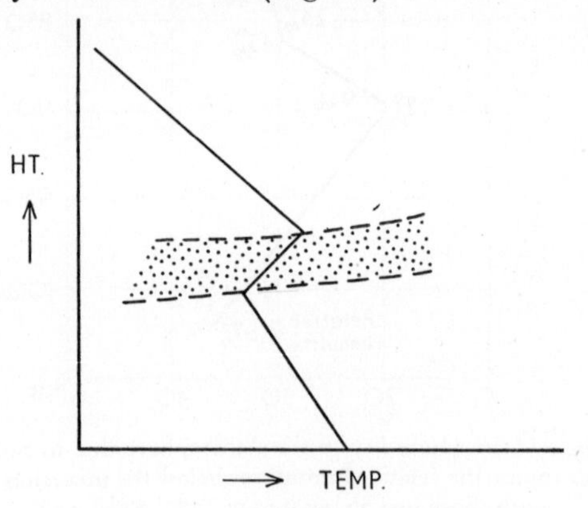

FIG. 18. — A Frontal Inversion

Note: The frontal zone is stippled. Such inversions may be revealed by temperature data recorded during an upper air ascent (see pages 110 and 123, Figs. 52 and 56, and Inset B Fig. 53, for examples).

THE STABILITY OF INVERSIONS

The most important feature of any type of inversion from the meteorological point of view is its *stability*. In Fig. 19, consider a layer of air extending from the surface to height H. A sample of air within this layer, on being lifted to height H from point A on the ground, would become cooler than its surroundings by an amount BX_1° F. (cf. Fig. 8). Should the E.L.R. become smaller (E.L.R.2), the sample, when lifted from A, would be cooler than its surroundings by an amount BX_2° F. at height H; should an inversion occur (E.L.R.3), the sample when lifted would be cooler than its surroundings by an amount BX_3° F. The value of BX_1° F.

or BX_2° F. or BX_3° F. is thus a measure of the tendency of the lifted air to return to its original position should it be disturbed; i.e. it is a measure of stability. This tendency increases as the E.L.R. diminishes, and becomes very pronounced in an inversion.

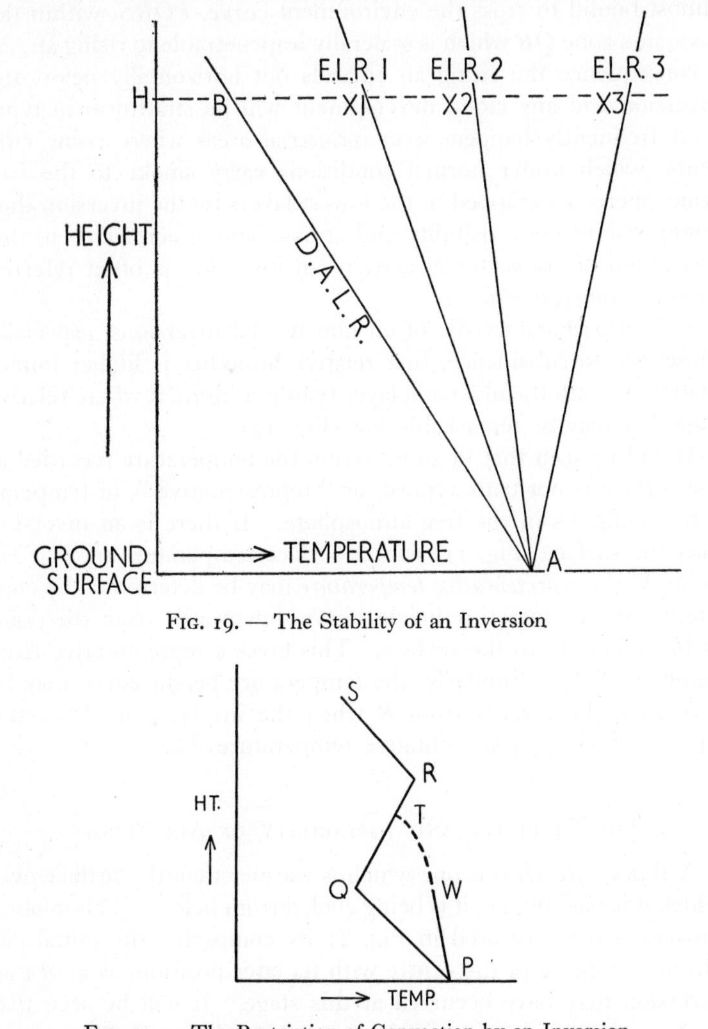

Fig. 19. — The Stability of an Inversion

Fig. 20. — The Restriction of Convection by an Inversion

It is for this reason that disturbances within an inversion are quickly absorbed and the convectional activity originating in unstable layers beneath an inversion is restricted to those layers. For example, when a path curve (*PWT*) (Fig. 20) for rising air occupies a position to the right of the environment curve *PQRS* in the lowest layers of the atmosphere, the path curve (*PWT*) is almost bound to cross the environment curve, *PQRS*, within the inversion zone *QR* which is generally impenetrable to rising air. As a consequence the rising air spreads out horizontally below the inversion and any cloud development will be stratiform in type. This frequently happens over industrial areas where rising currents, which under normal conditions carry smoke to the free atmosphere, are trapped in the lowest layers by the inversion thus giving rise to poor visibility and atmospheric gloom. Due to this restriction of convectional activity an inversion is often referred to as a " *convective lid* ".

It is also characteristic of all non-frontal inversions, especially those due to subsidence, that relative humidity is higher immediately beneath the inversion layer than it is above it where relative humidity may be remarkably low (Fig. 15).

It will be seen that in an inversion the temperature recorded at the surface is not truly typical, or " representative ", of temperature conditions in the free atmosphere. If there is an inversion near the surface (Fig. 11) with a surface temperature of $T°$ F. at point X, the ***representative temperature*** may be determined by continuing the temperature/height curve downwards from the point of inversion, Y, to the surface. This gives a representative temperature of T_R. Similarly, the temperature/height curve may be continued downwards from R when the inversion is above the surface to give a representative temperature T^1_R.

The Stability and Instability of Air Masses

A *Warm Air Mass* is one which is warmer than the surface over which it is passing, i.e. it is being cooled from below. This cooling process is demonstrated in Fig. 21 by comparing the initial environment curve in the centre with its later position, as at A ; an inversion may have occurred at this stage. It will be seen that such an air mass has acquired *increased stability*.

A *Cold Air Mass* is one which is colder than the surface over which it is passing, i.e. it is being warmed from below. This warming process is demonstrated in Fig. 21 by comparing the initial environment curve in the centre with its later position, as at *B*. It will be seen that such an air mass has acquired *greater instability*, especially in its lower layers.

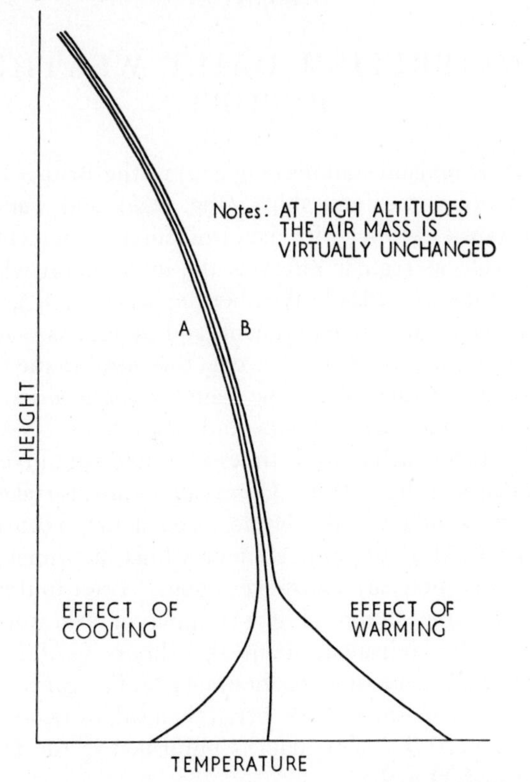

FIG. 21.—Warm and Cold Air Masses: Environment Curves

Chapter 2

THE BRITISH DAILY WEATHER REPORT

Reports from land stations (Fig 22*a*) in the British Isles, from fixed ocean weather ships (Fig. 22*b*) and various ships in transit together with data from aircraft on meteorological flights provide at regular intervals the information which forms the basis of the current Daily Weather Report (D.W.R.). Meteorological stations vary in equipment and functions [1] and in the amount and frequency of weather data they send to the forecasting headquarters at Dunstable. The main "*synoptic hours*" are 0000 hours, 0600 hours, 1200 hours and 1800 hours G.M.T., and tabulated data for each of these times are quoted in full on the front and back pages of the D.W.R. Observations are also taken at intermediate times such as 0300 hours, 0900 hours, 1500 hours and 2100 hours G.M.T. at some stations whilst at primary synoptic stations observations are taken every hour. Prior to the 1st April 1957 at some nine stations (Fig. 23) upper air data were obtained once during the afternoon, about 1500 hours G.M.T. and once during the night, about 0300 hours G.M.T. Since the 1st of April, 1957, these times have been changed to 0000 hours and 1200 hours G.M.T. This data is published in the Daily Aerological Record (D.A.R.).

At each observing hour the following data are noted:

(*a*) Observations: Instrumental

1. *Barometric Pressure*: this is recorded in *millibars* by means of a mercury barometer with scale and vernier attachment whereby the exact height of the column of mercury supported by the atmosphere can be measured. A barograph, which records atmospheric pressure continuously may also be used. All barometric readings are corrected for height of the station above sea level

[1] See *Meteorological Observers Handbook*, 1954, M.O. 554, pp. 3–10.

at the rate of 1 millibar for a rise of height of 30 feet in order that pressures between stations may be comparable. Corrections are also made for temperature, for reduction to standard gravity in latitude 45° N. and for index error.[1]

2. *Barometric Tendency*: this is the net difference, positive or

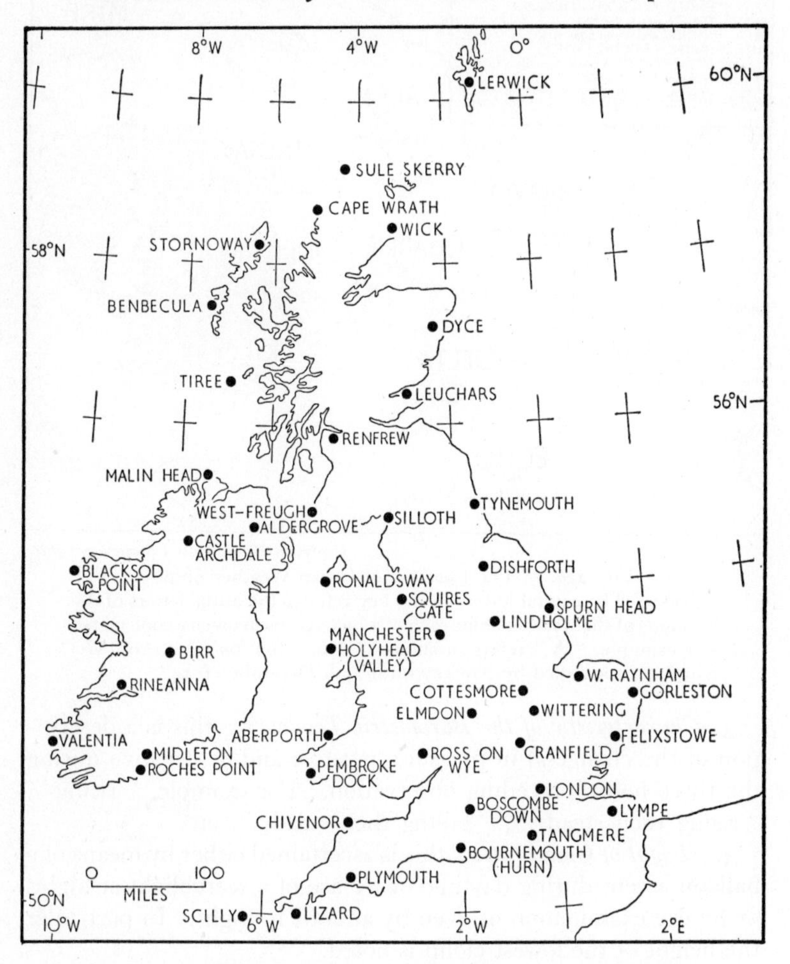

FIG. 22*a*. — The British Isles: Selected Meteorological Stations

[1] The reason for these corrections is as follows. The millibar is a thousandth part of a bar, the unit of atmospheric pressure, which is equal to 29·53 inches of mercury at 32° F. in latitude 45° N. at sea level.

negative, in millibars between the present reading of the barometer and the reading three hours earlier. Lines joining places of equal barometric tendency are termed *isallobars*.

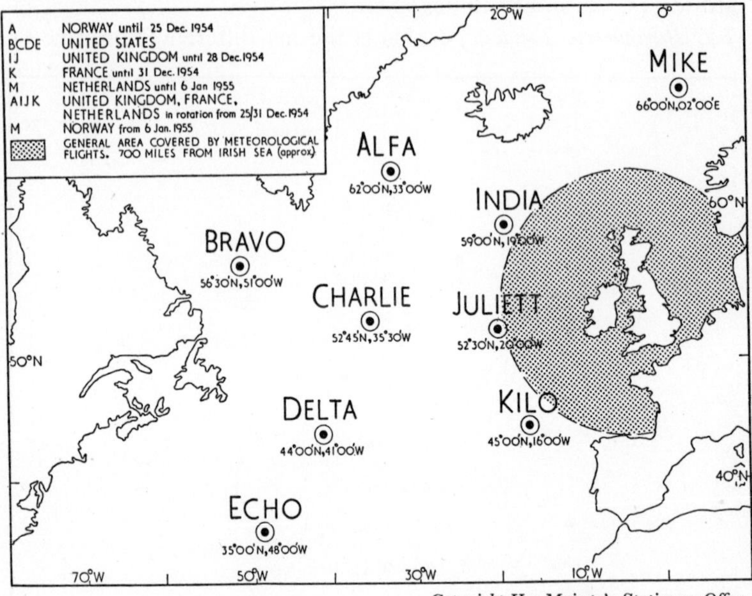

Copyright Her Majesty's Stationery Office.

FIG. 22*b*. — The Location of Ocean Weather Ships

Note : The capital letters in the key refer to the initial letters of the locations of the weather ships each of which has been given a code name. For example, " A " refers to station " Alfa " (62° 00′ N. 33° 00′ W.) which was occupied by Norway until 25th December 1954.

3. *Characteristic of the Barometric Tendency* : this is a description of the change(s) in pressure, positive and/or negative during the three hours preceding observation. For example, " rising ", " rising then steady ", " falling then steady ", etc.

4. *Height of Cloud Base* : this is ascertained either by means of a balloon ascent during daytime or by use of a searchlight at night, or by eye examination or even by aircraft in flight. In particular the height of the lowest cloud is noted.

5. *Temperature of the Air* : this is known as the *dry bulb temperature*. It is recorded by means of a mercury thermometer housed in a Stevenson Screen so that the bulb of the thermometer is about 4 feet above the ground level. The double roof, the

overlapping floor boards and the side louvres of the screen permit the free passage of air but prevent heat loss or heat gain by direct insolation and radiation and, in addition, the thermometers are protected from precipitation.

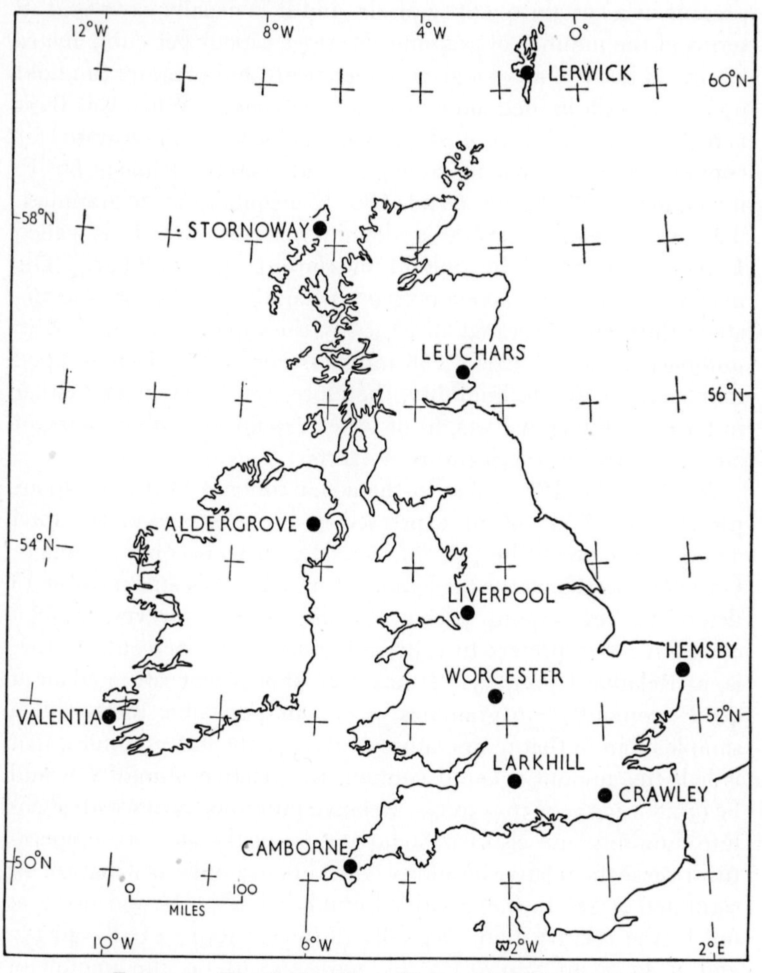

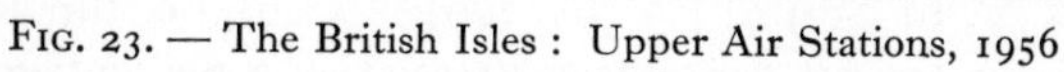
FIG. 23. — The British Isles : Upper Air Stations, 1956

6. *Humidity of the Air* : the air of the atmosphere always contains a quantity of water in the form of invisible vapour and most of the features of the weather are closely related to the ever-varying

proportion of water vapour present. The term which is applied to the dampness of the atmosphere is *humidity*; it may be expressed either absolutely or relatively.

Absolute Humidity refers to the actual amount of water vapour present in a certain quantity of air, and it is usually expressed in terms of the number of grammes of water vapour per cubic metre of air. A body of air at a given temperature and pressure can hold up to a certain limited amount of water vapour. When this limit is reached the air is *saturated.* For example, at 40° F. saturated air contains 6·56 grammes of vapour per cubic metre, while at 60° F. it contains 13·28 grammes, and at 80° F. it contains 25·29 grammes. This water vapour exerts a definite pressure which is called *Vapour Pressure.* The unit of measure is the millibar. The maximum value of vapour pressure occurs when the air is saturated; thus with saturated air at 40° F. the vapour pressure is 8·40 millibars, at 60° F. it is 17·68 millibars, and at 80° F. it is 34·98 millibars. Absolute humidity, therefore, can be expressed either in terms of the actual weight of water vapour per cubic metre of air or in terms of the pressure it exerts.

Relative Humidity refers to the actual amount of water vapour present in a body of air expressed as a percentage of the total amount that would be present were the air to become saturated. On many occasions the air is not saturated. It is still possible to determine the vapour pressure from tables, however, though common usage prefers to express humidity as a percentage, that is, as Relative Humidity. It has been shown that saturated air at 40° F. contains 6·56 grammes of vapour per cubic metre; if a sample of air at that temperature contains only 3·28 grammes, that is half the amount it could contain, the relative humidity would be $(3{\cdot}28 \times 100) \div 6{\cdot}56 = 50\%$. Relative humidity varies with absolute humidity and also with temperature of the air; as temperature rises so the relative humidity falls. For example, let a mass of air saturated at 40° F. (i.e. relative humidity 100%), be warmed: at 60° F. the relative humidity falls to $(6{\cdot}56 \times 100) \div 13{\cdot}28 = 49{\cdot}3\%$ and at 80° F. to 25·9%, $[(6{\cdot}56 \times 100) \div 25{\cdot}29]$, i.e. the amount of water vapour the air contains expressed as a percentage it could contain if it were saturated at that temperature.

Dew point: Conversely, when a mass of unsaturated air is cooled, the relative humidity rises until it reaches 100%. Beyond this point further cooling causes condensation of the excess vapour, (which the air is no longer able to hold), in the form of minute drops of water. The critical temperature at which this occurs is known as the *Dew Point*. For example, if the air temperature for a given station is 60° F. and relative humidity 49·3 %, a fall in temperature to 40° F. would render the air saturated. Thus 40° F. is the dew point of the air at that station.

For meteorological purposes the humidity and other associated properties of the air are most conveniently determined by *wet bulb* and *dry bulb thermometers*. These are mercury thermometers. One, the *dry bulb* thermometer (5 above) is normally mounted in the Stevenson Screen. The other, the *wet bulb thermometer*, also mounted in the Screen, has a muslin bag fitted evenly round the bulb. Cotton threads (the wick) which secure the bag are fed into a reservoir of distilled water so that the muslin is kept moist. Water passes along the wick to the muslin from which, unless the air is saturated, it evaporates into the air. The latent heat of evaporation[1] is drawn from the air immediately surrounding the wet bulb, causing its temperature to fall. This reduced temperature is recorded by the wet bulb thermometer. The lower the relative humidity of the surrounding air, the faster is the rate of evaporation from the muslin, and the lower the wet bulb reading. Only if the surrounding air is saturated will the readings of the wet bulb thermometer and the dry bulb thermometer be the same. Normally the difference is only a few degrees and it is known as the *depression of the wet bulb*. Knowing the dry bulb temperature and the depression of the wet bulb it is possible to determine dew point, relative humidity and vapour pressure from hygrometric tables.[2]

7. *Wind Force* : the direction, expressed in degrees from True North, and strength (Fig. 24*a*) of the wind are recorded continuously and automatically by an anemometer. In the absence of such an instrument, wind speeds may be estimated from the Beaufort scale (Fig. 24*a*) and wind directions by simple weather vanes.

When air begins to move horizontally according to the *pressure gradient* (i.e. the rate of change of pressure between two points) it blows from high to low pressure ; after the motion has con-

[1] See footnote, p. 11.
[2] Hygrometric Tables, 1940, M.O. 265 (4th ed.), H.M.S.O.

tinued for some time the flow tends to be along the isobars with low pressure on the left (when the observer is facing downwind)

Symbols for Wind Speed

M.P.H.	*Wind Force Speed kts.*	*Symbol*	*Simplified descriptions used in weather forecasts*
0	0		Calm
1– 2	1– 2		
3– 8	3– 7		Light (1–12 m.p.h. : 1–10 kt.)
9–14	8–12		
15–20	13–17		Moderate (13–18 m.p.h. : 11–16 kt.)
21–25	18–22		Fresh (19–24 m.p.h. : 17–21 kt.)
26–31	23–27		Strong (25–38 m.p.h. : 22–33 kt.)
32–37	28–32		
38–43	33–37		Gale (39–46 m.p.h. : 34–40 kt.)
44–48	38–42		Severe Gale (47–54 m.p.h. : 41–47 kt.)
49–54	43–47		
55–60	48–52		
61–66	53–57		
67–71	58–62		Storm (Over 54 m.p.h. : over 47 kt.)
72–77	63–67		
78–83	68–72		

(*Sources* : M.O. 515, Instructions for the preparation of Weather Maps, 1954. p. 6 ; M.O. 595, The Weather Map, 1956, p. 91.)

FIG. 24*a*. — Wind Force Tables

in the northern hemisphere. This deviation to the right is caused by an apparent force which operates at right angles to the wind direction. This force is known as the *geostrophic*[1] *force*. It can be shown mathematically that this same force acts whatever the wind direction and that it is proportional to the wind speed (V) and to the sine of the latitude (θ), i.e. geostrophic force varies as $V \sin \theta$. When the wind is blowing parallel to the isobars the geostrophic force balances the pressure gradient force and the resultant wind is known as the *geostrophic wind*. Obviously the closer together the isobars the greater the *pressure gradient force* and the greater will be the geostrophic force to balance it : so that the closer the isobars the stronger will be the geostrophic wind.

[1] *Geostrophic* — depending on the rotation of the earth.

In latitudes greater than 15° N. when isobars are more or less straight and parallel and are not changing rapidly with time a

The Beaufort Scale and Some Equivalents

Force	Description	*Equivalent speeds 33 feet (10 metres) above ground* — Knots, Mean	Knots, Limits	Miles per hour, Mean	Miles per hour, Limits
0	Calm	0	<1	0	<1
1	Light air	2	1– 3	2	1– 3
2	Light breeze	5	4– 6	5	4– 7
3	Gentle breeze	9	7–10	10	8–12
4	Moderate breeze	13	11–16	15	13–18
5	Fresh breeze	19	17–21	21	19–24
6	Strong breeze	24	22–27	28	25–31
7	Moderate gale *	30	28–33	35	32–38
8	Fresh gale	37	34–40	42	39–46
9	Strong gale	44	41–47	50	47–54
10	Whole gale	52	48–55	59	55–63
11	Storm	60	56–63	68	64–72
12	Hurricane	68	64–71	78	73–82

* Winds of Force 7, moderate gales, are not regarded as gales for the purpose of statistical summaries.

(*Source* : M.O. 554, *Observers Handbook*, H.M.S.O. 1952, pp. 74–5.)

FIG. 24*a*. (contd.)

steady balanced flow of air is possible. In these circumstances it has been found that the actual wind at 2,000 feet is given very closely by the geostrophic wind value calculated from the spacing and direction of the mean sea level isobars. This is very important to the meteorologist for it means that outside equatorial latitudes winds at about 2,000 feet can readily be estimated by placing a geostrophic wind scale (Fig. 33*c*) across the isobars on the surface weather map (Figs. 33*a* and 33*b* page 51).

Below 2,000 feet friction with the ground reduces wind speed at the surface so that the geostrophic force is also reduced and can no longer balance the pressure gradient force ; the result is that surface winds are usually inclined across the isobars towards the lower pressure (in the northern hemisphere) and are less strong than the corresponding geostrophic winds at 2,000 feet in the free atmosphere. It is for these reasons that the geostrophic winds are used in tracking air masses back towards their source region (see Chapter 3, p. 52).

(*b*) Observations : Non-Instrumental

1. *Present Weather* : any precipitation, atmospheric obscurity (fog, mist, haze, etc.), ground phenomena (dew, hoar frost, etc.), thunderstorms and the like which are observed at the hour of observation. These are noted according to a detailed classification of 100 present weather types (Appendix 2). Distinctive weather phenomena " near the station " or " during the hour preceding observation " may also be noted. Weather events of a critical nature and significance, notably " deteriorations " and " improvements ", are reported to Dunstable as they occur and quite independently of the hour of observation.

2. *Past weather* : sometimes a summary of all the events, sometimes just a record of the major event of the weather during the period since the last reported observation. The length of the period varies. It is 6 hours for reports at 0000 hours, 0600 hours,

Visibility

Visual range	*Verbal description*
Yards	
Less than 55	Dense fog
55–220	Thick fog
220–440	Fog
440–1,100	Moderate fog
1,100–2,200 ($1\frac{1}{4}$ miles)	Mist or haze
Miles	
$1\frac{1}{4}$– $2\frac{1}{2}$	Poor
$2\frac{1}{2}$– $6\frac{1}{4}$	Moderate
$6\frac{1}{4}$–$12\frac{1}{2}$	Good
$12\frac{1}{2}$–25	Very good
Greater than 25	Excellent

(*Sources* : M.O. 554, *Observers Handbook*, 1952, p. 44 ; M.O. 595, *The Weather Map*, 1956, p. 90.)

Fig. 24*b*.—Visibility Table

1200 hours and 1800 hours G.M.T., and 3 hours when intermediate reports at 0300 hours, 0900 hours, 1500 hours and 2100 hours are made. Past weather is classified according to 10 types (Appendix 2).

3. *Total Amount of Cloud*: this is estimated in eighths (*oktas*) of the sky covered (Appendix 2).

4. *Total Amount of Low Cloud*: again this is estimated in oktas.

5. *Types of Low, Medium and High Cloud*: on pp. 246–9 the details of the cloud types are tabulated, there being 10 types each of low, medium and high clouds (Appendix 2).

6. *Visibility*: the limit of horizontal visibility (Fig. 24*b*) is estimated by observing local features at known distances from the station. Alternatively, a visibility meter may be used to observe special lights of known candle power placed at known distances from the station.

7. *The State of the Ground*: whether the ground is dry, wet, flooded, frozen, etc. This is observed at every synoptic hour but is reported at 0600 hours and 1800 hours only.

(*c*) Observations: Additional

At 0900 hours and 2100 hours in the British Isles the following items are also reported:

1. *Rainfall*, in inches and/or millimetres, measured by a simple rain gauge.

2. *Bright Sunshine* in hours. A Campbell-Stokes sunshine recorder is used for this purpose. This instrument causes the rays from the sun to burn a trace on a card which is changed every twenty-four hours, and from which the hours of bright sunshine can be measured. It may be noted that though the sun may be visible to the observer it is possible for no sunshine to be recorded by the instrument; the intensity of the sunshine may be insufficient to cause a trace to be made on the card—hence the term "bright sunshine".

3. *Maximum and Minimum Temperatures* of the twenty-four hour period, recorded by special thermometers housed in the Stevenson Screen.

4. *Grass Minimum Temperature*, recorded by means of a minimum thermometer placed in supports just above the surface of

short grass, with the tips of the grass just touching the bulb.

5. *Earth Temperatures*: taken at 0900 hours only for depths usually of 1 foot, 2 feet, and 4 feet by means of a Symonds pattern thermometer. For shallower depths of 4 inches and 8 inches, right-angle, bent-stem thermometers are used.

6. *Upper Air Data*, which are obtained for temperature and humidity at specially selected stations at 0000 hours and 1200 hours by radio-sonde. These times have become operative since 1st April, 1957.

All this weather information is sent by telegraph and teleprinter in code (to facilitate its rapid transfer) to Dunstable where it is decoded and plotted on blank outline maps. To ensure uniformity and to facilitate interpretation, the codes[1] used, and the methods of mapping the information have been agreed on and are accepted internationally. Accurate decoding should reproduce the original observations as written or noted down by the observer.

The Station Model

The technique of plotting is based on the "*International Station Model*" (Fig. 25*a*) which consists of a circle, representing the location of the observing instruments on the ground, in and around which are grouped symbols and figures which represent the various elements. International agreement provides for the use of one (black) or two (black and red) colours in plotting the elements. For the British Isles D.W.R. red and black are used and are allocated as follows:

Black — total amount of cloud, wind direction, and wind speed, present weather, barometric pressure, temperature, form of low cloud, form of medium cloud, barometric tendency (positive) and characteristic of the barometric tendency (positive).

Red — dew point, visibility, past weather, form of high cloud, barometric tendency (negative) and characteristic of the barometric tendency (negative).

[1] *Instructions for Meteorological Telegraphy*, Air Ministry, M.O. 191/1 (1943), H.M.S.O.

Instructions for the preparation of Weather Maps, Air Ministry, M.O. 515 (1954) H.M.S.O.

Station Model

Figures are used for the following items :

- T_dT_d Dew point in whole degrees Fahrenheit.
- VV Visibility ; code numbers 0–100.
- PPP The last three digits of the barometric pressure at mean sea level in millibars and tenths of millibars. It is simple to see by inspection whether the digits 10 or 9 are missing from in front of the three digits quoted, since the usual pressure range for the British Isles is about 950 millibars to 1050 millibars.
- TT Dry bulb temperature of the air in degrees Fahrenheit.
- N_h The amount of low cloud in oktas (eighths).
- h Height of low cloud (code figure).
- pp Barometric tendency in tenths of millibars, e.g. a tendency of +1·4 millibars is plotted as 14.

Symbols [1] are used for the following items :

- N The total amount of cloud in oktas (eighths) of the sky covered.
- ww Present weather (classified into 100 types).
- W Past weather (classified into 10 types).
- (w) Weather during the hour preceding observation, i.e. immediate past weather. This is plotted to the right of the past weather symbol in black (classified into 14 types). There is no separate code ; the 14 types are included within the 100 types of ww.
- C_L Form of low cloud (classified into 9 types).
- C_M Form of medium cloud (classified into 9 types).
- C_H Form of high cloud (classified into 9 types).
- dd The wind direction is plotted in the form of an arrow originating at the circumference of the station circle and pointing in the direction *from* which the wind is blowing.
- ff The force of the wind is plotted by adding " feathers and solid pennants " to the end of the arrow (Fig. 24*a*). In plotting, the wind arrow is always inserted first to allow for any slight displacement of the other symbols or figures from their orthodox positions relative to the station circle.

[1] See Appendix 2.

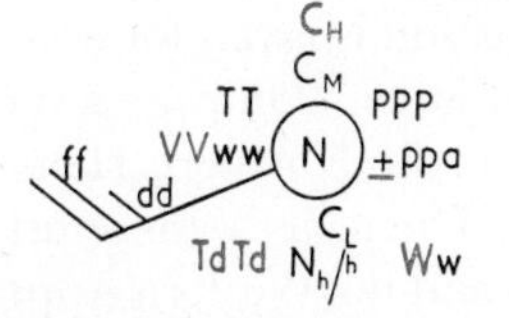

FIG. 25*a*. — The International Station Model for Land Stations

FIG. 25*b*. — Station Model for Cottesmore (Rutlandshire) for 26th November 1954 at 1800 hours G.M.T.

In the examples given in this book the meteorological data are given in the form of the station model and, in order that interpretation can be followed, sections of the Meteorological Office Code Book are given in Appendix 2. However, a " Code Book " is essential for the fullest interpretation of the D.W.R.

Above is the station model for Cottesmore (Rutlandshire) at 1800 hours, 26th November, 1954 (Fig. 25*b*). The interpretation is given below.

Temperature	47° F.
Dew point	46° F.
Pressure	980·3 millibars.
Barometric tendency	falling : 5 millibars.
Visibility	1½ miles.
Wind direction	170° from True North.
Wind force	13–17 knots.
Present weather	heavy continuous rain.
Past weather	rain.
Total amount of cloud	eight eighths (oktas).
Low cloud	stratus fractus.

N.B. Reference should be made to the Code Book M.O.515, *Instructions for the Preparation of Weather Maps*, 1954, for details concerning the above interpretation.

The Current British Daily Weather Report

The current British Daily Weather Report (D.W.R.) is a four-page folding leaflet. On page 1 observations are tabulated for some 55 land stations and for certain ships at 1200 hours and 1800 hours G.M.T. yesterday, i.e. the day prior to the day of issue of the report. On page 4 similar information is given for 0000 hours and 0600 hours G.M.T. on the day of issue. On page 2 there is a map showing the synoptic situation for the Northern Hemisphere at mid-day (1200 hours) yesterday. On page 3 there are three smaller maps, two for the British Isles and the Western Approaches at 1800 hours yesterday and 0000 hours today, and one map for most of Europe and the eastern North Atlantic at 0600 hours on the day of issue. Thus it is possible from the sequence of weather maps to follow the development and progress of a weather situation over the British Isles. At the bottom of page 3 are statements about the *General Synoptic Development*, the *Forecast for the British Isles* and the *Outlook for the next twenty-four hours*.

The Report has had this format (except for minor changes in July 1955) since 1st January, 1950. Prior to that date page 2 had a large map of the British Isles showing the station data and the weather situation in detail for 0600 hours on the day of issue. On page 3 was a large map of the Northern Hemisphere for the morning of the day of issue. This old format showed greater distribution of detailed weather in position in *space*. The new format shows more detail of the distribution and changes in *time*, and, in any event, station details on the front and back pages of the report are available for plotting.

Also to be included in the term Daily Weather Report is an Upper Air Section, i.e. the Daily Aerological Record (D.A.R.) which gives data for temperature, humidity and winds from the surface up to the level of 60 millibars, i.e. about 63,000 feet. It is obtainable separately and is always published a few days in arrears due to the vast amount of information to be collected from the Northern Hemisphere before maps can be compiled.

Techniques of Analysis and Interpretation

The Daily Weather Report via the station models expresses a summary of the *totality* of the weather over the British Isles at any given moment of time. It is a distillation of a vast amount of observational data which the weather forecaster has interpreted as a whole. This enables him to locate and identify frontal zones, especially since he has available also detailed charts showing the immediate past history of the weather situation he is examining. He is concerned with the practical interpretation of the D.W.R. for its own sake.

The purpose of this book, however, is to demonstrate the interpretation of the Report for the non-meteorologist, and in particular of the geographer. Moreover, this book is concerned with the inevitably bold simplification and standard classification of recognised weather types. To attain full understanding of the intricate complexities of whole entities, it is often necessary to isolate their parts, and analyse them separately. Then, having grasped the individual significance of each part, it is possible to appreciate more fully the collective significance of the parts within the whole. The danger of developing the wrong conclusions from studying the parts in isolation is fully countered by the re-integration of the parts for correlative study in the final stage. A geographer may, for example, trace off the contours or the drainage pattern or woodland areas from the 1 inch Ordnance Survey sheet to study them firstly in isolation and secondly in relation to the map as a whole.

The technique of interpretation of the D.W.R. advocated herein then is one *firstly* of selective analysis of weather elements in distribution, and *secondly*, of general correlation of the elements in relation to the synoptic situation as a whole. The *first* stage involves the selection of data from the report for separate plotting on outline maps. It would be unwise to list the weather elements in order of importance or "helpfulness" in assessing the full synoptic situation but it will be obvious that temperature, wind direction, barometric pressure and tendency, present weather and humidity (as reflected in temperature/dew point differences — see page 100) should normally be of primary significance in analysing the general situation. Then for each of the plotted elements isopleths[1] are interpolated at suitable intervals. Stages in the interpolation of isopleths are:

(*a*) The selection of proximate pairs of stations and the location of points between them through which an isopleth should pass, having regard to the relative values of the stations.

(*b*) The possible modification of the isopleth patterns, especially where stations are few or are scattered, in view of the background knowledge of geographical factors, e.g. land and sea distribution, or the nearness of large urban areas.

It is essential to note that:

(1) Isopleths should never cross, touch, join or bifurcate (except where two isopleths of the same value join to form a closed circuit).

(2) The values on one side of the isopleth should be consistently lower, and on the other side, consistently higher.

(3) The difference in value between adjacent isopleths should always be constant on a given map or series of maps.

(4) Isopleths should be smooth, usually curving lines (rarely straight) and their pattern should be "flowing" and symmetrical as far as possible.

[1] See Preface page v.

In some instances data may permit of more than one position for a given isopleth, the following alternatives often being available :

either (1) the *peninsula* extending out from the main trend of the isopleth (Fig. 26*a*).

or (2) the *island* separated from the main isopleth (Fig. 26*b*).

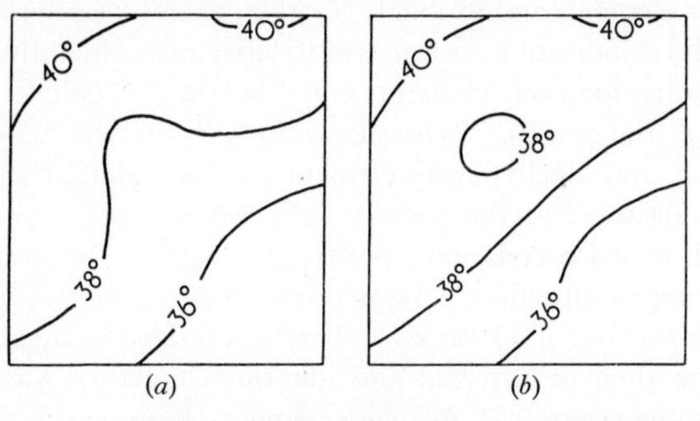

FIG. 26. — Isopleth Interpolation (*a*) the " Peninsula " (*b*) the " Island "

A *col* [1] in an isopleth pattern should always be defined by four isopleths, one opposite pair being identical in value and the other opposite pair being identical in value. The difference in value between the pairs should be the isopleth interval for the map (Fig. 27).

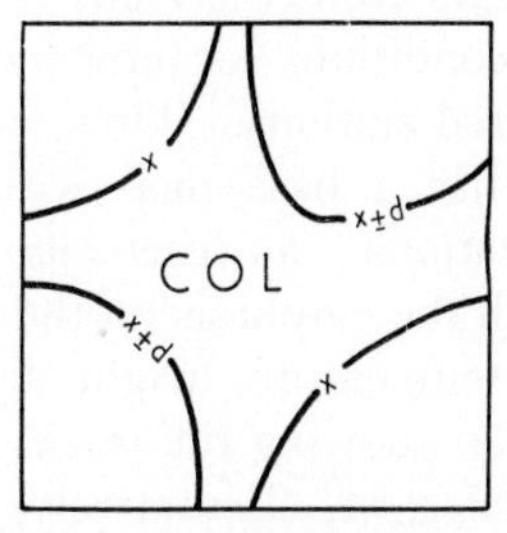

FIG. 27. — Isopleths of a Col

Note : At this col, " x " and " x±d " are the values of opposite pairs of isopleths respectively, where " d " is the isopleth interval.

When a satisfactory isopleth pattern has been constructed, the map is then " regionalised " ; that is, it is divided into *areas which*

[1] See also pp. 6 and 233.

appear to have relative uniformity, i.e. "*continuities*" so far as the particular element is concerned. Such areas are shown by *infrequent, widely spaced and irregular isopleths*. Boundaries, i.e. "*discontinuities*" between such areas are indicated by *close or bunched arrangement of the isopleths* lying perhaps *straight or slightly curving* across the map. When these discontinuities are sharp and occupy narrow zones, a clear regional change for this particular element, and probably for the general weather situation as a whole, is indicated. It is useful to label areas of continuity and discontinuity for each element, e.g. "warm", "cold", "sharp veer" (of the wind), "virtually steady" (of the barometer). After each, and ideally, every element has been plotted separately, isopleths drawn and the pattern subdivided, comparison of the maps will reveal correlations, positive or negative, in terms of the whole synoptic situation. Areas of marked *continuity* suggest *air masses, or portions of air masses*; sharp *discontinuities* suggest *fronts* which can then be inserted and identified together with the air masses they separate. A major danger, however, is that the approach is liable to be exclusively two-dimensional, that is, concerned only with conditions at the surface. Therefore, in addition to surface synoptic data obtained from the Daily Weather Report which are intensively dissected, analysed and interpreted, geostrophic wind scales [1] are used to track the course of the movement of air towards the British Isles, and temperature/height diagrams [2] based on data from the Daily Aerological Record are drawn which reveal conditions of temperature and stability at higher levels for selected stations. Thus, each example taken in subsequent chapters has a base map with data plotted for a selected network of stations; an inset map showing the general synoptic situation, with the emphasis on the pressure pattern; an inset map showing a temperature/height diagram and, wherever applicable, an inset map showing the tracks by which the air has reached the British Isles, or, alternatively, inset maps showing selected past stages in the development of the synoptic situation under review.

The British Isles have been taken as the area for analysis because there is a close network of stations within a compact unit and upper air information is readily available. On the other hand, fronts

[1] See p. 51. [2] See p. 53.

normally extend over large areas and only a portion, perhaps not the best developed portion, may lie across Britain at any given moment of time. This point is demonstrated more clearly by reference to air masses, only a small portion of which may cover the British Isles at any given moment of time.

Chapter 3

AIR MASSES

As previously noted, the general circulation of the atmosphere has a tendency to produce vast masses of air whose physical properties are more or less uniform horizontally and vertically within large areas. Air masses are represented by

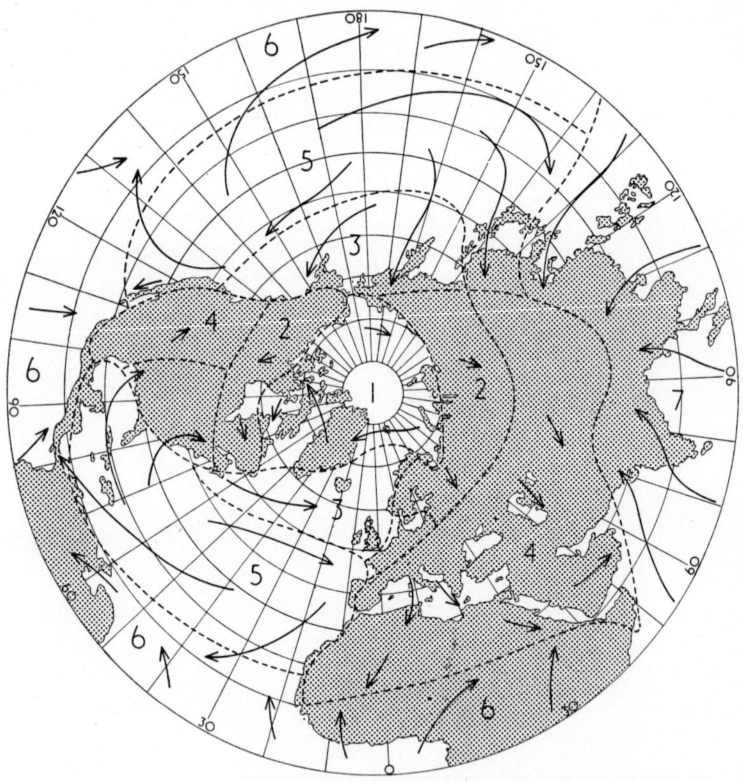

(After Petterssen 1956, by permission of McGraw-Hill Book Co. Inc.)

FIG. 28*a*. — Air Mass Source Regions: Northern Hemisphere in Summer 1. Arctic 2. Polar Continental 3. Polar Maritime 4. Tropical Continental 5. Tropical Maritime 6. Equatorial 7. Monsoon. The arrows indicate the main airflows

areas of "*continuity*" in horizontal distributions. The horizontal transition, i.e. *discontinuity*, or frontal zone, from one such mass to another is often relatively abrupt or sometimes more gradual depending on the degree of contrast between the air masses when they first come into contact, and the length of time they have been in contact, for the longer this period the greater will have been the mixing. Air masses acquire their homogeneous properties at the "*source region*" (Fig. 28) but by the time they reach the British Isles the properties acquired at the source region may have been considerably modified, for the air mass has travelled either south-

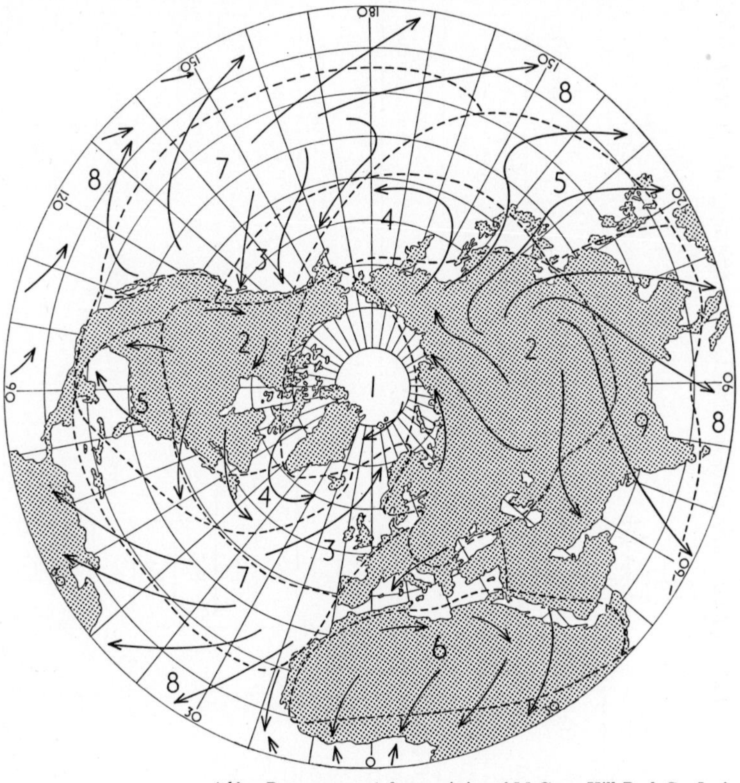

(*After Petterssen 1956, by permission of McGraw-Hill Book Co. Inc.*)

FIG. 28*b*. — Air Mass Source Regions ; Northern Hemisphere in Winter 1. Arctic 2. Polar Continental 3. Polar Maritime, or Transitional 4. Transitional 5. Transitional, or Tropical Maritime 6. Tropical Continental 7. Tropical Maritime 8. Equatorial 9. Monsoon. The arrows indicate the main airflows

General Classification of Air Masses affecting the British Isles (after Belasco)

Air mass		*Sub-division symbol*	*Source region*	*Main curvature of path to British Isles*	*Nature of path surface*	*Direction of approach to British Isles*
Tropical	Maritime	T1	South-west of Azores	Straight Anticyclonic	Oceanic	SW.
		T2				S. or SW.
	Continental	T3	Spain, Mediterranean or NW. Africa	Straight	Land and English Channel	SE. or S.
		T4	Southern Europe in summer	Anticyclonic		E. or SE.
Quasi-Tropical Maritime		TQ	43°–50° N. 15°–25° W.	Straight or Anticyclonic	Oceanic	SW., W. or NW.
Polar	Continental	A1	North of 50° N. and east of 25° E.	Cyclonic	Land and North Sea	NE., E. or SE.
		A2		Anticyclonic		NE., E. or SE.
	Maritime	P1	North and north-east of Iceland	Cyclonic	Oceanic	N. or NE.
		P2		Anticyclonic		N. or NE.
		P3	North and west of Iceland	Cyclonic		NW.
		P4		Anticyclonic		NW.
		P5		Cyclonic		W.
		P6		Anticyclonic		W.
		P7		Cyclonic		S. or SW.

FIG. 29. General Classification of Air Masses affecting the Weather of the British Isles (*After Belasco* 1952)

wards towards warmer areas, or northwards towards cooler areas. Furthermore, the amount of time taken by an air mass to reach the British Isles and the length and nature of the route it has followed will also influence the degree of modification which has taken place. Modifications begin at the base and develop upwards through the air mass so that the unaltered air mass characteristics are frequently found above the surface layer of air. It may be noted that the temperature of an air mass is changed not only by surface heating or cooling: almost equally important is warming by subsidence. In view of the above considerations a simple geographical classification of air masses has to be expanded to accommodate changes which occur *en route*. (Fig. 29.)

J. E. Belasco[1] has differentiated 19 types of air mass affecting the weather of the British Isles. Many of these are sub-types of the basic components mentioned earlier (i.e. Polar-Maritime, Polar-Continental, Tropical-Maritime and Tropical-Continental) indicating the source region and the orientation and curvature of the

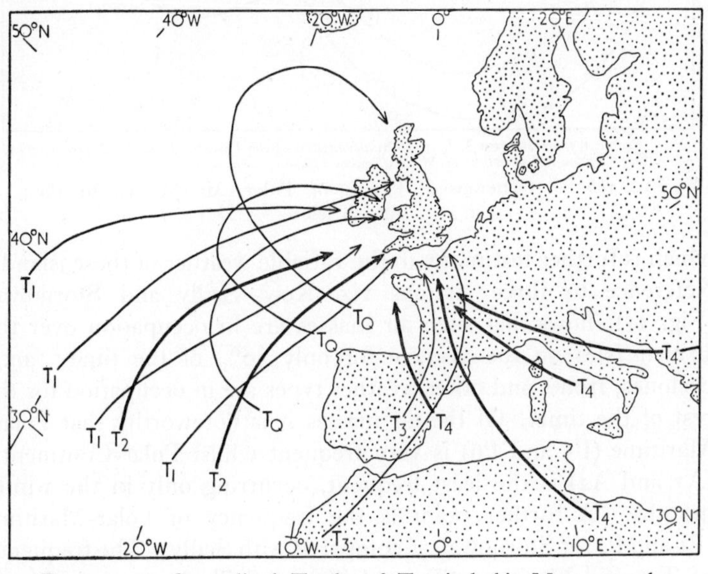

FIG. 30*a*. — Generalised Tracks of Tropical Air Masses to the British Isles

[1] Belasco, J. E., 1952, *Characteristics of Air Masses over the British Isles*, Air Min. Met. Office, Geophys. Mem. 87, M.O. 530*b*.

path to the British Isles. It will be seen that air masses may arrive over the British Isles from any point of the compass (Fig. 30)

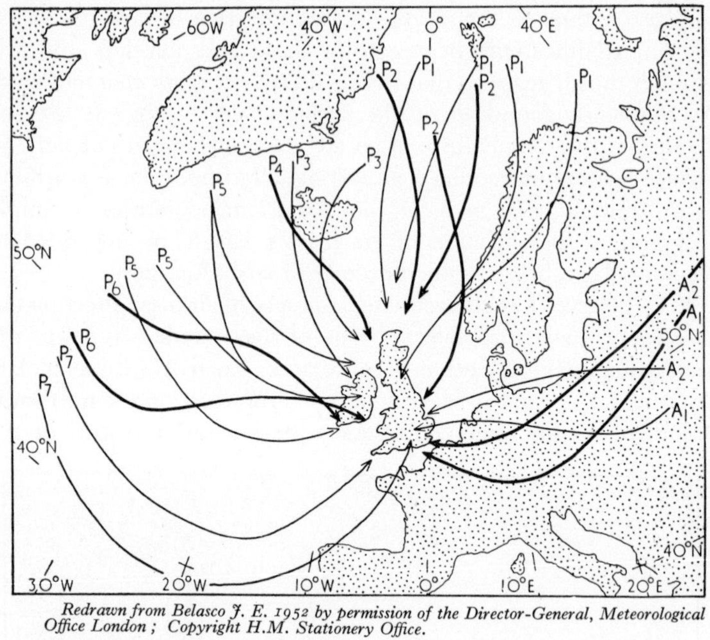

Redrawn from Belasco J. E. 1952 by permission of the Director-General, Meteorological Office London; Copyright H.M. Stationery Office.

FIG. 30*b*. — Generalised Tracks of Polar Air Masses to the British Isles

which is further testimony to the variable weather of these islands. Reference to three stations viz. Kew, Scilly and Stornoway (Fig. 31) shows that such air masses are in occupation over the British Isles on the average for only 50% of the time; anticyclones, fronts and other weather types are in occupation for the rest of the time. Of the air masses it is noteworthy that Polar-Maritime (P5 and P6) is very frequent whilst Polar-Continental (A1 and A2) is the least frequent, occurring only in the winter months. A further point is the frequency of Polar-Maritime (P1 and P2) at Stornoway as compared with Scilly. The frequency of Tropical-Maritime (T1 and T2) at Scilly as compared with Stornoway should also be noted as should the frequency of Tropical-Continental (T3 and T4) at Kew.

Not only do average daily mean temperatures differ at the surface according to the air mass in occupation but differences also occur up to 10,000 feet and more above ground level (Fig. 32). In fact such differences may occur up to 35,000 feet, above which temperature becomes constant at about −60° F. to −70° F.

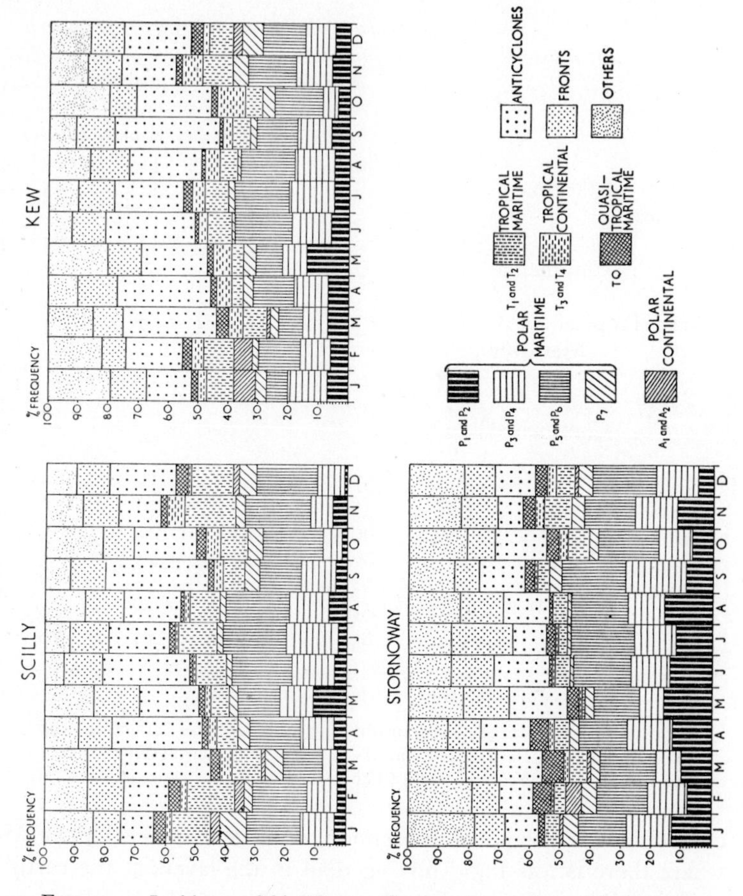

FIG. 31. — Incidence of Air Masses affecting the weather of the British Isles (*after Belasco*, 1952)

The recognition of air masses is now one of the foundation stones for a satisfactory understanding of the Daily Weather Report for " the synoptic chart at any time is a direct result of observations made within an air mass in temporary occupation, or is the result of the conflict between two air masses for possession, of the area ".[1] The meeting of air masses results in marginal mixing but experience has shown that in spite of such mixing by far the greater proportion of the air mass retains its individual

Air mass			*Average daily mean surface temperature at Kew* °F		*Average temperature at 10,000 ft.* (approx.) °F	
			*Summer**	*Winter**	*Summer*	*Winter*
Tropical	Maritime	T1	66	51	41	29
		T2	68	50	44	33
	Continental	T3	70	47	43	25
		T4	72	50	—	—
Quasi-Tropical Maritime		T_Q	63	45	37	24
Polar	Continental	A1	—	29	—	-8
		A2	—	30	—	-3
	Maritime	P1	57	34	19	-4
		P2	57	31	19	0
		P3	60	39	21	3
		P4	60	38	24	5
		P5	63	42	25	8
		P6	65	43	27	10
		P7	65	47	29	16

* August and February (after Belasco).

FIG. 32. — Average Temperature of Air Masses affecting the Weather of the British Isles at the Ground Surface at Kew and at 10,000 ft. (*after Belasco*, 1952) (Table)

characteristics fairly clearly defined, especially in the Upper Air where there is less rapid mixing than in the layers at the earth's surface. The meeting of air masses results in the displacement from the surface of the warmer air by the colder, denser air and this ascent produces condensation and precipitation. Those regions where air masses meet will have changeable weather affected by influences associated with each type of air mass and with the contact zone between them.

[1] Miller, A. A., 1953, *Air Mass Climatology*, Geography Vol. XXXVIII, p. 61.

For the purposes of the analyses which follow, the recognition of air masses may be based on those items found within the pages of the Daily Weather Report, namely :

(1) Surface temperature and its horizontal gradient.
(2) Dew point.
(3) Forms of cloud.
(4) Hydrometeors — i.e. bodies of solid or liquid water present in the air such as hail, snow, sleet, rain, drizzle, fog, etc.
(5) Visibility.
(6) Surface winds.

In some instances for the British Isles it may be possible to deduce the nature of the air mass from wind direction alone. For example, Tropical-Maritime air often arrives with south-westerly winds, Polar-Maritime air with north-westerly winds and Polar-Continental air with north-easterly winds. Generally, however, the wind direction, especially at one particular station may be misleading. For example, Polar-Maritime air circulating round a depression immediately to the south of Ireland may arrive as a

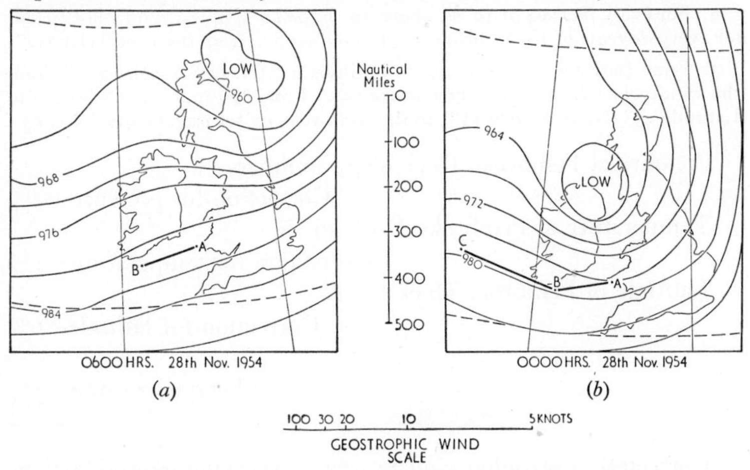

(c)

Maps redrawn from the Daily Weather Report of 28th November 1954 by permission of the Director-General, Meteorological Office, London. Copyright H.M. Stationery Office.

FIG. 33. — The Method of Tracking Air Masses using the Geostrophic Wind

Note : Nautical miles are used for horizontal distances because the geostrophic wind scale is given in knots.

southerly wind (P5 on Fig. 30); similarly, with an anticyclone centred to the west of Ireland, Tropical air arrives over Britain as a warm, damp current from the north-west (T_Q on Fig. 30). The identification of air masses whose properties have been modified in this way may be made by reference to a series of synoptic charts compiled for six hourly intervals. From Fig. 33 suppose it is required to find the source of the air arriving at Pembroke Dock (A). Place the *geostrophic wind scale*[1] (Fig. 33*c*)[2] on the chart (Fig. 33*a*) at Pembroke Dock and read off the geostrophic wind (=35 knots) from the spacing of the isobars at Pembroke Dock. Make corrections for pressure, temperature and latitude as shown below to obtain the correct geostrophic wind:

Note that the geostrophic wind scale used here (Fig. 33*c*) applies to the following conditions: Pressure 1,000 millibars; Temperature 50° F.; Latitude 55° N. or S.).

Corrections

1. For every *increase* of 10 millibars of pressure above 1,000 millibars *subtract* 1% from the wind velocity. For every *decrease* of 10 millibars of pressure below 1,000 millibars *add* 1% to the wind velocity.

2. For every *increase* of 10° F. above 50° F. *add* 2% to the wind velocity and for every *decrease* of 10° F. below 50° F. *subtract* 2% from the wind velocity.

3. From Latitude 55° (N. or S.) to Latitude 65° (N. or S.) *subtract* 1% from the wind velocity for each degree *above* 55°. From Latitude 55° (N. or S.) to Latitude 45° (N. or S.) *add* 1½% to the wind velocity for each degree *below* 55°.

Pressure at Pembroke Dock 984·2 millibars

Correction for pressure + 2%

Temperature at Pembroke Dock 46° F.

Correction for temperature − 1%

Latitude of Pembroke Dock 51° N.

Correction for latitude + 6%

Total correction + 7%

Corrected geostrophic wind 35 + 7% = 37·5 knots approximately.

In actual practice the corrections for surface pressure and temperature are usually neglected for, as will be seen from the example, they are very small and amount to only 1%, i.e. 0·35 knots. For this chart, therefore, it may be assumed that during

[1] Obtainable from Form M.O. 2373. [2] See p. 51.

the preceding three hours[1] the air has moved with the geostrophic speed at Pembroke Dock, i.e. 37 knots. Project back the air from the initial point for a period of three hours by drawing a line (*AB*), in the direction from which the wind has come, i.e. parallel to the isobars, of a length equal to the distance that the air has travelled; that is, $37 \times 3 = 111$ nautical miles. Similarly project back from *B* to *C* for a period of six hours using the geostrophic wind at *B*, determined by the spacing of the isobars at *B* for the chart drawn six hours previously (Fig. 33*b*). Repeat this process, using for each six hour period the geostrophic wind given by the synoptic chart for the mid-point of the period. In this manner the approximate path of the air at 2,000 feet may be determined. It does not follow, however, that air at higher altitudes follows this same track and it is not considered advisable to track back the air for a period greater than thirty-six hours.

Completely different air masses with similar immediate past histories can be indistinguishable if such data as have been mentioned already are the sole criteria considered. Identification can be confirmed by reference to *Upper Air* conditions. The construction of a temperature/height diagram from data provided by the Daily Aerological Record will show those portions of the air mass above the layer modified during transit from the source region.

Using the information provided by the Daily Weather Report it is possible to illustrate the various air masses which affect the weather over the British Isles. For the purpose of comparison each example is chosen at 0600 hours G.M.T. when the insolation factor is negligible and local effects are small and standardised. Each example is taken from the months of January and December so that actual surface temperatures are at least comparable. The Upper Air information from which the temperature/height diagrams are constructed is that for 1500 *hours G.M.T.* The reason for the different time taken is that in the winter months the surface layers of air are very frequently so cold at 6 a.m. that there is sometimes an inversion of temperature at the ground, or, if this has not developed, the cold is such that the air has been rendered stable.

[1] The initial point from which tracking begins is itself the mid-point of a six hour period — as determined by the times of the maps published in the D.W.R. Hence the first stage of the tracking is for a period of three hours only, but subsequent stages in the procedure involve the whole six hour period.

At night the surface of the ground radiates heat and so becomes cooler than the air immediately above it. By contact with the cold ground the lowest layers of the atmosphere are cooled in turn to a temperature lower than the layers above. The temperature/height curve resembles curve 1 (Fig. 34) : there is an inversion. After

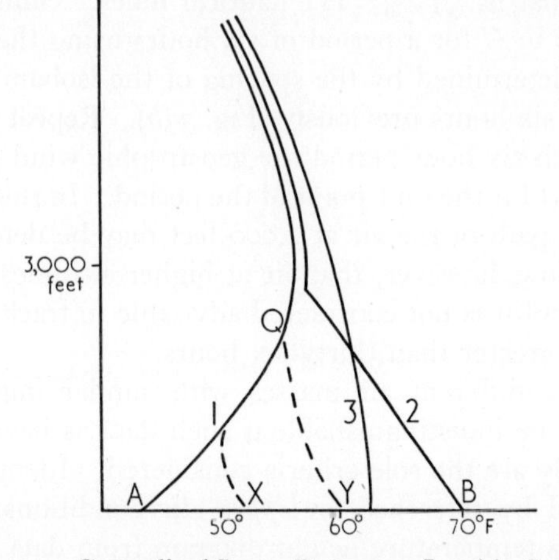

FIG. 34. — Generalised Lapse Rates over Land in Summer

sunrise the earth's surface is heated and warms the air in contact with it and simultaneously the higher layers are heated by direct radiation. The lapse rate near the ground changes from negative (as at *A*) to positive (as at *X*). As heating continues during the morning the warmed air rises from below and the inversion is gradually reduced (*X* to *Y*). At about mid-day the surface temperature reaches point *B* so that the temperature/height curve resembles curve 2. The outgoing radiation increases until about two hours after the sun has passed the meridian when balance is achieved between heat received and lost at the earth's surface. After this, radiation is greater and the temperature of the surface decreases. Again the lowest layers are cooled first ; the lapse rate decreases and once more the atmosphere becomes stable. By evening the condition shown by curve 3 has been attained. It is for these reasons that the temperature/height diagrams used here are for 1500 hours and not 0300 hours, the time nearer to that of the synoptic chart, for at 0300 hours most air masses are stable near the ground.

THE COLD AIR MASSES

The main sources are in Polar or Arctic regions (Fig. 28) but due to the spread of continental anticyclones in winter these source regions may extend into the centres of continents at that time of year. At the source (Fig. 35) they are characterised by:

(1) Low temperature.

(2) Low relative humidity, due to the low moisture capacity of air at low temperature.

(3) Stability, due to the intense cooling of the lower layers and consequent small lapse rate.

From Fig. 30 it will be seen that the tracks of these cold air masses are labelled P1, P2, P3, P4, P5, P6 and P7 and A1 and A2. All these tracks are towards warmer regions so that the lowest layers of the air are warmed (Fig. 35). The consequences of this are:

(*a*) The lapse rate is steepened (Fig. 35) so that instability results and strong ascending currents develop.

(*b*) Relative humidity increases if the track should be over warm ocean, and the warmer the ocean the greater will be the increase.

(*c*) Cumulo-nimbus and cumulus types of clouds are produced; that is, clouds of great vertical displacement. Precipitation takes place as short, sharp showers sometimes called *instability showers.*

(*d*) The inherent instability encourages the mixing of the air not only by turbulence [1] but also by convection. Thus the original properties of Polar air masses are liable to more rapid modification than those of Tropical air masses.

(*e*) Surface visibility is very good between showers due to the low temperature and the low humidity and also possibly due to the absence of concentrated dust layers which would be destroyed by the mixing.

THE WARM AIR MASSES

Tropical-Maritime: the chief sources of this air are the sub-tropical anticyclones which persist over the oceans about 30° N. At the source the air is characterised by:

(1) High temperatures derived from the influence of warm seas (Fig. 35).

(2) High humidity since abundant water vapour is available and

[1] *vide infra* footnote 1, page 56.

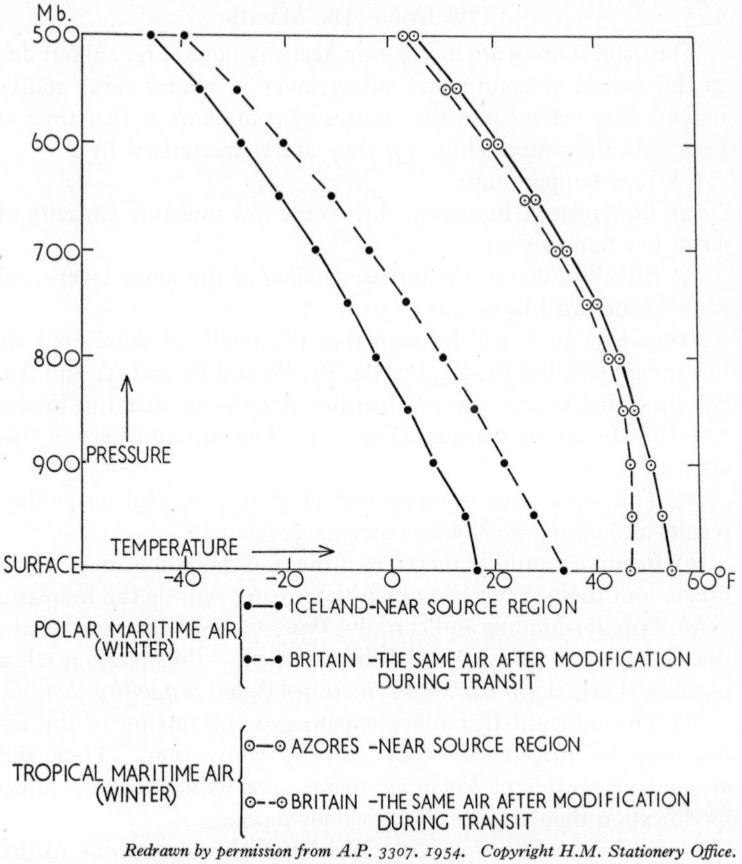

Redrawn by permission from A.P. 3307. 1954. Copyright H.M. Stationery Office.

FIG. 35. — Modification of Air Masses in Transit

the capacity of the air for moisture is high at high temperatures.

(3) A fair degree of stability. Moving to higher latitudes the air becomes cooled in its lowest layers by contact with the cooler land or sea. The results (Fig. 35) are :

(*a*) The lapse rate is greatly diminished, stability is greatly increased, convection and turbulence[1] are greatly reduced.

(*b*) The cooling of the lowest layers results in increased relative humidity and the dew point is soon reached.

[1] The term *turbulence* refers to the variable intensities of large-scale and small-scale air motion, e.g. gustiness, within a given mass of air. (See *Sutcliffe, R. C.* " Meteorology for Aviators ", pp. 95–6.)

(*c*) A combination of (*a*) and (*b*) can produce fog or stratus cloud, which is continuous, and steady drizzle or rain, especially if the air is lifted orographically. Sometimes, in contrast, however, there may be breaks in the cloud cover with resultant sunny periods.

(*d*) Visibility is poor.

Tropical-Continental: This type of air, more frequent over the British Isles in winter than in summer (Fig. 31), comes usually from North Africa (Fig. 28). At the source the air is characterised by:

(1) Very high temperatures and instability in summer and relatively high temperatures in winter.

(2) Low relative humidity at all seasons.

This type of air acquires moisture in the lower layers when it moves away from the source towards colder lands and this results in increased instability.

Selection and Analysis of Air Mass Examples

Having noted the major characteristics of the chief air masses, examples illustrating them will now be taken from selected Daily Weather Reports. It must be remembered that though all air masses have distinctive characteristics by which they may be recognised, yet one, or perhaps more, of those characteristics may be poorly developed or even unrepresented for a chosen example depending on the degree of modification which the air mass has undergone in transit.

The procedure of analysis, already outlined in Chapter 2 (page 39) may be reiterated. The first step is to obtain an indication of the source of the air by tracking it back for some twenty-four hours using the geostrophic wind. The next step is to discover whether or not the air is stable. This is achieved by the construction of a temperature/height graph from upper air data provided by the Daily Aerological Record for Liverpool on the afternoon of the day in question. From these two considerations it should be possible to arrive at a tentative conclusion as to the type of air mass involved.

Whether one air mass or more is in occupation can only be decided by reference to the plots of the separate elements which make up the weather at the time in question. These are plotted, therefore, in turn, isopleths are drawn and the regional pattern is marked. Here the point to observe is the occurrence of "*continuity*" in the pattern which would suggest the presence of an air mass. On the other hand, "*discontinuity*", i.e. any sudden change in an element over a considerable distance, would indicate frontal conditions, i.e. the presence of two or more air masses.

These diagrams will also serve to indicate the type of weather associated with a particular air mass.

Thus for each example the following information will emerge as the analysis proceeds :

(1) The type of air mass and whether only one is present.
(2) The weather associated with the air mass.

Cold Polar-Maritime Air : P1

18th January, 1955, 0600 hours G.M.T.

As can be seen from the map (Fig. 30*b*) P1 air tracks can either be direct to the British Isles, following a southerly course exclusively over the sea, or rather less direct over Scandinavia, following a south-south-westerly course partly over the sea and partly over the land. That which arrives by the more direct sea route used to be termed "Arctic" but now it is described as "cold Polar-Maritime".

What evidence is available to suggest that the air mass (Fig. 36) is cold Polar-Maritime? Firstly, the Polar source of the air is shown quite conclusively if the origin of a sample of air be tracked geostrophically, for example, from Stornoway on 18th January at 0600 hours. It will be seen (inset A, Fig. 36) that the sample was near Bear Island (74°30′ N. 19°00′ E.) at midnight on 16th January, 1955. The route to Britain was south-westwards passing between Iceland and Norway, and then southwards to Stornoway.

On its journey from the source region over the Barents Sea the air moved into warmer latitudes and so in theory must have been warmed from below and would have tended to become unstable. On this occasion, however, even at 1400 hours the surface temperature was so low (38° F.) that the air was stable to 900 mbs. It will be noted (inset map B, Fig. 36) that the air was unstable from 900 mbs. to 715 mbs. In fact, if the surface temperature at Liver-

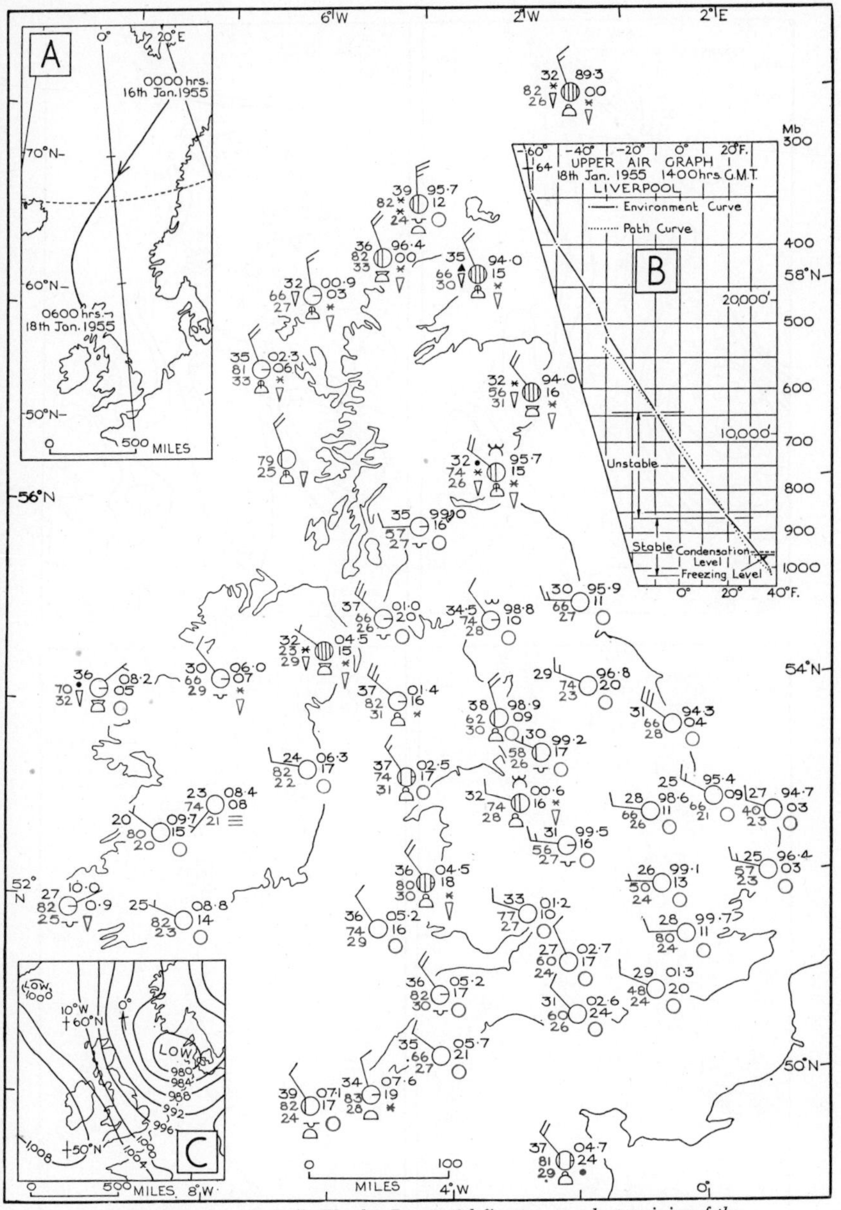

Maps redrawn from the Daily Weather Report 18th January 1955 by permission of the Director-General, Meteorological Office, London. Copyright H.M. Stationery Office.

Fig. 36. — Selected Data for 18th January 1955 : 0600 hrs. G.M.T.
Cold Polar Maritime — P1
Inset A — Track Map ; Inset B — Upper Air Graph
Inset C — Isobars : 0600 hrs. G.M.T. 18th January 1955

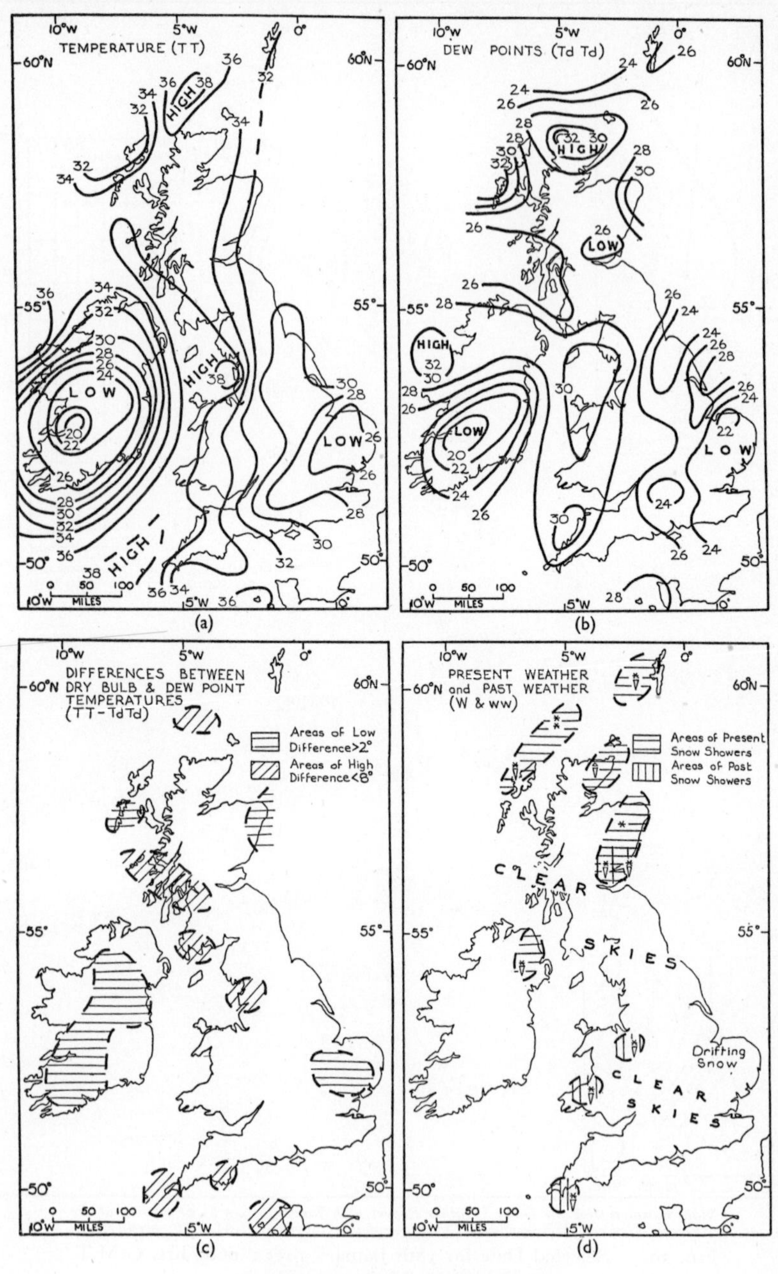

Fig. 36 (*contd.*). — (*a*), (*b*), (*c*), (*d*)

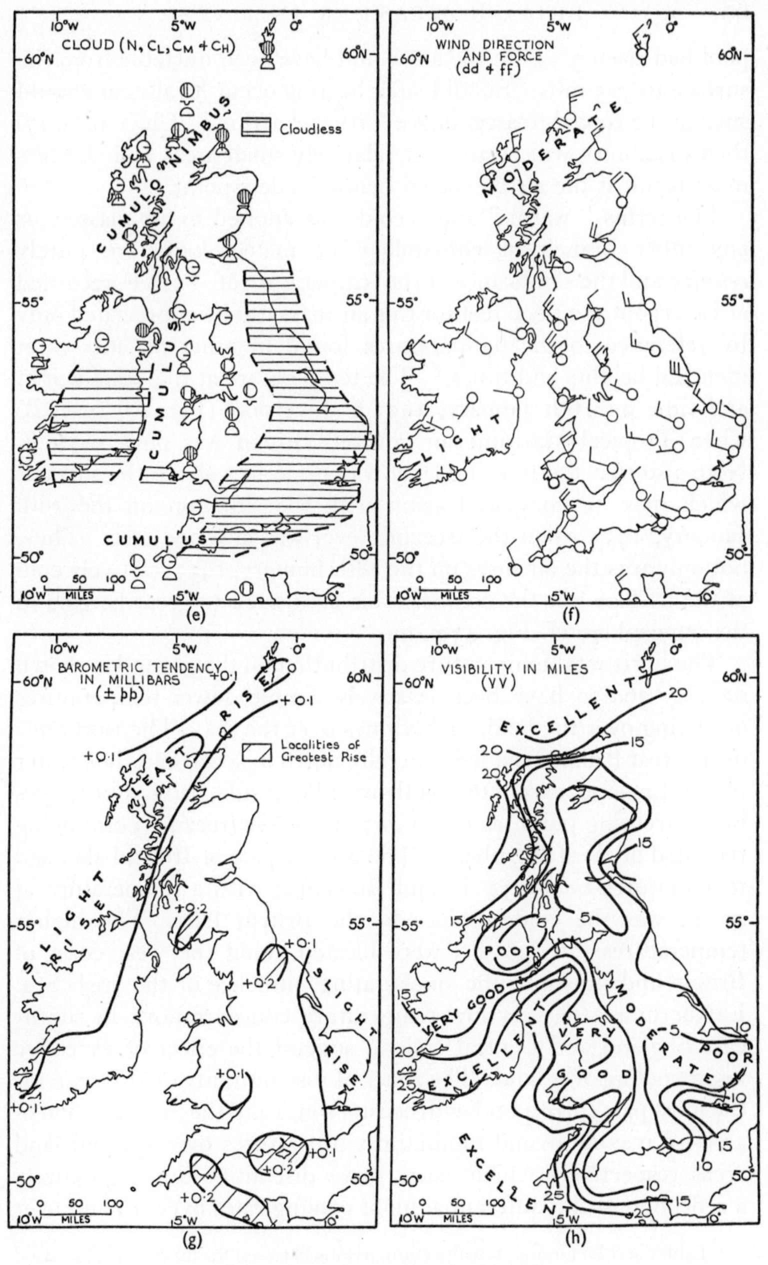

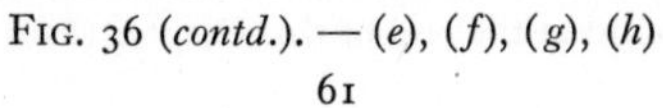

FIG. 36 (*contd.*). — (*e*), (*f*), (*g*), (*h*)

pool had risen 3°–4° F. the air would have been unstable from the surface to 715 mbs. Should such heating occur locally, or should such air be forced to ascend (see " trigger action ", Ch. 1 page 17) then instability will occur over relatively small areas and showers must result if the air be cooled below its dew point.

The terms " warm " and " cold " as applied to air masses, or any other branch of climatology or meteorology, are purely *relative* and the signficance of the temperature of – 51° F. recorded at Liverpool at 24,000 feet for this air mass can be appreciated only by reference to the temperatures found in other air masses at identical heights and times.[1] The temperature at the same height and time on 16th January, 1953 at Liverpool (Fig. 40, Inset B) when Tropical-Maritime air covered Britain was only – 23° F. Note also that the freezing level was 1,000 feet above the surface, which may be compared again with the situation on the 16th January, 1953 when the freezing level was at 8,000 feet. Thus, not only was the air mass on the 18th January, 1955 relatively cold at the surface but the coldness was continued to great heights in the atmosphere cf. Fig. 43 p. 99.

The horizontal temperature distribution on the ground is shown on Fig. 36*a* to have been relatively simple, lower temperatures occurring over the land, higher ones over the sea. The isotherms over Great Britain trended generally north to south and the greater part of England, except the south-west Peninsula, had temperatures below freezing point, as much as 7° F. below freezing point being recorded at West Raynham. The greater part of Ireland also had temperatures below 32° F. and Rineanna, with a temperature of 20° F. was the coldest place in the British Isles. The higher temperatures (36°–38° F.) were located along the west coast of Britain and illustrate the ameliorating influence of the Irish Sea. Furthermore, the very low temperature concentrations in south-east England and Central Ireland suggest the effect of excessive night cooling over land. The zones of discontinuity on this map for the most part correspond with coastal zones and the juxtaposition of areas of maximum and minimum temperatures over sea and land areas respectively which cause these discontinuities are entirely a reflection of the differential night cooling rates over sea and over

[1] Tables and Diagrams showing comparisons between the air masses discussed in the text are to be found at the end of this chapter (Figs. 42 and 43).

land. Reference to the following table will show that the morning of the 18th January, 1955 was cold for the time of year.

Station	*Temperature °F. 18th January, 1955*		*Average*[1] *Daily Temperature* °F.	*Average*[1] *Minimum Temperature* °F.
	0600 *hours*	1200 *hours*		
Kew	30	37	40·1	35·7
Pembroke Dock	36	39	43·8	41·1
Stornoway	32	30	40·5	37·1
Scilly	39	42	46·3	43·7
Felixstowe	25	35	39·5	35·9
Birr Castle	23	33	39·6*	34·3*

* Average for 1881–1915: other averages for 1921–50

The dew point distribution (Fig. 36*b*) was somewhat irregular though generally higher over sea and coastal areas, e.g. over the Irish Sea, the South-West Peninsula and North Scotland. Even so, the air had to cool to below 32° F. over the greatest part of the land before condensation could have occurred and conditions develop for ground frost to form.

The isopleths of the difference[2] between dry bulb and dew point temperatures (Fig. 36*c*) show that whilst the greater part of Ireland had differences of 2° F. and less, it was only in East Anglia and North-east Scotland elsewhere that such low differences occurred. In contrast, differences were high, as much as 6° F. over the greater part of Wales, 11° F. at West Freugh and 15° F. at Scilly, for example. *Dry air* (with relative humidity of less than 60%)[3] was present over the greater part of the country and reference to hygrometric tables shows that the relative humidity at West Freugh was 55% and at Scilly it was 62%. This is not surprising for air at low temperatures has a low capacity for moisture.

As previously noted,[4] cold air masses moving southwards are

[1] In this Table and subsequent similar Tables in Chapters 3 and 5, the average temperatures quoted have been abstracted from M.O. 571. *Averages of temperature for Great Britain and Northern Ireland 1921–50.* H.M.S.O. 1953. Similar data for stations in Eire have been abstracted from M.O. 236. *Book of Normals of Meteorological Elements for the British Isles for periods ending 1915.* H.M.S.O. 1919.

[2] See Fig. 44 p. 100.

[3] This is the official Meteorological Office definition.

[4] See p. 55.

warmed from below and as a result they become unstable. This can occur throughout an air mass but it is more usual for it to happen over relatively small areas due to local influences. The temperature/height graph (Fig. 36 inset B) indicates instability above 900 mbs. so that wherever the air was lifted locally to that height instability showers were the result. These are well shown on the map depicting " past weather " and " present weather " (Fig. 36*d*) on which showers of snow and hail are widespread from the Shetland Islands to Lands End.

Cloud amounts (Fig. 36*e*) show that large areas of East and South-east England, and South and Central Ireland were free from cloud, as indicated also by the clear skies in the present weather map (Fig. 36*d*). It was the cloudless state of the sky which permitted loss of heat by radiation on a grand scale thus accentuating the low, early morning temperatures in these localities. Elsewhere, cloud amounts were generally slight with exceptions at Aberporth, Aldergrove, Dyce, Wick and Lerwick where the convective cumulus and cumulonimbus clouds reported are again evidence of instability.

The map of wind force and direction (Fig. 36*f*) shows a gradual change in both force and direction from the north to the south of the British Isles. Moderate winds blow from the north-north-west in the extreme north, light winds from the north-west in Northern England, Northern Ireland and the South-west Peninsula whilst light westerly winds are found over Southern Ireland, Central, East and South-east England, suggesting, by their direction, that the winds, coming generally from the north-west, were bringing cold Polar air to the British Isles. As there are no lines of discontinuity in either force or direction in Fig. 36*f* a Polar air mass would appear to have been in occupation.

Except at Cape Wrath (Fig. 36*g*) pressure was rising everywhere, changes were slight and the barometer more or less steady, again indicating the presence of just one air mass. Only three localities, West Freugh, Plymouth-Guernsey and Tangmere-Bournemouth had rises greater than 0·2 millibars.

The good visibility (Fig. 36*h*), a notable feature of Polar air in general, is well shown. Except at Aldergrove where snow showers had decreased visibility, 10 to 25 miles visibility obtained over Ireland. The greater part of England had visibilities of from

6 to 10 miles except in the Midlands and East Anglia where it was less than 5 miles. On the whole coastal areas reported visibilities greater than 25 miles.

The isobars on inset map C, Fig. 36, are relatively widely spaced over the greater part of the British Isles and trend slightly west of north to east of south. They show none of the sudden changes in direction associated with fronts. Their wide spacing is evidence of the light to moderate winds already noted except in North Scotland where the closer spacing indicates stronger winds.

All the isopleth patterns (Fig. 36*a–h* inclusive) are generally simple and only locally complex. The general lack of extensive discontinuities, (except those parallel to the coast and attributed to land/sea effects) and the relatively simple nature of the temperature/height diagram illustrates the fact that one air mass covered the British Isles at 0600 hours on 18th January, 1955. That it was a Polar-Maritime air mass is shown by:

(*a*) The track (Fig. 36, inset A) of the air from the Arctic, and the winds blowing from the north-west.

(*b*) Low humidity due to low temperatures.

(*c*) Very low temperatures; all stations also reported the ground frozen or ice covered.

(*d*) The showery weather due to local instability.

(*e*) The very good visibility.

It is of interest to add here that this type of air mass is very rarely experienced in July over Britain (Fig. 31) owing to the rather rapid modifications which the air undergoes in this month as it moves over the warmer seas or lands. It is most active in the winter months, especially in North Scotland though these conditions can extend over the whole of the British Isles.

Polar-Maritime Air: P1

4th January, 1954, 0600 hours G.M.T.

In the previous example the air mass under consideration had come directly southwards from the Polar source region following a route exclusively over sea areas. However, air over the British Isles at 0600 hours on the 4th January, 1954 had followed a somewhat different route. The geostrophic path of a parcel of air located at Felixstowe (Fig. 37, inset A) shows that the air was in the vicinity of the White Sea (65° N. 40° E.) in the early hours of the previous day. Thus, the air, probably derived from a Polar source over the Arctic Ocean, passed southwards over a land route across Scandinavia for the first half of its journey to Britain. The second half of its journey lay across the North Sea in a south-westerly direction, a sea crossing of such length as may account for the surface relative humidity of 83% at Liverpool as compared with 73% at the same station for the previous example.

The surface temperature at Liverpool at 1400 hours 4th January, 1954 of 39° F. was quite low and the temperature/height graph (inset B, Fig. 37) shows stable air conditions. Even so, an increase of some 6° F. at the ground would have caused instability. The condensation level was low at 600 feet and the freezing level was at 1,600 feet. The temperature at 24,000 feet was −30° F. which may be compared with −51° F. which was recorded at the same level at the same time of day on the 18th January, 1955 when P1, cold Polar-Maritime air, covered the British Isles (cf. Fig. 43). Note that the air has been warmed considerably on its journey for the corresponding European weather chart for 0600 hours shows surface temperatures in Finland to have been below 10° F., in Southern Norway generally about 20° F. and in Denmark 30° F. This warming is also shown on the upper air graph (inset B, Fig. 37) for below 750 millibars (7,600 feet) the curve shows a trend to the right. Thus the air moved over cold land and then warm sea on its journey to the British Isles.

The general pattern presented by the isothermal distribution (Fig. 37*a*) reveals an area of cold air extending southwards over the whole of the British Isles. However, the pattern is somewhat modified by the pronounced area of relatively warm air extending northwards over the Bristol Channel, Cardigan Bay and the Irish Sea, which separates areas of low temperature over Central England (e.g. the lowest temperature was 35° F. at Elmdon) and Ireland (the lowest temperature was 31° F. at Aldergrove and Rineanna). Further, it is consistently clear that relatively high temperatures were recorded at coastal stations; for example, Culdrose 43° F., Blacksod Point 46° F., Cape Wrath 41° F., Tynemouth 46° F. and Gorleston 42° F. These features of the isothermal distribution may be attributed to the differential rates of cooling or heating over land and sea. Zones of steep temperature

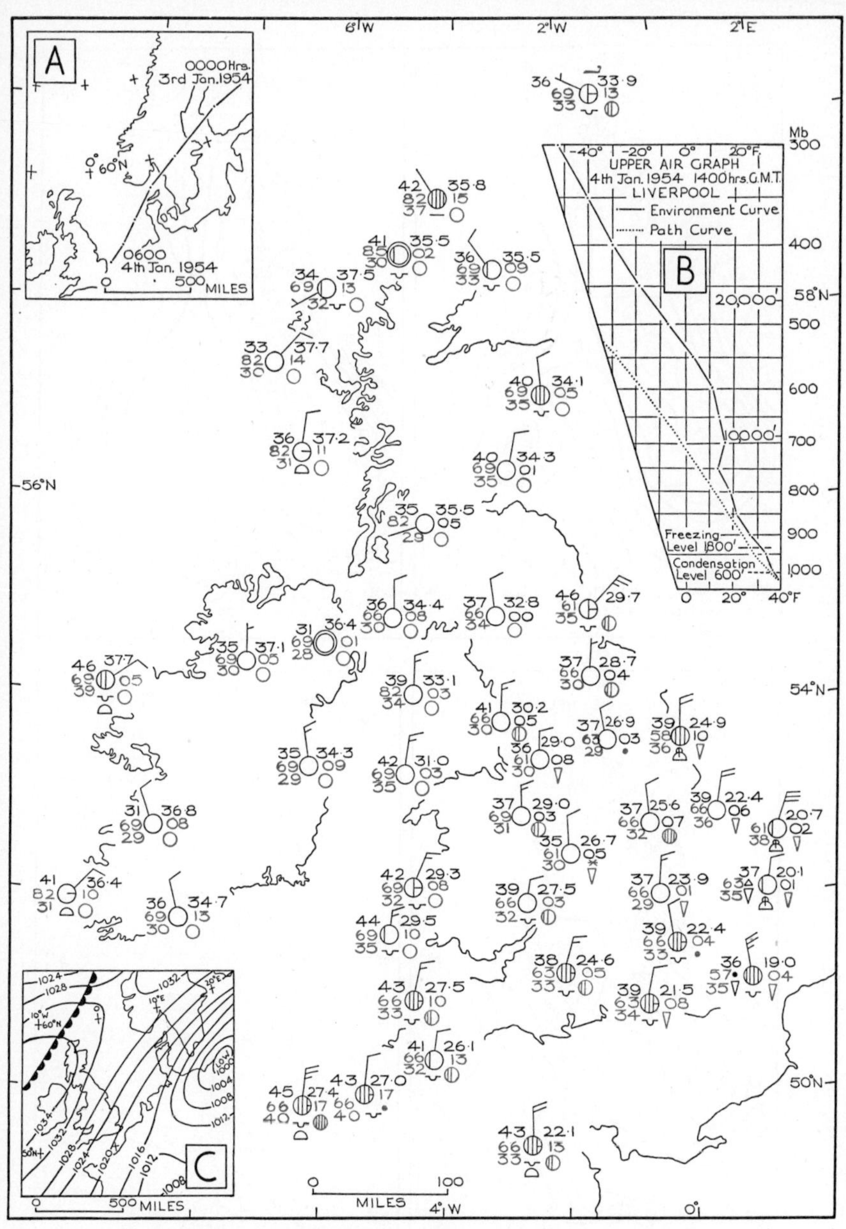

Maps redrawn from the Daily Weather Report 4th January 1954 by permission of the Director-General, Meteorological Office, London. Copyright H.M. Stationery Office.

FIG. 37. — Selected Data for 4th January 1954 : 0600 hrs. G.M.T.
Polar Maritime — P1
Inset A — Track Map ; Inset B — Upper Air Graph
Inset C — Isobars : 0600 hrs. G.M.T. 4th January 1954

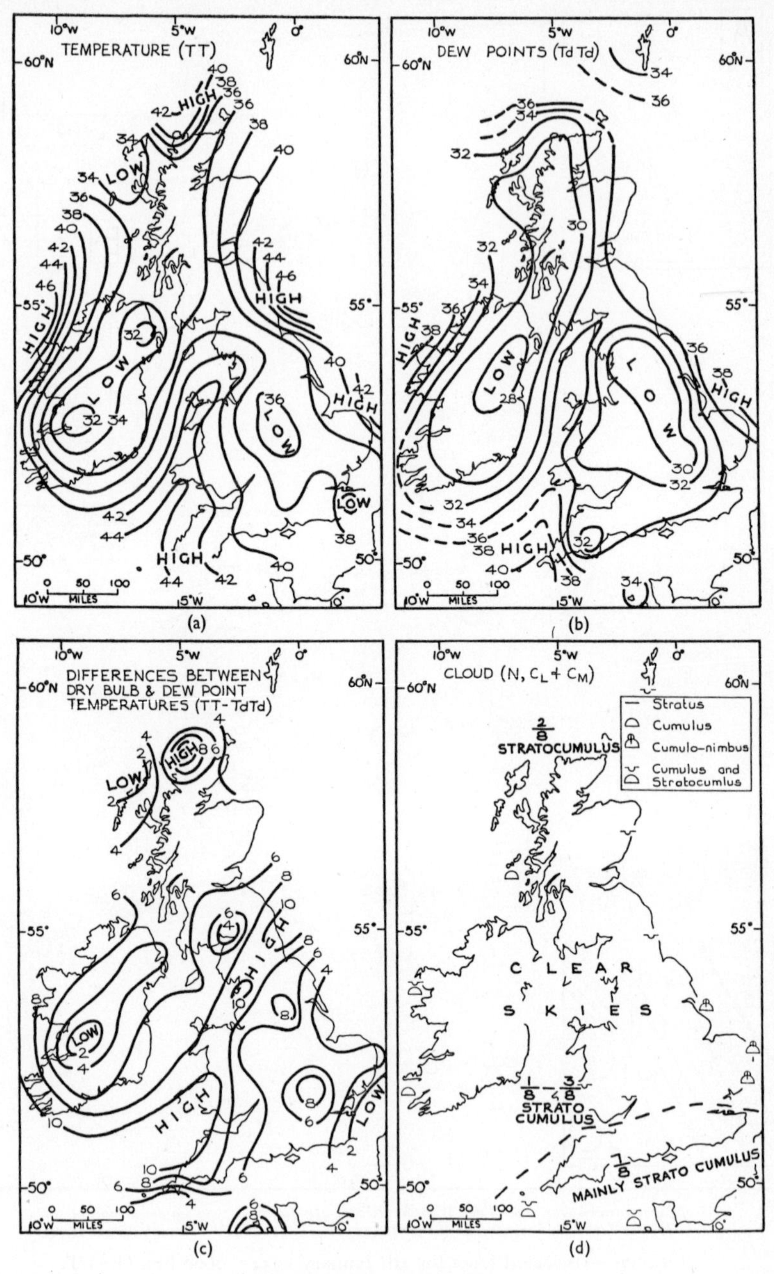

FIG. 37 (*contd.*). — (*a*), (*b*), (*c*), (*d*)

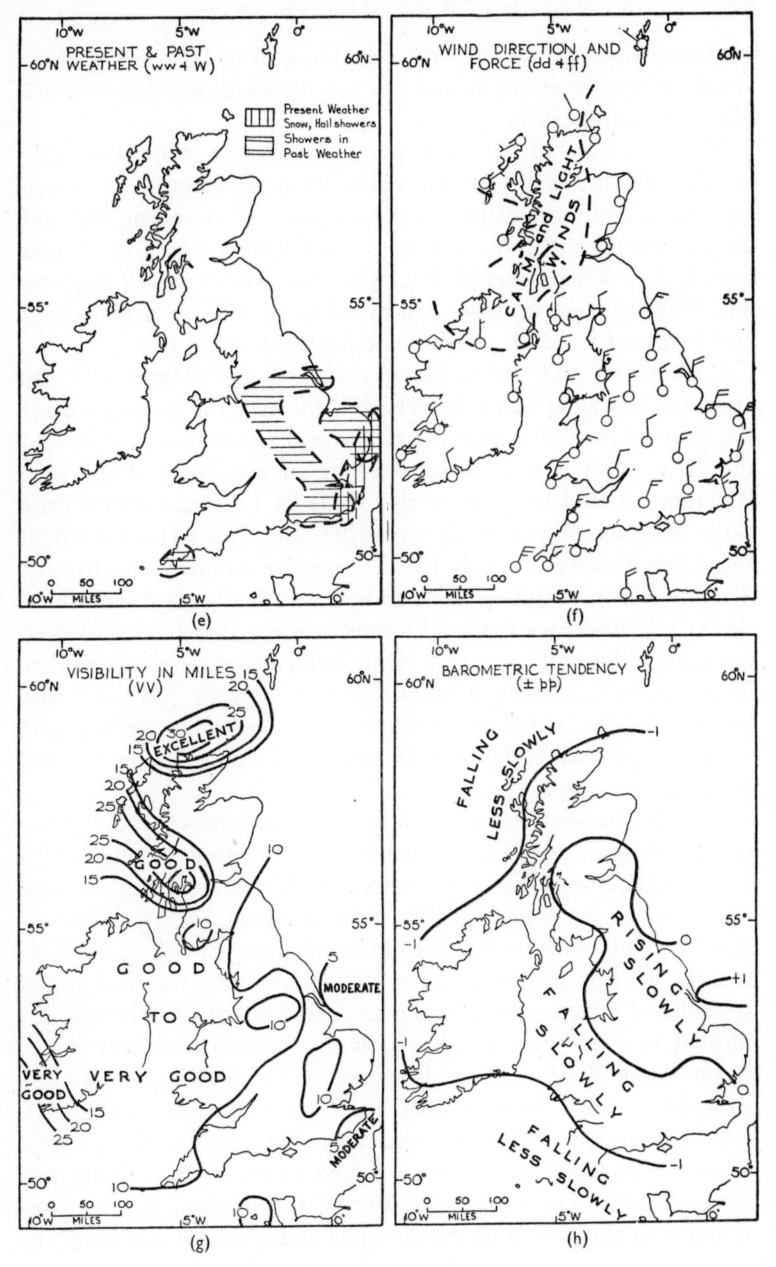

FIG. 37 (*contd.*). — (*e*), (*f*), (*g*), (*h*)

gradient consistently follow the coastlines, in Ireland and Eastern Great Britain for example, and it is very doubtful whether they are of frontal significance.

The character of the dew point distribution map (Fig. 37*b*) is essentially the same as that revealed by air temperatures. There are two inland areas of low dew points (30° F. over England and 28° F. over Ireland) in contrast to coastal areas which in general have higher dew points (38° F.). Over the greater part of England and Wales air temperatures had to fall to 32° F., and over Ireland and Scotland to 30° F., before condensation could occur.

Considering this air is being classified as " Maritime " the atmosphere was in fact relatively dry, for over the greater part of the country the differences between the dry bulb temperature and the dew point temperature were relatively great (Fig. 37*c*). Reference should be made to the Table in Fig. 44. Noteworthy is the belt extending from Tynemouth to St. Anne's Head in which the differences were mainly 10° F.; relative humidity was 65% at Tynemouth and Squires Gate, and 70% at Pembroke Dock whilst the 11° F. difference reported locally at Cape Wrath is equivalent to a relative humidity of 64%. Only in Kent was relative humidity high, viz. 89%. Many stations reported " dry air " in the " past weather ", i.e. a relative humidity of less than 60%[1]; this cannot be plotted on the D.W.R. as there is no symbol for it in the past weather code.

Clouds present were mainly strato-cumulus (Fig. 37*d*); though only in southern England was the cover extensive. In East Anglia, coastal districts reported cumulonimbus clouds though the amounts were slight. This type of cloud has great vertical development which is evidence of the instability of Polar air. Note that the development of cumulonimbus clouds was localised and of sporadic occurrence as were the associated instability showers indicated in the " past weather " in the general area of Central, Eastern and South-eastern England. The distribution of such showers in the " present weather " was more restricted to the coastal areas of Suffolk, Essex and Kent (Fig. 37*e*); in these coastal areas the showers were of snow whilst in the Scilly Islands they were of rain. The easterly location of the showers may be associated with the arrival of the air mass as north-east winds off the

[1] See footnote p. 63.

North Sea, and with local uplift as the air meets the land after a sea crossing.

Winds (Fig. 37*f*) were from a northerly or north-easterly quarter and were moderate to strong except in North-west Scotland where they were light and variable in direction with some stations reporting calms.

As may be expected in air from a Polar source visibility in general was good — 10 to 15 miles (Fig. 37*g*) and locally up to 30 miles (Sule Skerry and Cape Wrath).

The pressure gradient was relatively weak (Fig. 37*h*) in Scotland and North-west Ireland as shown by the widely spaced isobars (inset map C, Fig. 37) and it is reflected in the light winds and calms (Fig. 37*f*). Over the rest of the British Isles isobars were evenly spaced and relatively close together having a general trend NNE. to SSW. Pressure was high generally and was changing only very slowly (Fig. 37*g*).

To summarise, at 0600 hours on the 4th January, 1954, the north-easterly origin of the air, its relative coldness, and the northerly direction of the surface winds, together with the instability showers and general absence in all patterns of such discontinuities as are associated with fronts, would all appear to indicate the presence of one air mass only, which was of Polar origin. Further, the long journey over Scandinavia has given this air mass many features of "continentality", for example, its relative dryness, and it would appear that air masses of this type are in many ways intermediate in character between Polar-Maritime air masses on the one hand and Polar-Continental air masses on the other. The example clearly demonstrates how air masses can be much modified in transit from their source to the British Isles.

As noted above there appear to be no discontinuities in these general patterns such as would be associated with frontal conditions. However, there is some evidence of a broad contrast between weather over North-west Scotland and over South-east England, which demands some explanation. This contrast is not apparent in either the dry bulb temperature (Fig. 37*a*) or the dew point temperature (Fig. 37*b*) distributions but it is visible on the "past" and "present weather" map (Fig. 37*e*). All the showers occurred in South-east England, for example. Again the calms on the wind map are confined to North-west Scotland. Also visibility (Fig. 37*g*) appears to have been much better over North-west Scotland than over South-east England. The reason for these differences could be that whilst South-east England with straight isobars was under the influence of the Polar air mass in question, North-west Scotland with more widely spaced and curving isobars was probably under the influence of an anticyclone located some 300 miles to the west of Ireland as is shown by the inset map C (Fig. 37).

Polar-Maritime Air : P5

16th January, 1954, 0600 hours G.M.T.

It has been previously noted that air originating to the west and north-west of Iceland (P3 to P7 types inclusive, (Fig. 30)) can follow one of several tracks to Britain. Some, e.g. P3 and P4, come relatively direct from the north-west; others, e.g. P5, are less direct arriving from a westerly point whilst one or two, P7 for example, reach Britain from the south-west after an even longer sea journey. These types of Polar-Maritime air inevitably have varied characteristics. The average daily mean surface temperature at Kew, for example, has been noted by Belasco,[1] to lie between 39° F. for P3 air, and 47° F. for P7 air, in winter (Fig. 32). In the summer months the differences are not as marked. The average temperature at 10,000 feet (approx.) is 3° F. and 16° F., respectively, in winter.

To illustrate the characteristics of Polar-Maritime air masses coming from a westerly direction the synoptic situation for the British Isles on the 16th January, 1954 at 0600 hours will now be studied. At this time, a steady westerly air stream was established consequent upon the eastward movement the preceding day of a deep depression to the Baltic Sea area.

If a sample of air over Central Ireland at 0600 hours on 16th January, 1954 be traced back geostrophically (inset map A, Fig. 38) it will be seen that the air was in a position between Iceland and Greenland (63° N. 32° W.) in the early hours of the 15th January, thus indicating the likelihood of a Polar source of the sample. A southerly track was taken to 60° N. and then a more

[1] See p. 50. *op. cit.* Belasco, 1952.

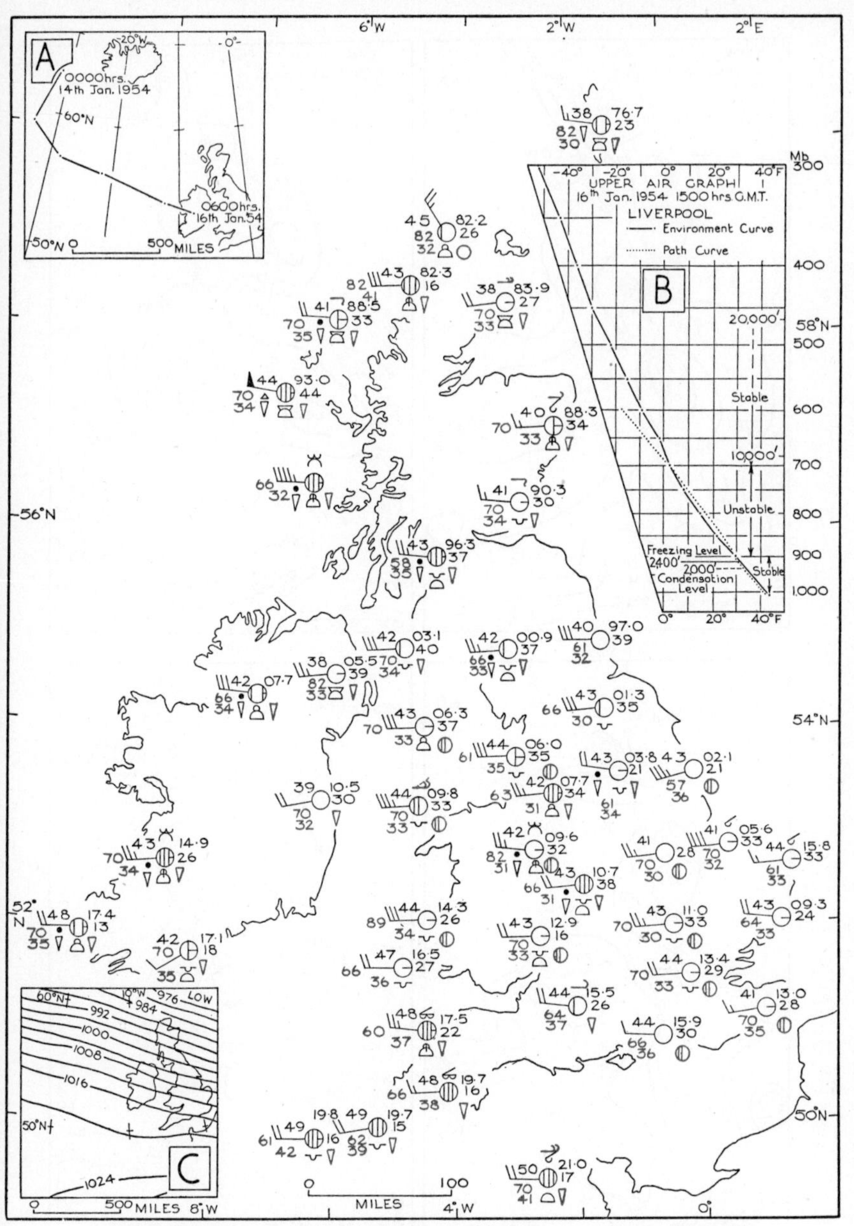

Maps redrawn from the Daily Weather Report 16th January 1954 by permission of the Director-General, Meteorological Office, London. Copyright H.M. Stationery Office.

FIG. 38. — Selected Data for 16th January 1954 : 0600 hrs. G.M.T.
Polar Maritime — P5
Inset A — Track Map ; Inset B — Upper Air Graph
Inset C — Isobars : 0600 hrs. G.M.T. 16th January 1954

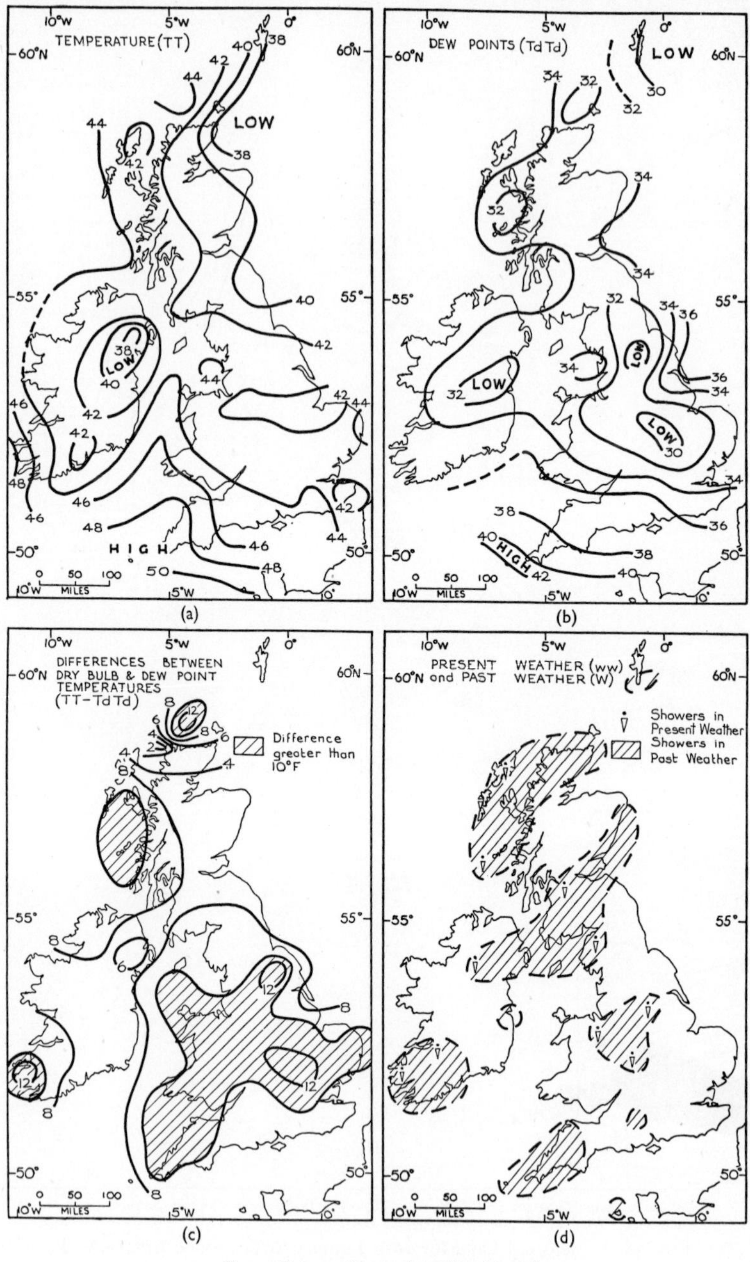

FIG. 38 (*contd.*). — (*a*), (*b*), (*c*), (*d*)

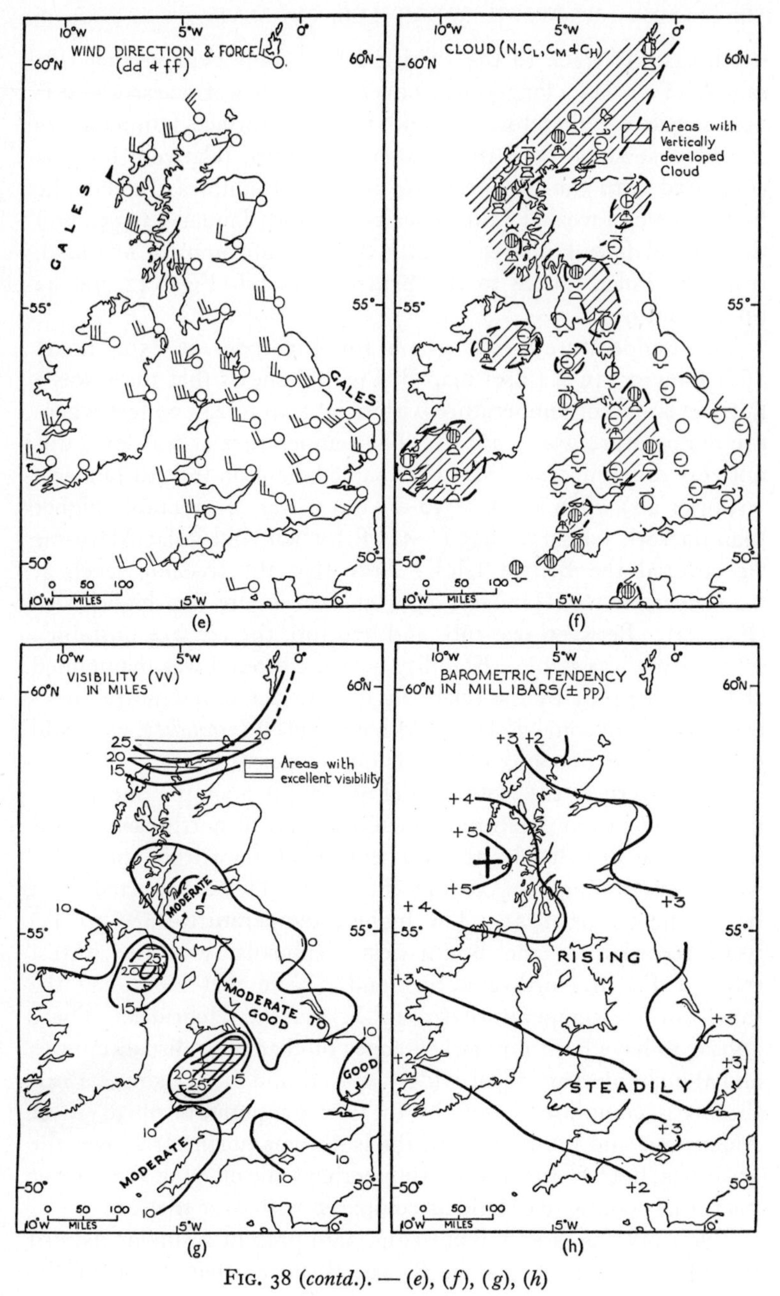

FIG. 38 (*contd.*). — (*e*), (*f*), (*g*), (*h*)

south-easterly track to the British Isles. It is evident that this sample of air had a long journey over relatively warm seas and it is not surprising, therefore, to find that the surface temperatures recorded at stations in the British Isles were relatively high as compared with the two previous air mass examples studied, the first of which revealed a direct sea route (18th January, 1955), and the second (4th January, 1954) a direct route, mostly overland, from the Polar source to the British Isles (cf. Figs. 42 and 43 pp. 98 and 99).

The temperature/height graph for Liverpool at 1500 hours 16th January, 1954 (inset map B, Fig. 38) shows that there was a fairly even fall of temperature with height up to 24,000 feet where the temperature was −36° F. The temperature at this level was not very different from that at the same height on the 4th January, 1954 (P1 air) when it was −30° F. but it was considerably higher than on 18th January, 1955 (−55° F.) when cold Polar-Maritime air covered the British Isles. Note that the freezing level, at 2,200 feet on 16th January, 1954 at 1500 hours was higher also (Fig. 43). Between 900 mb. and 720 mb. the air was unstable; otherwise it was stable. Stability near the ground was maintained at Liverpool only by the relatively low surface temperature, however; a rise of some 2° F. would have caused *instability*, as would have any forced cooling of the air due to ascent.

The pattern of the isotherms (Fig. 38*a*) is a simple one with a general fall in temperature from south-west to north-east. Over most of the British Isles the temperatures came within the somewhat limited range of 40°–44° F., as might be expected in a homogeneous air mass. The highest temperatures (48°–50° F.) were recorded in the South-west Peninsula, and the lowest (38°–40° F.) in North-east Scotland. Note that Kent had the same surface temperature (*c.* 42° F.) as the Hebrides. There appear to have been no marked zones of change or discontinuities and the simple pattern of widely spaced and rather sinuous isotherms is complicated only by the low temperature of 38° F. at Aldergrove and by the turn of the isotherms northwards over the Irish Sea, both features indicating perhaps the effect of the greater nocturnal cooling over land as compared with over the sea.

The isopleths of dew point (Fig. 38*b*) present a similar pattern though the values are some 8°–10° F. lower than those of the temperature distribution just considered. The dew point distribution indicates that over the greater part of the Midlands and North-east England the air would have had to cool to 32° F. before condensation could occur; elsewhere, cooling to 34° F. would have produced the same result except in Devon and Cornwall where condensation would have occurred at 38°–40° F. Generally speaking, the highest dew points were reported at coastal stations and the lowest ones at inland stations indicating the prominence of local land-sea effects and suggesting the absence of frontal discontinuities.

It has been noted previously (p. 55) that Polar air at the source has a low relative humidity due to the incapacity of air at low temperatures to hold very much moisture. On moving to warmer latitudes the capacity for holding moisture is increased as air temperature rises. In spite of the oceanic path in this example, the map (Fig. 38*c*) showing the isopleths of the difference[1] between the dry bulb and dew point temperatures is characterised by large areas where the difference is greater than 10° F. Most of Southern England had differences of 10°–13° F. which may be equated with a relative humidity of 67%; Northern England and Ireland had differences of 7°–9° F. (relative humidity 73%–76%). Isolated examples of large differences were reported at Tiree (12° F. = relative humidity 63%) and Sule Skerry (13° F. = relative humidity 60%). Perhaps dryness to this degree is not typical of Polar-Maritime air, though "bracing" weather, implying cool, relatively dry conditions, is to be expected.

Winds (Fig. 38*e*) were consistently from the west, between WSW. and WNW. and there were no discontinuities in the pattern. These winds were strong generally and along the east coast and in the Hebrides they reached gale force, e.g. Spurnhead 35 knots and Tiree 43 knots.

The showery precipitation characteristic of Polar air is well shown on Fig. 38*d*. On 16th January, 1954 at 0600 hours G.M.T. widespread showers were reported mostly in the "past weather" but also in the "present weather" mainly in the north and west rather than in the east and south of the British Isles, as may be expected when a WNW. airstream is forced to ascend over high ground for the first time.

[1] See Fig. 44, p. 100.

Except in North-west and Central Scotland, parts of the East Midlands, South Lancashire, the South-west Peninsula and Ireland, cloud amounts were generally low (Fig. 38*f*). Many of the stations located in lowland areas reported stratus cloud. Others, particularly in highland areas, reported cumulus and cumulonimbus clouds characterised by vertical development to a marked degree, again indicating unstable conditions within the air mass.

Visibility (Fig. 38*g*) varied somewhat but with the exception of Renfrew it was generally greater than 7 miles. Most stations reported 12½ miles visibility and some areas had visibility greater than 20 miles. For one station in the far north of Scotland, Aldergrove, and Aberporth, visibilities were greater than 25 miles. Such unusually excellent visibility may be associated with Polar air (between showers of rain) due to the low humidity of the atmosphere, which, at coastal stations is also free from atmospheric pollution.

Barometric pressure was rising everywhere and was not changing rapidly (Fig. 38*h*). A rise of from two to three millibars appears to have been about the average barometric change which is very slight when comparison is made with the frontal situations dealt with later. (See Chapter 4.)

The isobars (inset map C, Fig. 38) were straight and closely spaced. They trended from north-west to south-east, and the situation is one which is usually denoted in the weather forecast by the phrase " a westerly airstream covers the British Isles ".

It is now possible to review the evidence as to why this example is firstly concerned with one air mass only, and secondly to consider why the air mass should be labelled Polar-Maritime P5.

In all the distributions considered it will be evident that there are no discontinuities such as to suggest the presence of fronts. The key note is of homogeneity. The consistencies are so strong as to mask local expression of the moderating influence of the sea.

The geostrophic track of the air, the strong westerly winds, the moderate temperature and the dryness of the atmosphere (a feature unusually well developed in this example), the showery precipitation, and the excellent visibility are all strong indications of a *polar* origin of the air mass under review.

In conclusion, it is evident that one air mass covered the British

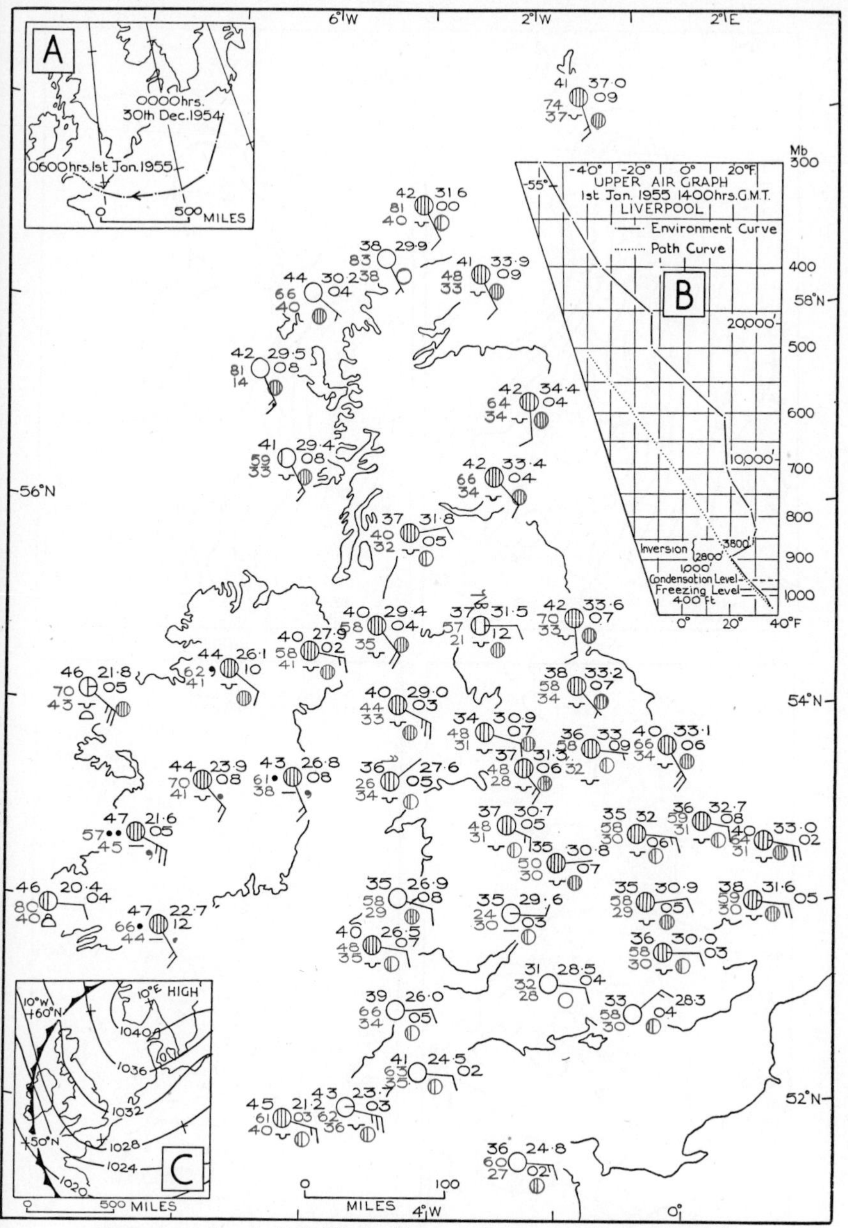

Maps redrawn from the Daily Weather Report 1st January 1955 by permission of the Director-General, Meteorological Office London. Copyright H.M. Stationery Office.

FIG. 39. — Selected Data for 1st January 1955 : 0600 hrs. G.M.T.
Polar Continental — A2
Inset A — Track Map ; Inset B — Upper Air Graph
Inset C — Isobars : 0600 hrs. G.M.T. 1st January 1954

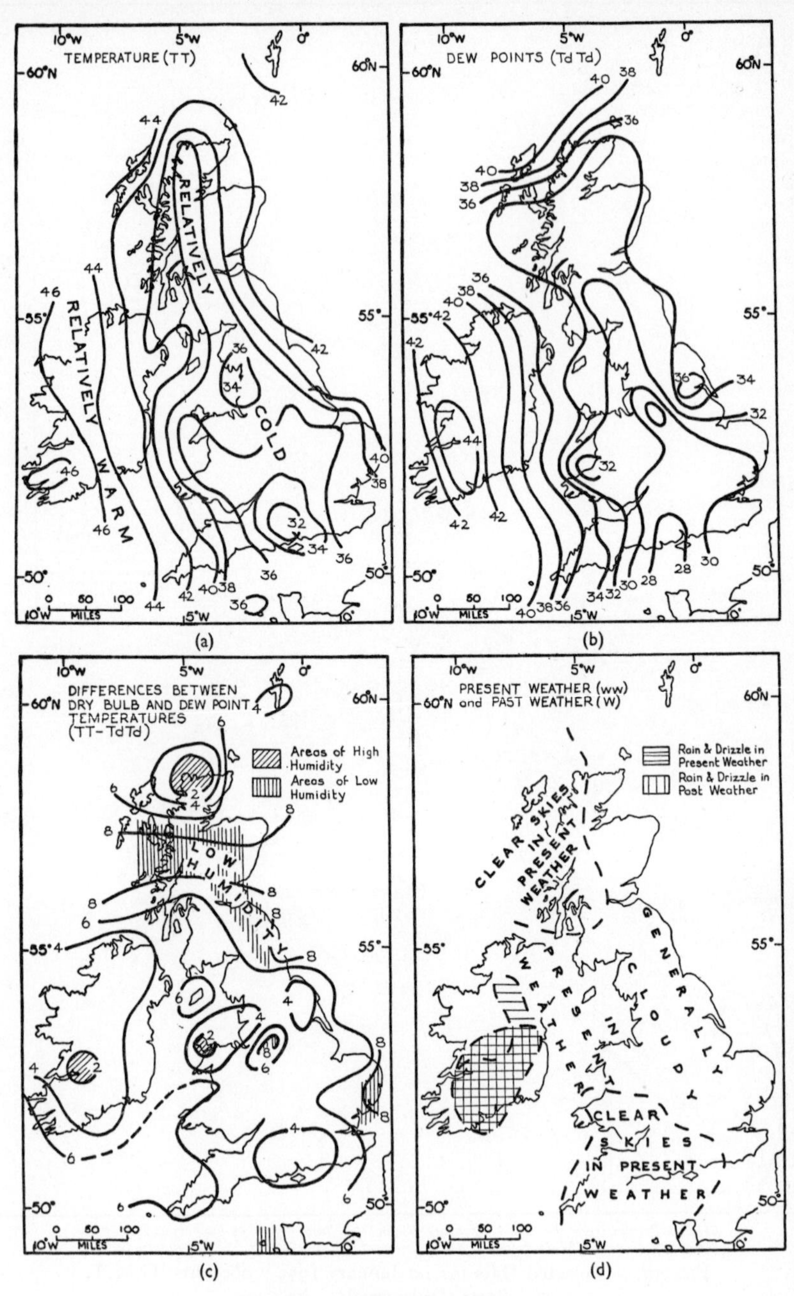

FIG. 39 (*contd.*). — (*a*), (*b*), (*c*), (*d*)

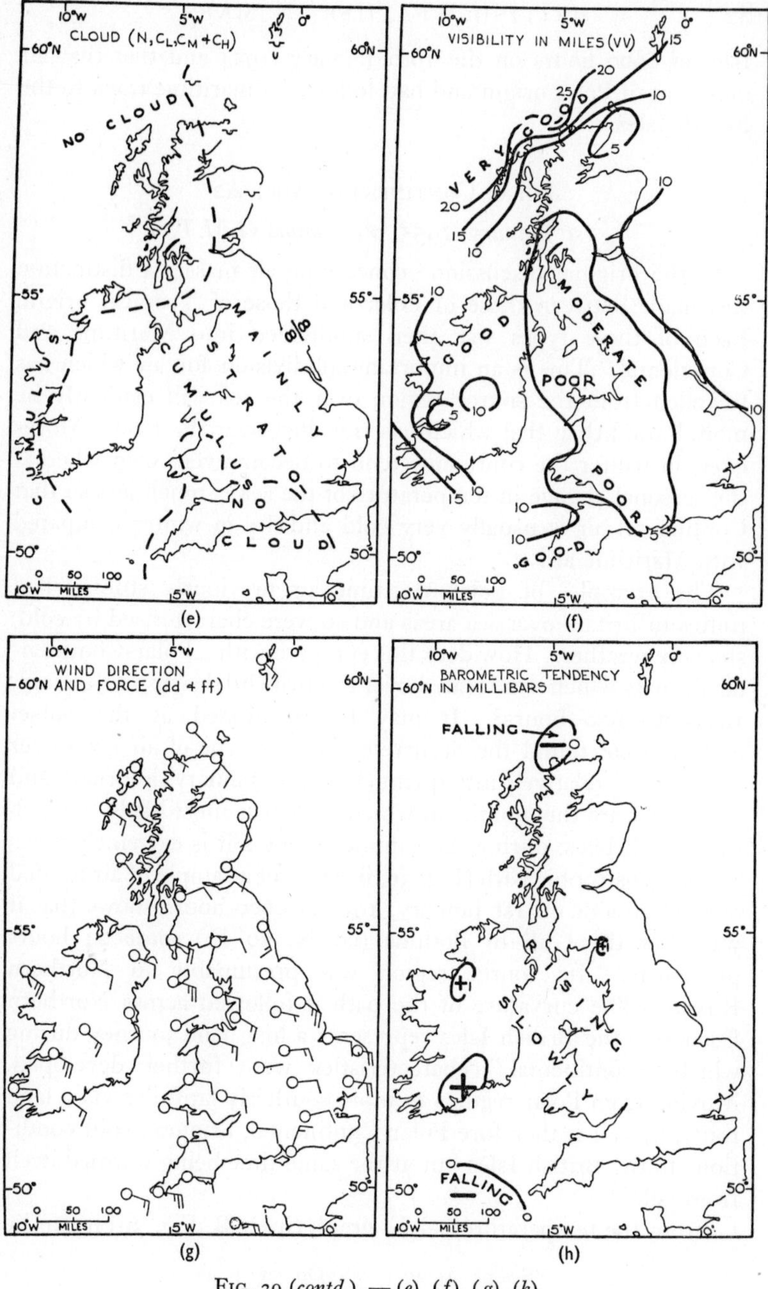

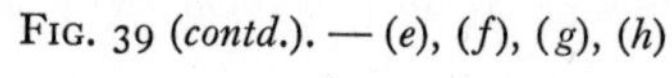

FIG. 39 (*contd.*). — (*e*), (*f*), (*g*), (*h*)

Isles at 0600 hours on the 16th January, 1954 and that that air mass was of Polar origin and had followed a maritime track to the British Isles.

POLAR-CONTINENTAL AIR: A2

1st January, 1955, 0600 hours G.M.T.

In the original discussion [1] concerning air masses a distinction was made between those of Polar and those of Tropical origin. Each of these types was then subdivided into Maritime and Continental. This is an important subdivision for air which has travelled from the source region over the sea will evidently be more humid than that which has travelled over the land. Moreover, in winter the continents tend to become very cold whereas the seasonal change in temperature of the sea is much less so that Continental air is usually very cold and dry in winter compared with Maritime air.

The examples of Polar-Maritime air previously studied had routes to Britain over sea areas and so were characterised by cold, showery weather. How does this compare with a Polar-Continental air mass which was located over the British Isles on 1st January, 1955 at 0600 hours? It may be mentioned at the outset that Belasco[2] found the occurrence of this type of air mass over Britain to be relatively infrequent (Fig. 31). January, February and December are the months in which this air is most likely to reach the British Isles; during the summer months it is extremely rare.

The geostrophic path (Fig. 39, inset A) of a sample of air located over Dartmoor on 1st January, 1955 at 0600 hours shows that it was over the Gulf of Bothnia (60° N. 20° E.) some 24 hours previously. Its source region was presumably in Northern Russia. The curvature of the path it followed across Northern Europe to the British Isles represents a long land journey during which "continental" characteristics were further developed. Moving from Polar regions to more southerly latitudes via a land route, this air is therefore Polar-Continental, bringing cold conditions to the British Isles but at the same time being warmed itself from below.

From the temperature/height graph (inset B, Fig. 39) it can be

[1] See pp. 45–47 [2] Op. cit., p. 49.

seen that the air would have been unstable in its lowest layers if the temperature were to have risen a further 2° F. However, a marked inversion is located at 905–850 millibars[1] above which there are conditions of great stability. In fact the general aspect of the graph as a whole is one of stability. Note that the temperature at 24,000 feet was −35° F., that the freezing level is at 800 feet (at 1400 hours) and that the condensation level is at 1,200 feet all of which may be compared with the situation at the same station (Liverpool) at the same time (1400 hours) on 7th December, 1953 when Tropical-Continental air covered the British Isles, viz. air temperature of −32° F. at 24,000 feet, a freezing level at 7,500 feet and a condensation level at 3,200 feet.[2] It is of interest to note that relative humidity at the ground at Liverpool was 67%, and that relative humidity increased to a value of 92% at 890 mb.[3] just beneath the inversion. However, there was a very sudden drop in the value of the relative humidity above the inversion until at 780 mb.[4] it was less than 2%. Thus, the characteristic dryness of Continental air appears to have been increased by the effects of an inversion.[5]

The pattern of isotherms (Fig. 39*a*) reveals a belt of cold air lying north-south over Great Britain; for example, Tangmere 33° F., Boscombe Down 31° F., Manchester 34° F. and Cape Wrath 38° F. These low temperatures are probably partly explained by nocturnal cooling over land facilitated by incomplete cloud cover the preceding night and partly by the persistence of cold easterly winds. The highest temperatures occurred over Ireland and the Western Isles; for example, Scilly (45° F.), Valentia and Blacksod Point (46° F.), Stornoway (44° F.) and Lerwick (41° F.). The isotherms trend north to south with stations on the east coast of the British Isles having reported lower temperatures than stations on the west coast of Ireland in the same latitudes. The pattern is essentially a simple inverted " V " shape which is perhaps dominated by the weak cold front which lay over western Ireland and the Hebrides, and which is moving to the west so causing continental conditions to spread westwards from Europe (inset C, Fig. 39).

[1] This is equivalent to a height range of 3,700 to 4,700 feet.
[2] See Fig. 43 p. 99.
[3] This is equivalent to a height of 3,000 feet.
[4] This is equivalent to a height of 6,500 feet.
[5] See Chapter 1, p. 21.

The isopleths for dew point (Fig. 39*b*) present a pattern which repeats the one discussed above for again the area about the Isle of Wight had the lowest dew point temperatures of 28° F. Northwards from this region " V " shaped isopleths extend to include dew points of 33° F. at Wick and Tiree. The highest dew points were reported in Western Ireland (Rineanna 45° F., Blacksod Point 43° F.). Most of England and Wales had dew points below 32° F. and the greater part of Great Britain had dew points below 34° F. In Ireland dew points varied from 36° F. on the east coast to 42°–44° F. on the west coast. The only marked zones of change in horizontal distribution are located in the Hebrides (Stornoway 40° F., Benbecula 34° F.); in Ireland (Aldergrove 36° F., Castle Archdale 41° F.) and in South-west Wales (Aberporth 29° F. Pembroke Dock 35° F.). Whilst these discontinuities may be significant it is difficult to say at this juncture whether there were two air masses or only one covering the British Isles at this time.

Large differences[1] of 6°–8° F. between dry bulb and dew point temperatures are the rule rather than the exception (Fig. 39*c*). Thus relative humidity in general was low and " dry air ", i.e. 60% relative humidity, was frequently reported in the " past weather " observations. The distribution of the isopleths is somewhat complex with low differences locally, such as Holyhead (93%), being adjacent to high differences locally, as at Manchester (72%). Northern Scotland, with differences of 8° F. had a general relative humidity of 73% whilst the differences of 5° F. reported over most of England and Wales may be equated with a relative humidity of 82%.

Concerning the " past weather " and " present weather " (Fig. 39*d*) the greater part of England was generally cloudy, but in North-east Scotland, South-west England and South Wales clear skies predominated. Rain and drizzle had developed only in Central and Southern Ireland where humidity was somewhat higher than elsewhere. This may quite well be associated with the weak cold front which has already been noted to lie over those areas.

Cloud amounts (Fig. 39*e*) were generally eight-eighths, except in South-west England, South Wales, the west coast of Ireland and the Hebrides all of which reported no cloud. The dominant cloud type was strato-cumulus, a layer type of cloud, located at 2,000 to

[1] See Fig. 44 p. 100.

3,000 feet which corresponds to the height of the inversion on the temperature/height graph (inset B, Fig. 39). It would appear that the cloud formation can be associated with the presence of the inversion and thus this cloud cannot be taken as being typical of Polar-Continental air. Further, examinations of D.W.R.'s for the previous day (31st December, 1954) in any event indicate the persistence of old warm sectors with associated strato-cumulus cloud over the British Isles.

Visibility was very good only in the Hebrides (Fig. 39*f*), elsewhere it was moderate to good, with poor visibility over the Severn Estuary and the Irish Sea. Undoubtedly, this moderate visibility is not in this instance truly characteristic of Polar air and again it can be explained by the trapping of dust, etc. beneath the inversion already noted.

Winds (Fig. 39*g*) blew from the east and were generally light to moderate in strength as can be expected from the widely spaced isobars (inset map C, Fig. 39) which trend NNW. to SSE. An exception had to be made when the west coastal areas of Ireland were considered for here a cold front was marked by stronger winds, though they were still from the east. Pressure was generally high (Tynemouth 1033·6 millibars) and was tending to increase slightly (Fig. 39*h*). The whole pressure pattern (inset C, Fig. 39) shows part of an anticyclone whose centre was over Norway so that the British Isles lay in its south-west quadrant and therefore received easterly winds as they flowed clockwise round the high pressure centre.

Thus, in summary, the track of the air, its coldness and dryness together with the fact that there was a cold front moving westwards over Ireland, would point to the presence of Polar-Continental air over Britain at 0600 hours on 16th January, 1954, but the development of the inversion prevented the incidence of the showery conditions and the occurrence of excellent visibility which are both normally associated with Polar air.

Tropical-Maritime Air: T1

16th January, 1953, 0600 hours

The air masses so far considered originated in cold, high latitudes of the Northern Hemisphere and have been classified as

Polar. They travelled southwards to relatively warmer middle latitudes and consequently were warmed from below. The present example is of air which originated in the more southerly (lower) latitudes of the Northern Hemisphere.[1] The geostrophic track of a sample of air at Stornoway at 0600 hours on 16th January, 1953 shows that some time previously the air was in a position 50° N. 20° W., that is, 650 miles west of Land's End. It came from a source well to the south-west of the British Isles and has moved north-eastwards to relatively cooler latitudes via an oceanic route (inset map A, Fig. 40).

At its source Tropical-Maritime air is generally characterised by high temperature, high humidity and a fair degree of stability. Contact with the cooler land, or as in this example, with the cooler sea, on its northward journey causes cooling from below; a diminished lapse rate results, in fact an inversion may be formed. These developments are conducive to increased stability. The relative humidity is increased and the dew point is soon reached with the result that fog and stratus cloud frequently develop accompanied locally by drizzle and light to medium, steady rain and generally moderate to poor visibility. A descriptive analysis of the present air mass will reveal the extent to which it conforms with this standard pattern for Tropical-Maritime air masses.

From the temperature/height graph (inset B, Fig 40) which is based on data for Liverpool at 1500 hours 16th January, 1953 note that the air has been so extensively cooled on its journey northwards that there is a marked inversion from 950 mbs. to 900 mbs.[2] — a zone of great stability. Below the inversion the air was stable also. Note that the *representative temperature* [3] should be in the region of 54° F. at the ground. The temperature at 24,000 feet was − 23° F. which is somewhat higher than that recorded at the same height and time of day at Liverpool on 18th January, 1955 when the temperature was − 51° F. and cold Polar-Maritime air covered the British Isles. The freezing level, too, at 1500 hours on 16th January, 1953, was not reached until 8,300 feet which is appreciably higher than for any example so far considered. The condensation level, on the other hand, was quite low at 700

[1] cf. Fig. 42.
[2] This is equivalent to a height range of 1,300 feet to 2,800 feet.
[3] See p. 24.

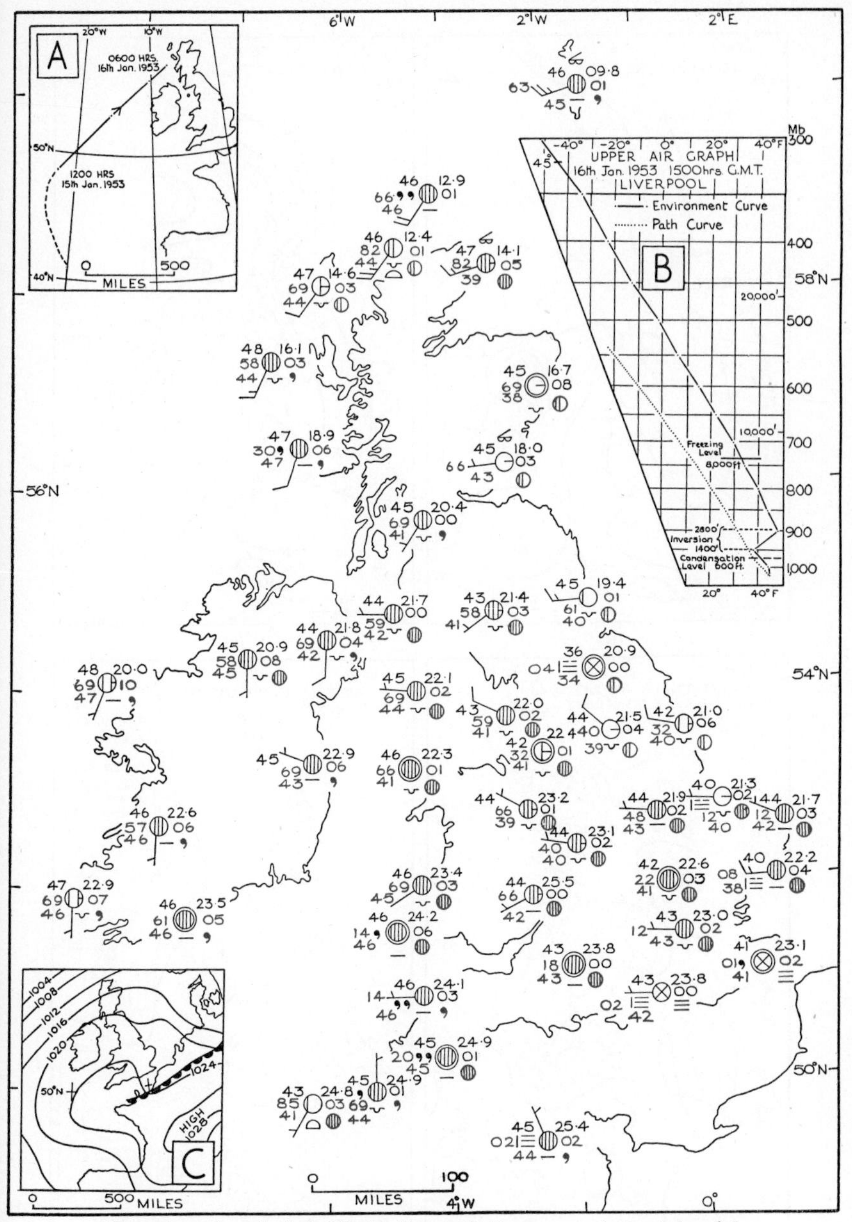

Maps redrawn from the Daily Weather Report 16th January 1953 by permission of the Director-General, Meteorological Office, London. Copyright H.M. Stationery Office.

FIG. 40. — Selected Data for 16th January 1953 : 0600 hrs. G.M.T.
Tropical Maritime — T1
Inset A — Track Map ; Inset B — Upper Air Graph
Inset C — Isobars : 0600 hrs. G.M.T. 16th January 1953

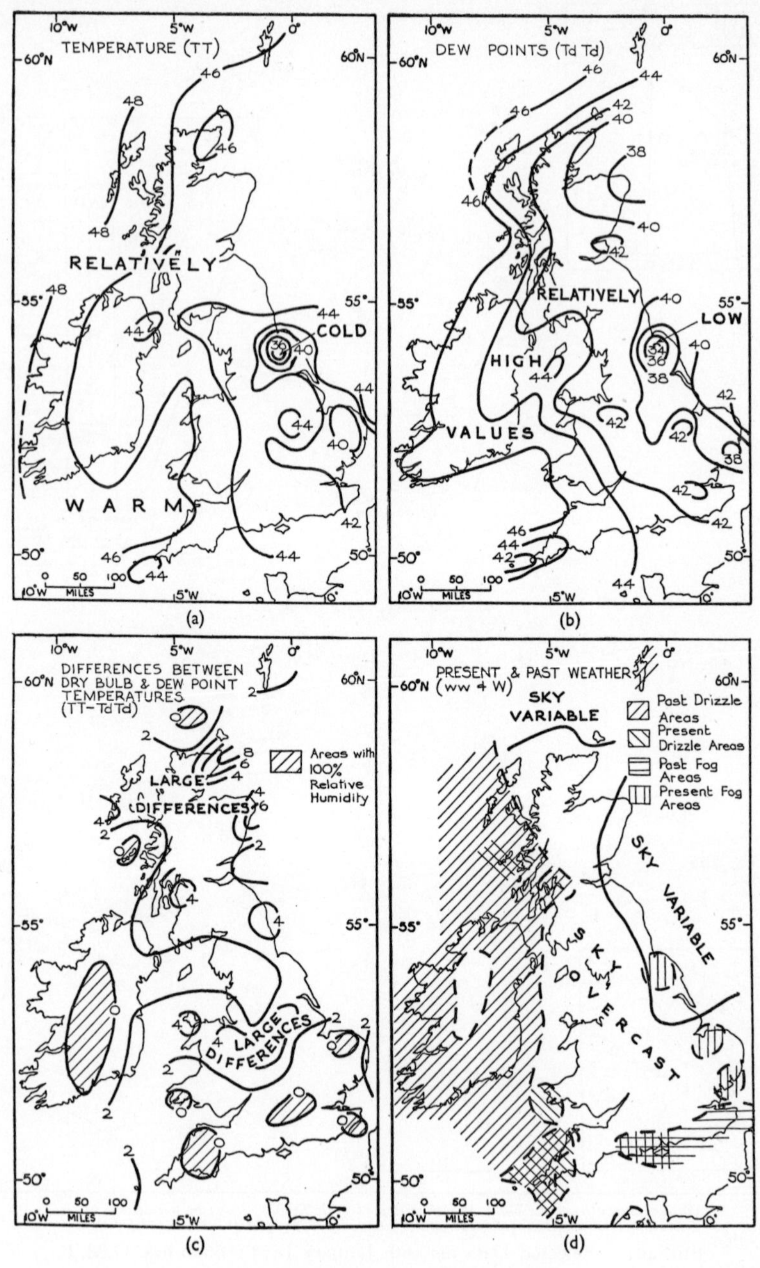

FIG. 40 (*contd.*). — (*a*), (*b*), (*c*), (*d*)

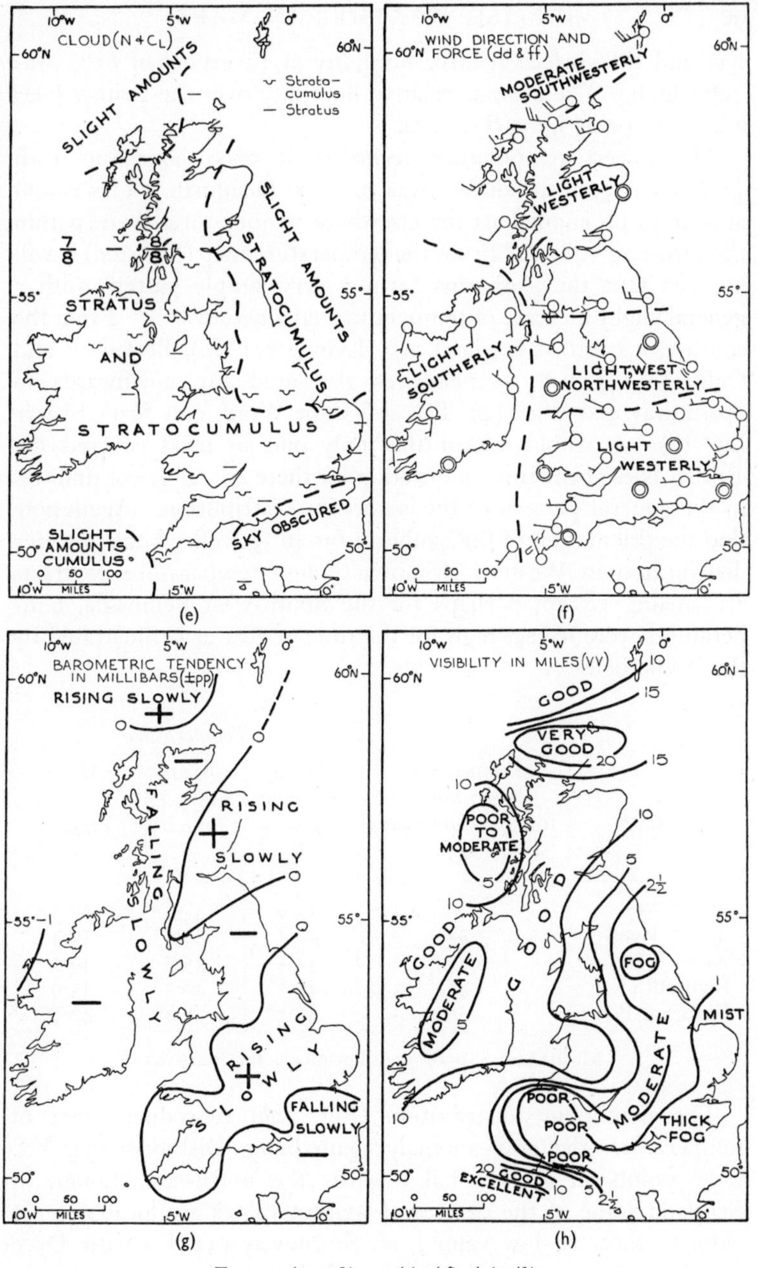

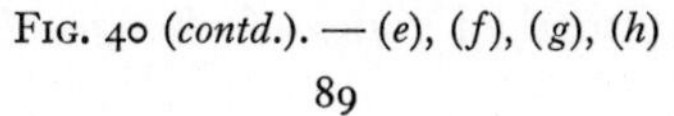

FIG. 40 (*contd.*). — (*e*), (*f*), (*g*), (*h*)

feet and the surface relative humidity at Liverpool of 85% was quite high. The average relative humidity over the British Isles was high, being 93% (Fig. 43).

The lowest temperature recorded at 0600 hours on 16th January, 1953 at the surface was 36° F. at Dishforth. This would appear to be anomalous for elsewhere temperatures were within the range 40°–48° F. From the temperature map (Fig. 40*a*) it will be seen that the isotherms form a very simple pattern with a general slight increase of temperature northwestwards. From the south-east coast of England, e.g. Lympe (41° F.), Plymouth and Culdrose (45° F.), temperatures rise gradually northwards to Stornoway and Wick (47° F.), and Cape Wrath and Skule Skerry (46° F.). It would appear that only one air mass covered the British Isles at the time in question for there are no discontinuities in the general pattern of the isothermal distribution. Again note that the orientation of the isotherm for 46° F. reflects the land/sea distribution in Western Britain although temperature contrasts are small. Except perhaps for the South-west Peninsula, temperatures were in fact high for the time of year as is illustrated by the Table below.

Station	*Temperature 0600 hours 16th January, 1953* °F.	*Temperature*		
		Mean maximum January °F.	*Mean minimum January* °F.	*Mean daily January* °F.
Stornoway	43	43·9	37·1	40·5
Spurn Head	42	42·4	36·5	39·4
Kew	47	44·5	35·7	40·1
Plymouth	45	47·5	40·3	43·9
Blacksod Point	48	46·5*	38·8*	42·7*

* Means for 1881–1915 : other means for 1921–1950

The dew point distribution (Fig. 40*b*) reproduces that of temperature, the only anomaly again being Dishforth (34° F.). Dew points in general fall towards the north-east though in Scotland some of the centres of highest values are located quite close to those of low value ; cf. Stornoway (44° F.) with Dyce (38° F.). Even so, marked zones of change of any great extent are absent from the map. Over the greater part of Scotland cooling to 39°–42° F. would have produced condensation; cooling to 40°–42° F. over the greater part of England and to 42°–45° F. over Wales and 44°–46° F. over Ireland and the South-west Peninsula would also have produced condensation.

The dry bulb/dew point temperature differences[1] (Fig. 40*c*) show that over Central Ireland and isolated parts of England and Wales south of a line Aberystwyth to the Wash, the air was at its dew point (i.e. relative humidity 100%). Elsewhere in these areas the differences of 2° F. may be equated with relative humidity of 93%. In Central England and North Wales the differences of 4° F. indicate 85% relative humidity whilst north of the line Spurn Head to Silloth the relative humidity was 90% except at the east coast stations of Dyce and Wick where the low values of 80% and 74% respectively were recorded. Note that the moist areas were often coastal, especially on the south and west coast where orographic uplift could cause cooling to the dew point with resultant fog and drizzle.

This point is illustrated in the map of "past" and "present weather" (Fig. 40*d*) which shows that those areas with the air at or near its dew point coincide with the fog areas of East, South-east and Southern England and the drizzle area of the South-west Peninsula. In the "past weather" the drizzle area was much more extensive than at 0600 hrs. G.M.T. for it occupied almost the whole of Ireland, the west coast of Scotland and coastal portions of the South-west Peninsula. It is noteworthy that the D.W.R. for 0000 hours on the 16th January, 1953 showed that stations in these areas were reporting dry bulb and dew point temperatures to be the same.

With the exception of the Hebrides and the east coast from Dyce to the Wash, cloud amounts were small (Fig. 40*e*). The cloud types were generally stratus and strato-cumulus with the latter predominant and the amounts were generally seven-eighths to eight-eighths. The height of this cloud between 2,000 to 2,800 feet is significant when reference is made to the inversion already noted on the temperature/height graph.

Wind direction (Fig. 40*f*) was generally from westerly points except over Ireland where it was southerly. Wind force was light except in Northern Scotland where it was moderate. The light

[1] See Fig. 44, p. 100.

winds and calms in South-east England no doubt facilitated the formation of the fog in that area and favoured its persistence; Felixstowe, for example, had fog, first reported at 0000 hours on the 15th January, 1953.

Barometric pressure was high everywhere ranging from 1024·8 millibars at Scilly to 1009·8 millibars at Lerwick (inset map C, Fig. 40). Pressure gradients were weak except in the far north of Scotland where the isobars were more closely spaced evidencing stronger winds. Many stations reported no change in pressure during the preceding 3 hours (Fig. 40*g*) or very slight rises or falls mostly of less than 0·5 millibars.

As might be expected for Tropical air, visibility was not very good except at Scilly and the north coast of Scotland and Ireland (Fig. 40*h*). The frequency of only "good" to "moderate" visibility with extensive areas of "poor" visibility and local fog patches may be compared with visibilities reported when Polar air covered the British Isles[1].

In conclusion, therefore, the track of the air from the south-west, its stability, its high and homogeneous surface temperature indicate that *Tropical* air was in occupation over the British Isles at 0600 hours on 16th January, 1953. Moreover, the high humidity, high dew points, drizzle with low stratus cloud and fog are typical expressions of a *Maritime* origin and *Maritime* journey from warmer latitudes.

TROPICAL-CONTINENTAL AIR: T4

7th December, 1953, 0600 hours G.M.T.

The tropical origin of a sample of air with a surface temperature of 51° F. over Berry Head near Torquay at 0600 hours on 7th December, 1953 is illustrated in inset A, Fig. 41 which shows it was off the coast of North Africa (38° N. 10° E. approx.) on the evening of the 6th December. After crossing the Mediterranean Sea, France and the English Channel this air reached Britain as a warm current from a predominantly easterly direction. On its journey from the source region, which was presumably the North African Desert, the air must have been cooled from below and so was very stable (inset B, Fig. 41). Thus the surface temperature at Liverpool at 1400 hours on 7th December was 48° F. which is

[1] FIG. 37*g*, p. 69.

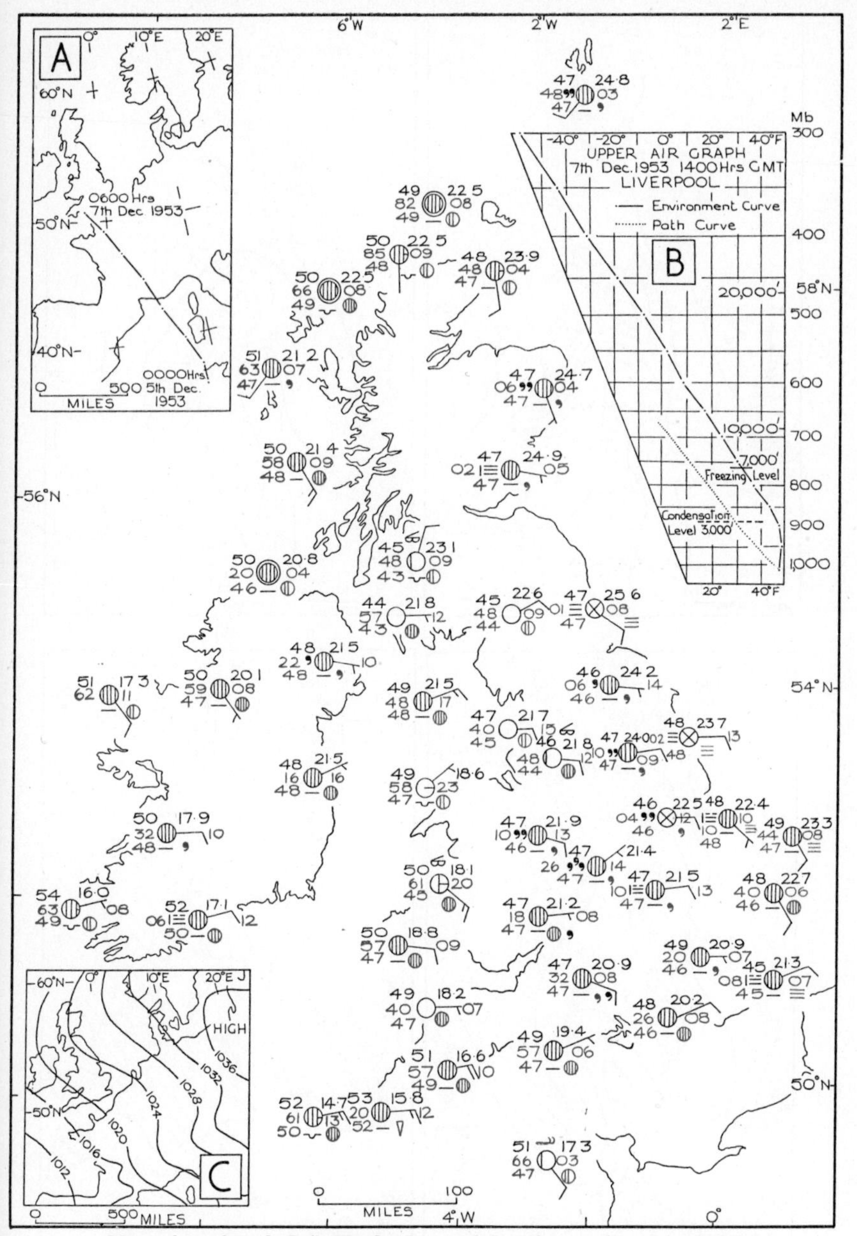

Maps redrawn from the Daily Weather Report 7th December 1953 by permission of the Director-General, Meteorological Office, London. Copyright H.M. Stationery Office.

FIG. 41. — Selected Data for 7th December 1953 : 0600 hrs. G.M.T.
Tropical Continental — T4
Inset A — Track Map ; Inset B — Upper Air Graph
Inset C — Isobars : 0600 hrs. 7th December 1953

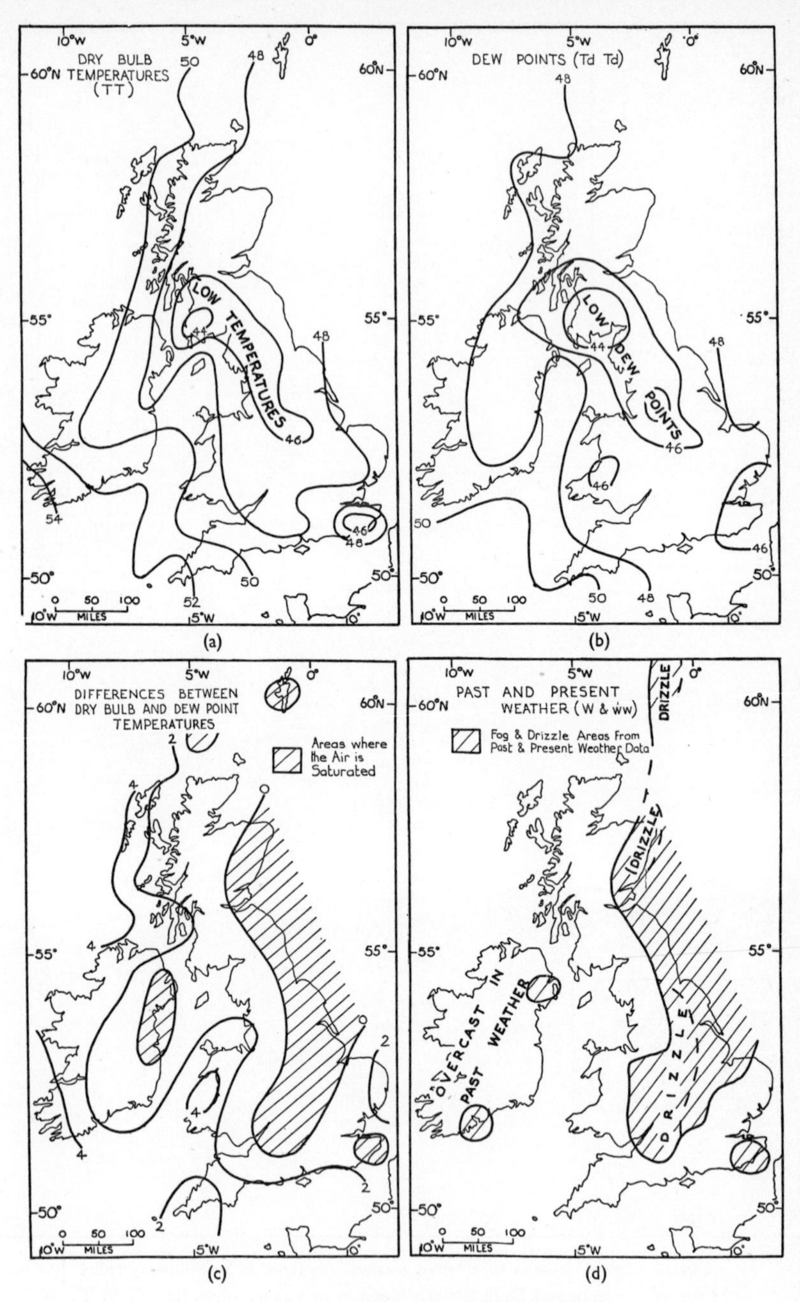

FIG. 41 (*contd.*). — (*a*), (*b*), (*c*), (*d*)

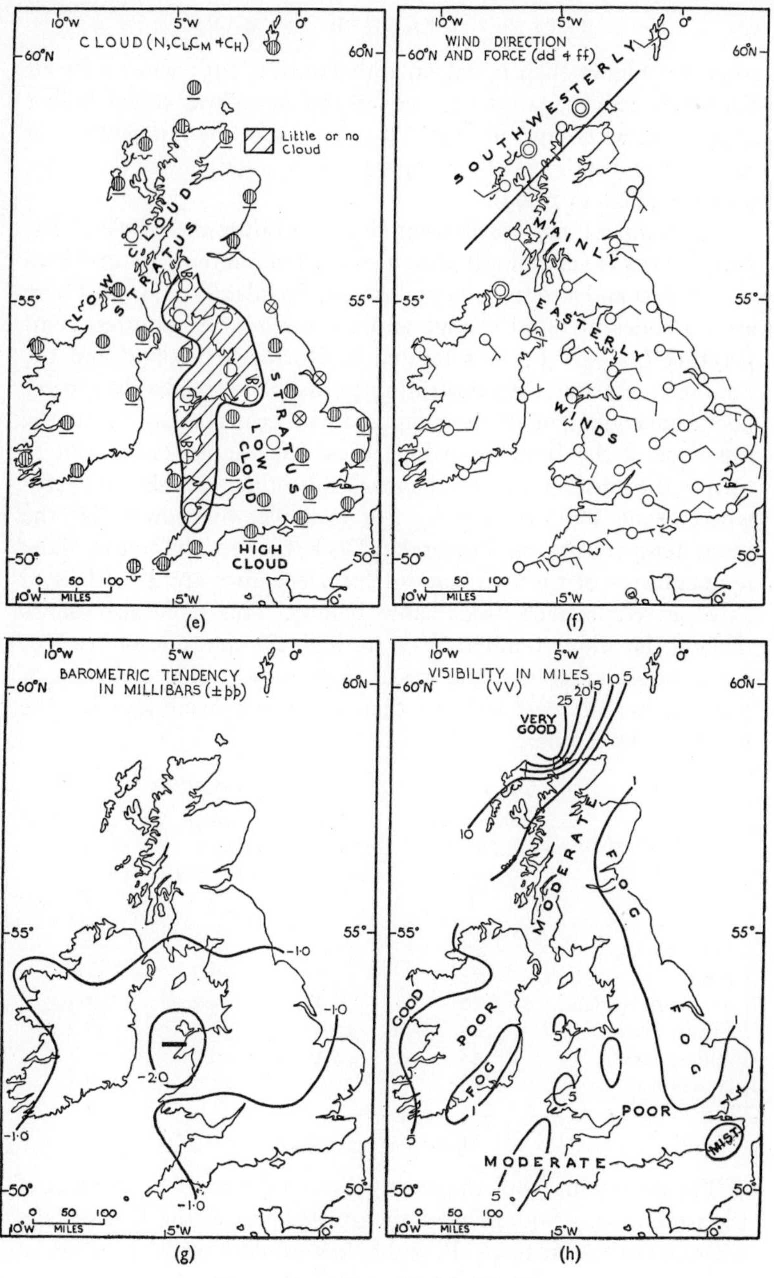

FIG. 41 (*contd.*). — (*e*), (*f*), (*g*), (*h*)

some 10° higher than it was on 18th January, 1955 when a P1 air mass was in occupation[1]; the freezing level was much higher (7,500 feet as compared with 1,500 feet) and the temperature at 24,000 feet was −32° F. compared with −51° F. on the other occasion (Fig. 43 p. 99).

The temperature distribution (Fig. 41*a*) over the whole of the British Isles is very simple with a gradual fall in temperature from west to east and also from coastal stations to inland stations. There are no zones of rapid change and the main zone of lowest temperature (44°–46° F.) was located in Northern England and the Southern Uplands demonstrating perhaps the relatively greater nocturnal cooling inland as compared with coastal areas. Note the influence of the Irish Sea which caused isotherms crossing it to turn to the north — in fact, the maritime influence is shown everywhere along the west coast. For example, Stornoway has the same temperature as Pembroke Dock though the mean daily temperatures of the two stations for December are 41·7° F. and 45·2° F. respectively (see Table below). This table also shows that on the whole temperatures are high for the time of year for it may be seen that temperatures at 0600 hours 7th December, 1953 were higher at most stations than the mean maximum for the month of December.

Station	*Temperature* 0600 *hours* 7*th December* 1953 °F.	*Temperature*		
		Mean maximum December °F.	*Mean daily December* °F.	*Mean minimum December* °F.
Felixstowe	48	43·9	40·7	37·5
Scilly	52	49·7	47·2	44·6
St. Anne's Head	50	48·0	45·2	42·3
Spurn Head	48	43·6	40·9	38·2
Aldergrove	48	44·3	40·7	37·1
Stornoway	50	45·0	41·7	38·4

Means for 1921–1950

The dew point isopleth pattern (Fig. 41*b*) reflects closely that of the isotherms. Note that for the greater part of the British Isles a cooling of the air to 48° F. and below would have been sufficient

[1] See p. 99.

to cause condensation; compare this with the dew point of 34° F. which was characteristic on the morning of 1st January when Polar-Continental air covered the British Isles (Fig. 39).

The distribution of the differences between[1] the temperature and the dew point (Fig. 41*c*) shows that extending along the east coast of Great Britain from Dyce, to Lincolnshire and well into the Midlands and as far west as Ross-on-Wye was an area in which the air was already saturated and it is not surprising to find that this coincides with the fog and drizzle area shown on the map depicting "past" and "present weather" (Fig. 41*d*). Note that the fog area was mostly coastal, being succeeded inland by the drizzle area. Similarly, moist air with fog and drizzle were reported along the east coast of Ireland, north and south of Dublin. The relatively higher differences in West Wales, Western Ireland and in the Western Islands should also be noted.

Cloud cover (Fig. 41*e*) was generally abundant except along the west coast from Prestwick to Chivenor. Usually the cloud was stratus, variable in height, though generally with a cloud base below 1,000 feet.

Surface winds (Fig. 41*f*) were generally from the east and south-east except in the extreme north, and therefore blew from the North Sea on to the East Coast. On a journey over water such warm air is capable of taking up moisture which, in this instance, ultimately formed first fog and then drizzle when progressively cooled to its dew point as it came into contact with the colder land especially in the Midlands. Having passed over the highlands of Wales, the Pennines and the Lake District such air would descend and be warmed adiabatically. It would then be capable of holding more water vapour so that the west coast stations at this time were not only free from drizzle and fog but also reported relatively low humidities (see Table below) and small amounts of cloud. During the crossing of the Irish Sea further moisture was acquired so that

Station	*Dry bulb temperature* °F.	*Dew point* °F.	*Relative humidity* %
Aberporth	50	45	82
Squires Gate	47	45	92

[1] See Fig. 44, p. 100.

on reaching Ireland the sequence already noted was repeated with Aldergrove and Dublin reporting saturated air with fog and drizzle. The light to moderate winds reported are a reflection of the

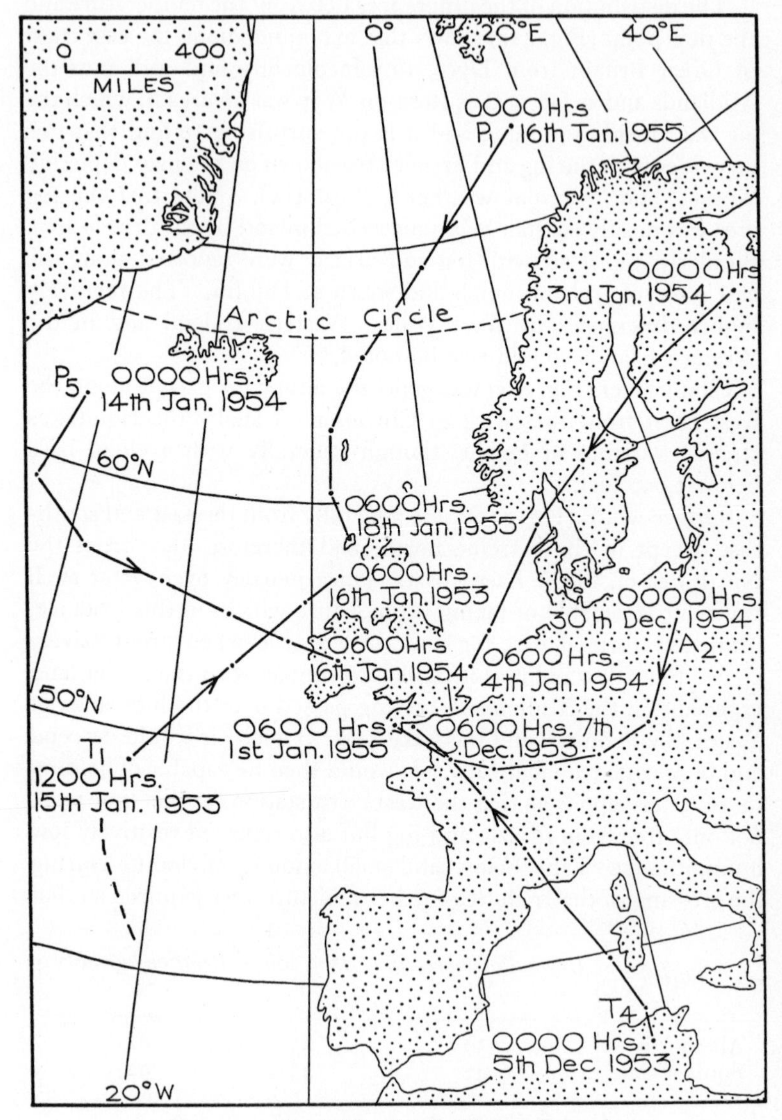

FIG. 42. — Track Map for the Various Examples

Air Mass	Location of sample at 0000 hours previous day	Route to British Isles	Stability	Surface temp. Liverpool at 1400 hours °F.	Temperature at 24,000 feet at 1400 hours °F.	Freezing level, feet	Condensation level, feet	Average surface wind direction	Average temp. of chart °F.	Average dew point of chart °F.	Average relative humidity of chart %	Average relative humidity: 1400 hours Liverpool at surface %
Cold Polar-Maritime (P1) 18/1/55	74° 30′ N. 19° 00′ E.	SW. Oceanic	Stable to 900 mb. then unstable to 715 mb.	38	−51	1,000	1,000	northerly	31·7	26·6	78	73
Polar-Maritime (P1) 4/1/54	65° N. 40° E.	SW. over land and sea	Conditional	39	−30	1,600	600	northerly	38·6	32·5	79	83
Polar-Maritime (P5) 16/1/54	63° N. 32° W.	E. over sea	Conditional	44	−36	2,200	2,000	westerly	43·1	33·8	67	68
Polar-Continental (A2) 1/1/55	60° N. 20° E.	SW. over land	Stable (Inversion)	38	−35	800	1,200	easterly	39·4	34·2	83	79
Tropical-Maritime (T1) 16/1/53	50° N. 20° W.	NE. over sea	Stable (Inversion)	45	−23	8,300	700	westerly	44·5	42·5	93	85
Tropical-Continental (T4) 7/12/53	38° N. 10° E.	N. over land and sea	Stable	48	−32	7,500	3,200	easterly	48·5	47·0	96	89

Fig. 43. — *Comparison of Air Mass Examples*

Dry Bulb °F.	*Difference between Dry Bulb and Dew Point Temperatures* °F.															
	0	**1**	**2**	**3**	**4**	**5**	**6**	**7**	**8**	**9**	**10**	**11**	**12**	**13**	**14**	**15**
80	100	97	94	91	88	85	82	79	77	74	72	69	67	65	63	60
78	100	97	93	91	87	85	82	79	77	74	72	69	67	65	63	60
76	100	97	93	90	87	85	82	79	76	74	71	69	66	64	62	60
74	100	97	93	90	87	85	82	78	76	74	71	68	66	64	62	60
72	100	97	93	90	87	84	82	78	76	73	71	68	66	64	61	59
70	100	97	93	90	87	84	82	78	75	73	71	68	66	63	61	59
68	100	97	93	90	87	84	82	78	75	73	71	68	66	63	61	59
66	100	97	93	90	87	84	81	78	75	73	70	68	65	63	61	58
64	100	97	93	90	87	84	81	78	75	73	70	68	65	63	60	58
62	100	97	93	90	87	84	81	78	75	73	70	67	65	62	60	58
60	100	97	93	90	87	84	81	78	74	72	70	67	65	62	60	58
58	100	97	93	89	86	83	81	78	74	72	69	67	64	62	59	57
56	100	97	93	89	86	83	80	77	74	72	69	66	64	61	59	57
54	100	97	93	89	86	83	80	77	74	72	69	66	64	61	59	57
52	100	97	93	89	86	83	80	77	74	71	69	66	63	61	59	56
50	100	96	93	89	86	83	80	77	74	71	69	66	63	61	59	56
48	100	96	93	89	86	83	80	77	74	71	68	66	63	61	58	56
46	100	96	93	89	85	83	80	76	73	71	68	65	63	61	58	56
44	100	96	93	89	85	83	79	76	73	70	68	65	63	60	58	55
42	100	96	93	89	85	83	79	76	73	70	67	65	62	60	57	55
40	100	96	93	89	85	83	79	76	73	70	67	65	62	60	57	55
38	100	96	93	89	85	82	79	76	73	70	67	65	62	59	57	55
36	100	96	93	89	85	82	79	75	72	70	67	64	62	59	57	54
34	100	96	93	89	85	82	78	75	72	69	67	64	61	59	56	54
32	100	96	92	89	85	82	78	75	72	69	66	64	61	59	56	54
30	100	96	92	89	85	82	78	75	72	69	66	64	61	58	56	53
28	100	96	92	88	85	82	78	75	72	69	66	64	60	58	56	53
26	100	96	92	88	84	81	78	75	72	68	66	63	60	58	55	52
24	100	96	92	88	84	81	78	75	72	68	65	63	60	57	55	52
22	100	96	92	88	84	81	77	74	71	68	65	63	60	57	54	52
20	100	96	92	88	84	81	77	74	71	68	65	62	59	56	54	52

Relative Humidity, Per Cent. (to the nearest whole number).

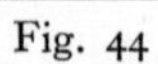

Fig. 44

isobaric pattern for there was high pressure over the whole of the British Isles (inset map C, Fig. 41) and isobars were widely spaced. The isallobars (Fig. 41*g*) show a general fall in atmospheric pressure everywhere for this time.

In summary, there can be little doubt that judging from the geostrophic track of the air, its stability and generally high temperature a *Tropical* air mass covered Britain at the time and on the day in question. However, although its route from North Africa across Europe was over land areas which cooled it from below rendering it stable, nevertheless in crossing the North Sea and Irish Sea it was capable of taking up water vapour to acquire uncharacteristically high humidities accompanied by fog on east facing coasts and drizzle in their immediate hinterlands with associated poor visibility (Fig. 41*h*). The synoptic situation (see inset C, Fig. 41) constituted the westward extension over the British Isles of a ridge of high pressure from a centre over Eastern Europe.

Chapter 4

FRONTS

General Characteristics

Air masses have been described in the preceding chapter as vast portions of the atmosphere possessing characteristics, e.g. of temperature and humidity, of general uniformity and *continuity* which are revealed in their horizontal distributions. In geographical parlance, air masses may be referred to as the " regions " of the atmosphere, having height as well as length and breadth. Separating air masses are zones or slices of the atmosphere characterised by gradation and *discontinuity* which are discernable both on the ground and in the upper air. Such zones are termed *fronts* and in many ways they constitute the " regional boundaries " of the atmosphere. Transitions between areas of uniformity within the atmosphere may be sharp or gentle ; and adjacent areas of uniformity may be greatly contrasted or almost similar. Thus the properties of frontal zones may extend into flanking areas or alternatively may be narrowly restricted. At best a line at ground level or a sloping plane through a vertical section of the atmosphere is just a convenient way of showing diagrammatically where the transition actually occurs between one air mass and the next. This transition is shown on the weather map or upper air graph by a line, which, it must be stressed, is purely a simple way of representing a complex zone of transition.

The theory of the origin of the mid-latitude depression and the development of its warm sector flanked on either side by cold air has been described in simple terms in Chapter 1 (see pp. 6–9). The accompanying diagrams (Fig. 45) illustrate in three-dimensional form the development of a mid-latitude depression from birth through maturity to final decay. The accompanying maps (Fig. 46) trace the life history of an actual depression, " Low 'C' ", between the 28th November, 1954 and the 1st December, 1954. The maps are simplifications of the Daily Weather Reports issued for this period. At birth, stage (*a*) (Fig. 45) and particularly at maturity, stage (*b*), two fronts, the *warm front* and the *cold front* respectively, are in evidence. At each front two different types of air mass, one warm and Tropical the other cold and Polar are in contact. The cold air is dense and heavy, and at the cold front undercuts the warm air which, being less dense and lighter, in its turn overrides the cold air at the warm front. For the cold front the slope is about 1 in 50 ($=1°\ 9'$ to the horizontal) on the average; for the warm front it is about 1 in 150 ($=0°\ 23'$ to the horizontal). The steeper angle of the cold front as compared with the warm front is partly explained by the effect of the friction of the earth's surface in relation to the direction of movement of each front

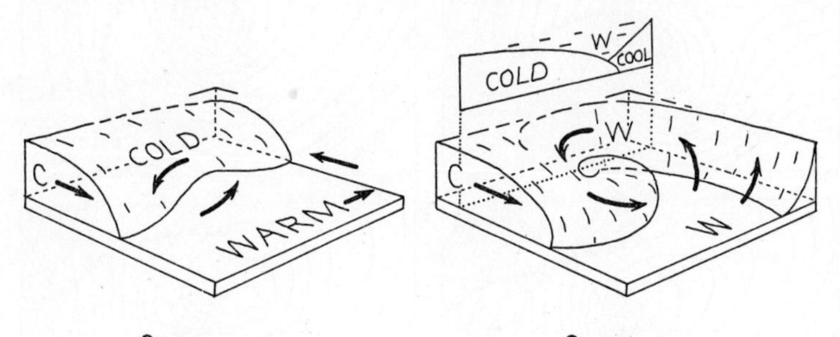

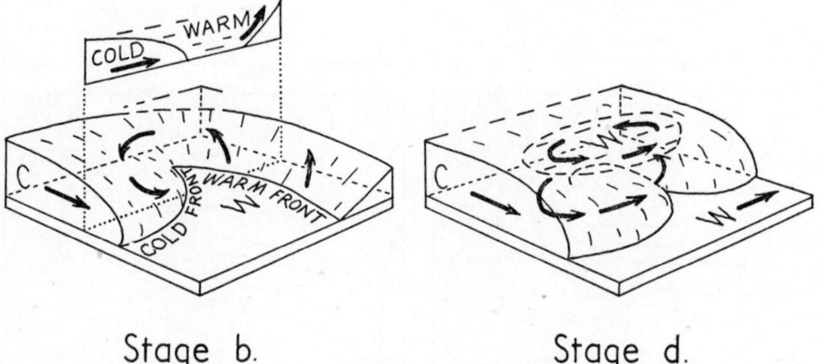

Adapted from Strahler 1951, by permission of John Wiley and Sons Ltd.

FIG. 45. — Development of a Mid-Latitude Depression: Northern Hemisphere
(*a*) Early development; (*b*) Mature stage; (*c*) Occluded stage; (*d*) Full occlusion prior to decay

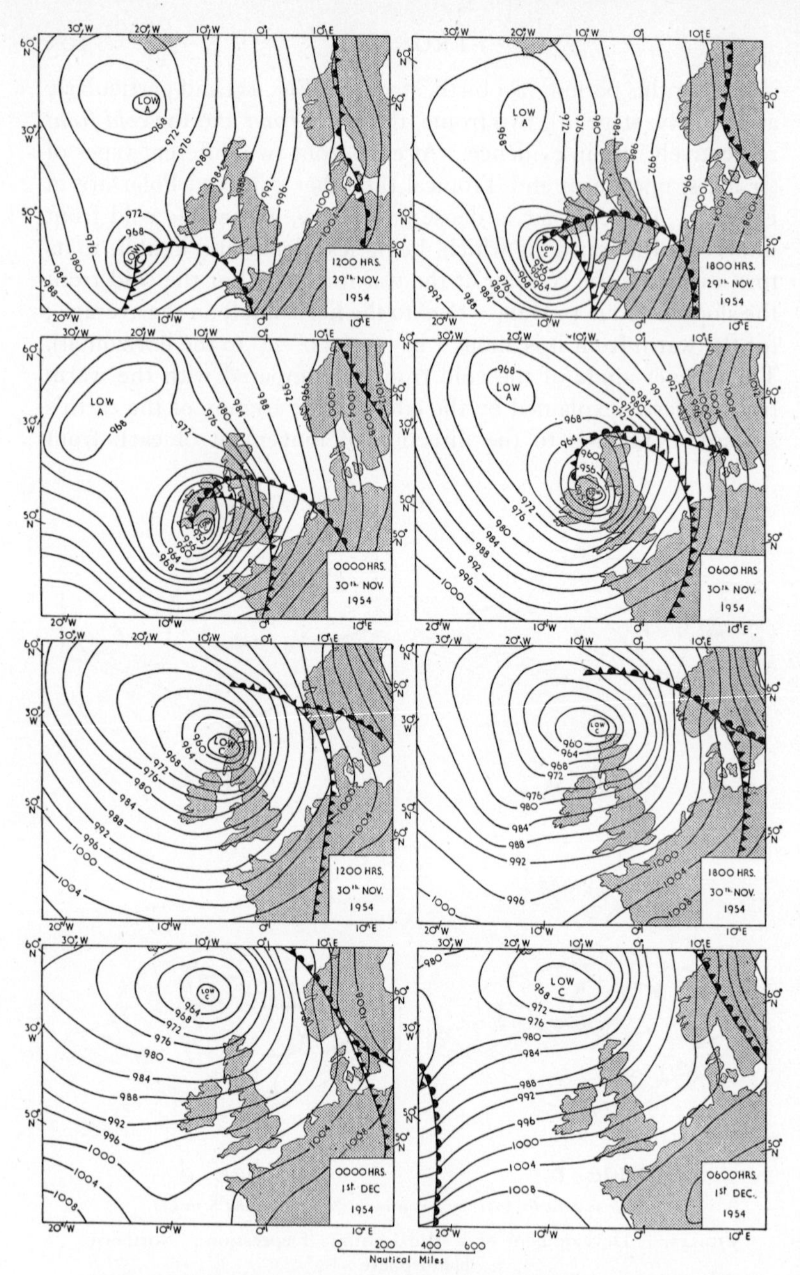

Maps redrawn from the Daily Weather Reports of 28th November 1954, 29th November 1954, 30th November 1954 and 1st December 1954 by permission of the Director-General, Meteorological Office, London. Copyright H.M. Stationery Office.

FIG. 46. — The Life History of Low " C " : 28th November 1954 to 1st December 1954

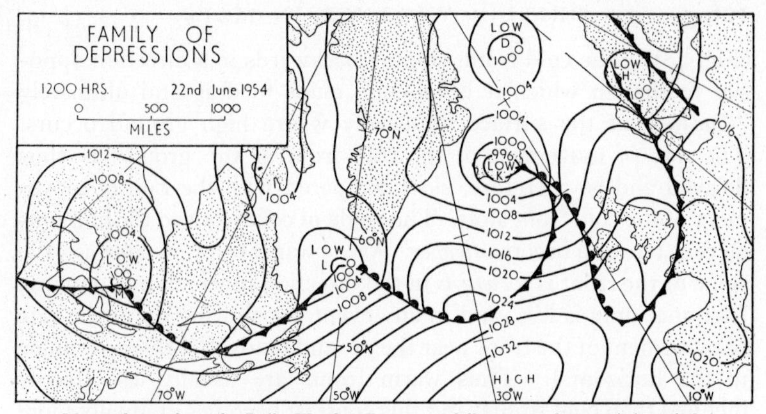

Map redrawn from the Daily Weather Report 22nd June 1954 by permission of the Director-General, Meteorological Office, London. Copyright H.M. Stationery Office.

FIG. 47. — A Family of Depressions : 1200 hrs. 22nd June 1954

Note : Along the Polar Front mid-latitude depressions often develop in a series, or " family ", moving generally eastwards across the North Atlantic towards the British Isles. Each successive depression follows a path further to the south than its predecessor until the last one of the " family " is so far south as to permit the Polar air behind its warm sector to break through the Polar Front to enter the Trade Winds circulation.

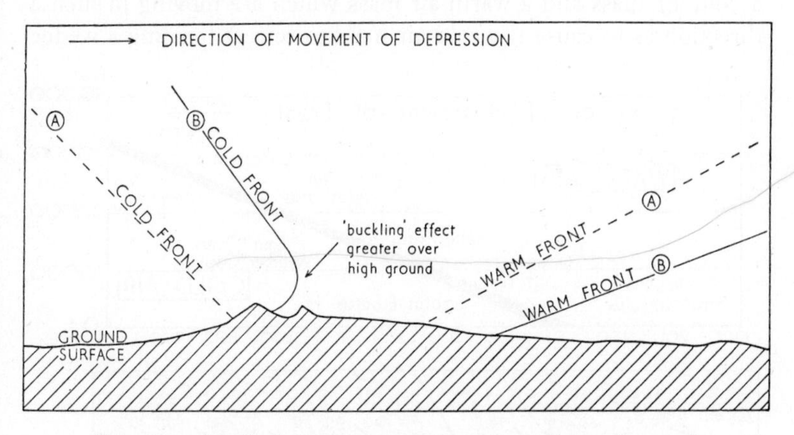

FIG. 48. — Idealised Sections through a Warm Sector Depression Showing the effects of Friction of the Earth's Surface on the Inclination of the Warm and Cold Fronts

A — earlier positions ; B — later positions

(Fig. 48). The cold front, sloping backwards in a direction opposite to that in which it is moving, tends to drag and ultimately "*buckle*" at the surface, especially where high ground occurs. The rate of movement of the cold front at the ground is thus delayed and is, therefore, slow compared with the rate of movement of the cold front aloft. The angle of cold front to the horizontal thus tends to become *steeper*. At the warm front, in contrast, the slope of the front is *forwards* in the direction in which it is moving, frictional drag is less, and in any event the slowing up of the rate of movement of the front near the ground tends to *decrease* its angle to the horizontal. Thus warm fronts are usually less steeply inclined than cold fronts, and this contrast becomes gradually more marked as the depression moves and develops towards the occlusion stage (see pp. 7–9). Also the fact that the cold front tends to move faster than the warm front would emphasise this contrast. The angles of slope of fronts in Fig. 48 and other similar diagrams are shown greatly exaggerated.

The Warm Front

The warm front may be defined as that zone of contact between a cold air mass and a warm air mass which are moving in such a direction as to cause the cold air mass to retreat forming a wedge

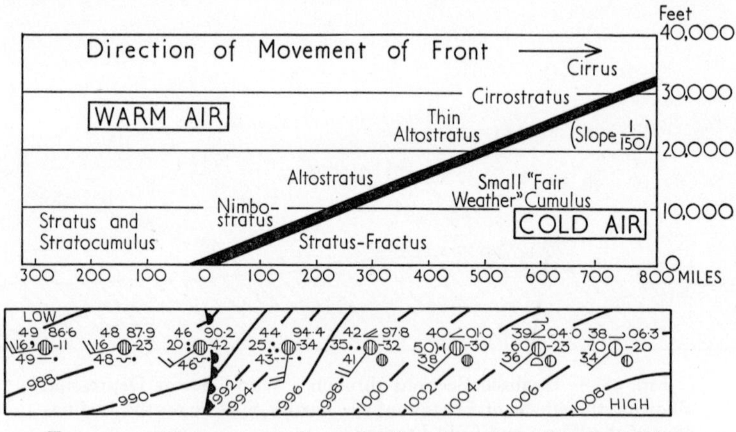

FIG. 49. — Diagrammatic Cross-Section through an Idealised Warm Front

Note : The Warm Front zone is shown in black. The Upper diagram is a vertical cross-section ; the lower diagram is the corresponding horizontal synoptic distribution at the ground.

which is over-ridden by the advancing and ascending warm air mass. Figs. 49 and 50 illustrate diagrammatically the structure of the warm front and the sequence of events associated with its approach, arrival and passage. These events are summarised

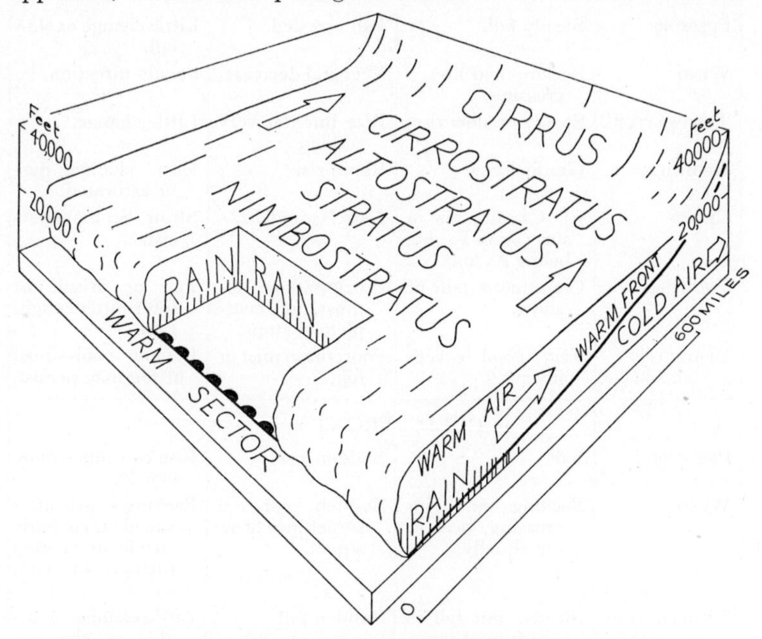

FIG. 50. — Block Diagram of an Idealised Warm Front. The line representing the Warm Front on the ground has its identifying projections on the side towards which the front is moving

below in Fig. 51. Since the plane of the warm front is sloping towards the direction of movement of the front, it is in the upper air at 30,000 feet ($5\frac{1}{2}$ miles above sea-level), and perhaps higher, that the first signs of the approach of the warm front appear — tufted cirrus clouds often called " mares' tails ". Such clouds develop some 500 to 700 miles in advance of the warm front on the ground. They are followed by cirro-stratus and successively lower and thicker cloud, including alto-stratus, nimbo-stratus and stratus-fractus. Pure stratus or strato-cumulus may also be present but these clouds are more typical of the area behind the warm front, in the warm sector. Light, steady rain develops some 200 to 300 miles in advance of the front and becomes increasingly heavier as the

Summary of Frontal Characteristics for Warm and Cold Fronts
(After Sutcliffe)*

Element	*In advance*	*At the passage*	*In the rear*
	WARM	FRONT	
PRESSURE	Steady fall.	Fall arrested.	Little change or slow fall.
WIND	Backing and increasing.	Veer and decrease.	Steady direction.
TEMPERATURE	Steady or slow rise.	Rise but not very sudden.	Little change.
HUMIDITY	Gradual rise.	Rapid rise.	Little change, may be saturated.
CLOUD	Ci, Cs, As, Ns in succession Fs, Fc, below As and Ns.	Low Ns and Fs.	St or Sc may persist.
WEATHER	Continuous rain or snow.	Precipitation almost, or completely, stops.	Fair or drizzle or intermittent slight rain.
VISIBILITY	Very good except in rain.	Poor, often mist or fog.	Usually poor—mist or fog may persist.
	COLD	FRONT	
PRESSURE	Fall.	Sudden rise.	Rise continues more slowly.
WIND	Backing and increasing, becoming squally.	Sudden veer and sometimes heavy squall.	Backing a little after squall, then fairly steady or veering further in later squall.
TEMPERATURE	Steady, but fall in pre-frontal rain.	Sudden fall.	Little change. Variable in showers.
HUMIDITY	Little change.	Sudden fall.	Variable in showers but generally low.
CLOUD	Ac, As then heavy Cb.	Cb with Fs, Fc or Ns, very low.	Lifting rapidly followed by As, Ac. Later, further Cu or Cb.
WEATHER	Usually some rain perhaps thunder.	Heavy rain, perhaps thunder and hail.	Heavy rain for usually short period. Sometimes more persistent. Then fine followed by further showers.
VISIBILITY	Poor, perhaps fog.	Temporary deterioration followed by rapid improvement.	Very good.

* *Meteorology for Aviators*, Air Ministry Publication 1699, 1946, p. 187.

Fig. 51

front approaches ; if the temperature is low enough this precipitation may fall as sleet or snow. Rain, sleet or snow, at the warm front is caused by the ascent of the warm air over the wedge of cold air, which leads to expansion, cooling and condensation evidenced in the accumulation of progressively lower and thicker cloud types and the development of rain, sleet or snow, of increasing intensity as the warm front approaches. The precipitation occurs over a relatively wide belt, e.g. 200 to 300 miles; it is continuous, and may take six to ten hours to pass over a given station. The warm front moves at a slower rate than the cold front as a rule. It follows that relative humidity increases steadily as the warm front approaches, the air becoming saturated or nearly so at the beginning of the rain belt some 200 miles in advance of the front. Also, temperatures rise gradually until the front is about 50 miles away ; thereafter there is a rapid rise in temperature which is continued until the passage of the front. Atmospheric pressure falls steadily till the front arrives, after which it falls only very slightly or is perhaps generally steady behind the front in the warm sector. Winds tend to back and increase in strength in advance of the front, and to veer and decrease in strength, assuming a relatively constant direction, behind it. Exceptionally good visibility well in advance of the front in the Polar air is followed by a progressive deterioration until it becomes very poor at and behind the front in the Tropical air where misty, drizzly, muggy weather may persist in the warm sector because of the very high humidity, warm temperatures, and dominant low cloud, viz. strato-cumulus, stratus or stratus-fractus. However, these conditions may be relieved locally by patches of brighter weather with less humid air and the cloud cover thinning out and perhaps breaking in places.

It is important to visualise the structure of the warm front in three dimensions. By reference to Figs. 45 and 50, it will be seen that the warm front, normally, is a vast curved slice of the atmosphere extending upwards very gradually from a curved line or zone along the ground into the upper air at the "tops" of the air masses. The graphs (Fig. 52) illustrate diagrammatic vertical profiles in advance and behind warm fronts of different intensities. The profiles marked "*y*" taken some distance in advance of the front, show part of the wedge of cold, Polar air underlying the warm front zone which is represented by an inversion which varies in intensity according to the degree of development of the front. Above the inversion is the warm Tropical air overriding the cold air beneath. The profiles marked " *x* ", taken in the warm sector behind the fronts, show an uninterrupted fall of temperature

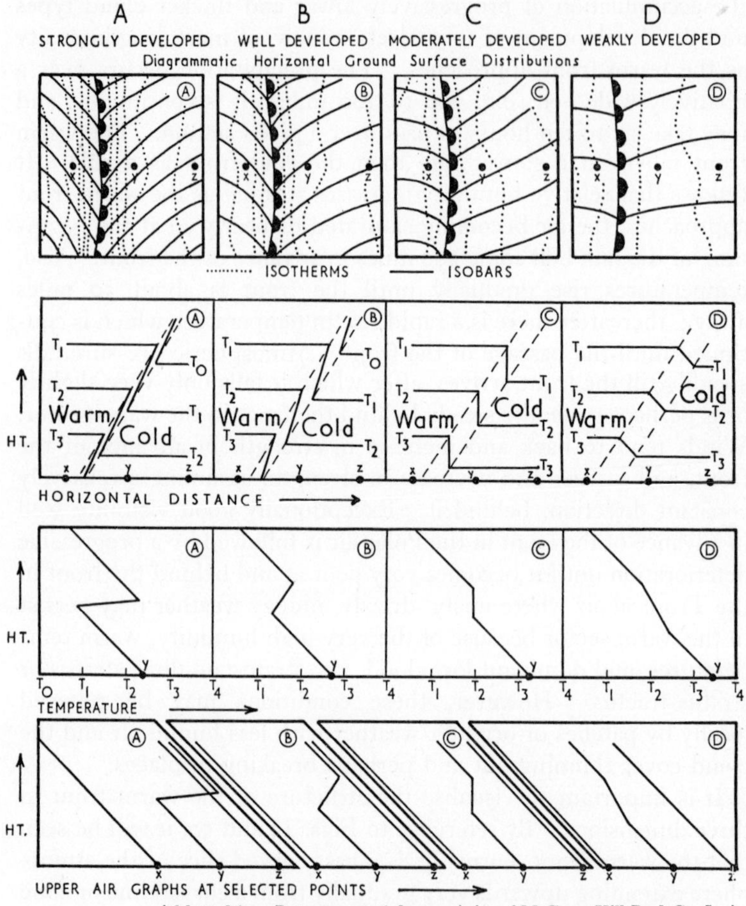

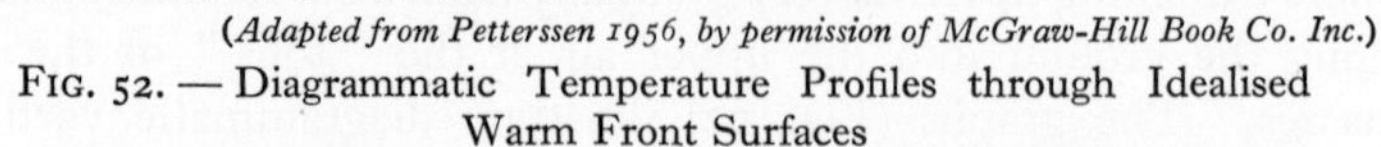

(*Adapted from Petterssen 1956, by permission of McGraw-Hill Book Co. Inc.*)

FIG. 52. — Diagrammatic Temperature Profiles through Idealised Warm Front Surfaces

Note : The top set of four diagrams shows the horizontal distribution on the ground of the isobars and isotherms for warm fronts of different intensities. The next set of diagrams immediately below shows the corresponding vertical distributions of temperature. The bottom two sets of diagrams show corresponding upper air temperature graphs for positions *x*, *y*, and *z* marked in all the diagrams.

upwards through the warm Tropical air of the warm sector. Similarly, the profiles marked " *z* ", taken in the cold sector in advance of the fronts, show an uninterrupted fall of temperature upwards through the cold Polar air.

All the foregoing refers to the average, standard " text-book" warm front. In actual experience, deviations from this basic pattern are much more frequent than approximations to it. One of the best examples of a warm front to occur in recent years over the British Isles was that from 6.0 a.m. on the 7th February, 1948. The Daily Weather Report for this time will now be analysed in detail.

Each analysis in this chapter contains three procedures, each of which provides evidence of the position and identity of frontal " *discontinuities* " and of the air mass " *continuities* " flanking them. These three procedures are :

(1) Analysis of horizontal distributions of surface synoptic data.

(2) The geostrophic plotting of the routes to the British Isles followed by samples of air. Alternatively, when this is impracticable, due to a combination of (*a*) long time intervals (6 hours) between charts on the D.W.R. and (*b*) excessive curvature of the isobars, an examination is made of preceding synoptic situation thus revealing stages in the development of the weather situation under review.

(3) Analysis of upper air data for selected stations.

The *first* procedure reveals the frontal *discontinuities* and flanking air mass *continuities* in terms of horizontal distributions of surface synoptic data. The *second* procedure assists the identification of the types of air present, and the way the weather situation under review has developed. The *third* procedure assists in the recognition of types of air and types of discontinuity present and provides evidence leading to a fuller interpretation of the weather situation in general.[1]

The Warm Front : 7th February, 1948 0600 hours, G.M.T.

Surface Synoptic Data

In Fig. 53 a selection of data is given for the British Isles for the above time and date. In Figs. 53*a–h* separate [1] elements have

[1] Refer back to method of analysis, pp. 39–43.

been plotted, isopleths have been inserted, discontinuities marked in, and distributions labelled. Fig. 53*a* for air temperatures reveals a NNW.–SSE. zone of discontinuity where closely aligned isotherms indicate a steep temperature gradient. To the west, over Ireland, Wales and South-west England, is an area of uniformly high [1] temperatures, averaging about 49° F.; isotherms in this area of continuity are widely spaced and irregular in pattern. To the east, over Scotland and Eastern England, is an area of uniformly low [1] temperatures, averaging about 38° F.; isotherms in this area of continuity are again more widely spaced and irregular in pattern. Some standard of comparison may be obtained by quoting the average means of daily minimum temperature (1901–30) [2] for February for those two areas. For Ireland, Wales and South-west England the figure is about 38° F.; for Scotland and Eastern England it is about 35° F. Thus at 6.0 a.m. on the morning of 7th February, 1948 in the western parts of the British Isles temperatures were certainly high for the time of year, and also for the time of day. The eastern parts of the British Isles, on the other hand, had temperatures only a little higher than the average minimum for the time of day and year. The general distribution of air temperatures then already suggests the presence of part of a warm air mass over the western areas of the British Isles, separated from colder air over Eastern Britain by a well defined frontal zone.

The distribution of dew points (Fig. 53*b*) reveals a similar pattern to that of temperature. A clearly marked belt of bunched, and almost straight, isopleths lies across South-west Scotland, North-west England, the Midlands and South-east England. To the west of it is a region of relatively high dew points (45° F.); to the east is a region of relatively low dew points (36° F.). A more direct indication of the distribution of atmospheric humidity is shown in Fig. 53*c* on which are plotted the differences[3] between air temperature and dew point for each station. For convenience, the areas where these differences are less than 2° F. have been shaded; they are the areas where the air is most moist and nearest to saturation, i.e. the areas where cloud formation and precipitation

[1] *N.B.*, i.e. *relatively* high, *relatively* low.

[2] *Climatological Atlas of the British Isles*, H.M.S.O., 1952, Plates 1–12, pp. 34–45.

[3] See Fig. 44, p. 100.

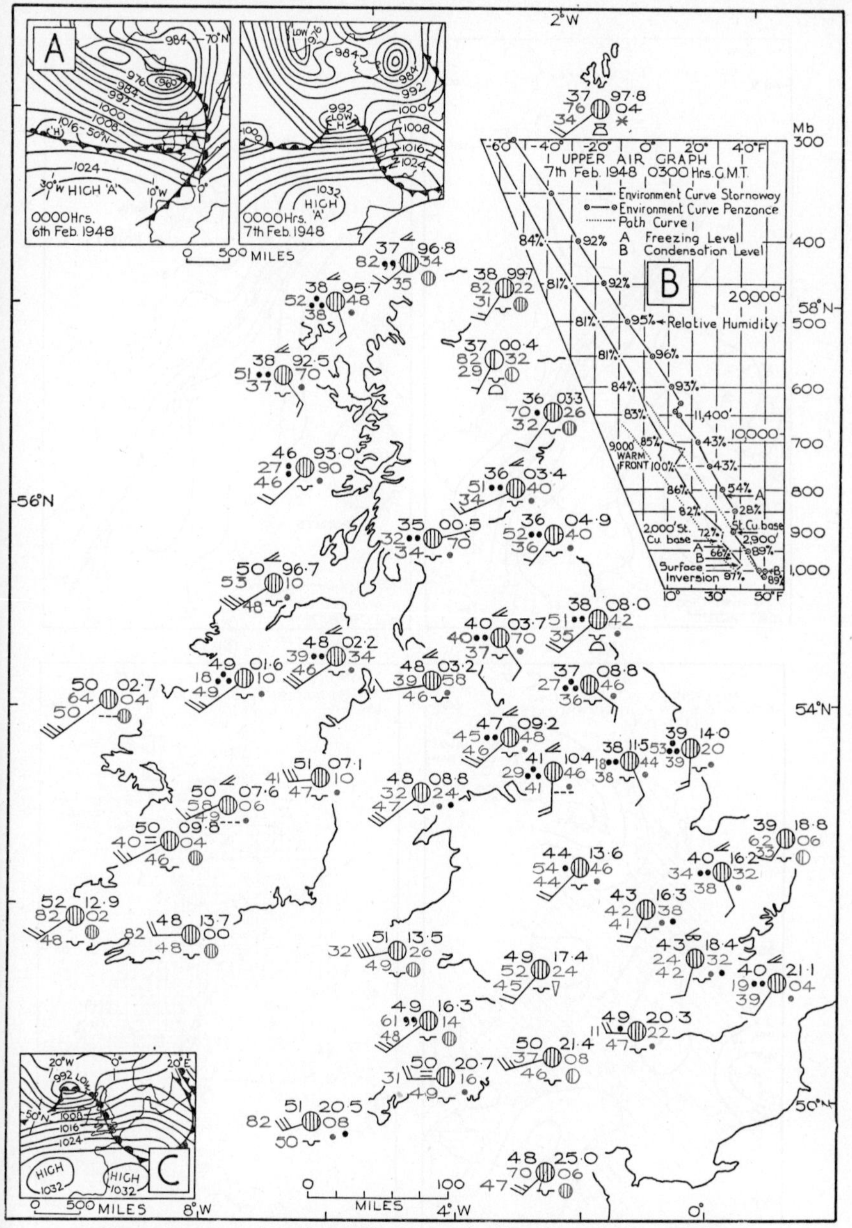

Maps redrawn from the Daily Weather Report 7th February 1948 by the permission of the Director-General, Meteorological Office, London. Copyright H.M. Stationery Office.

FIG. 53. — Selected Data for 7th February 1948 : 0600 hrs. G.M.T.
The Warm Front
Inset A — Previous Synoptic Situations ; Inset B — Upper Air Graphs
Inset C — Isobars : 0600 hrs. G.M.T. 7th February 1948

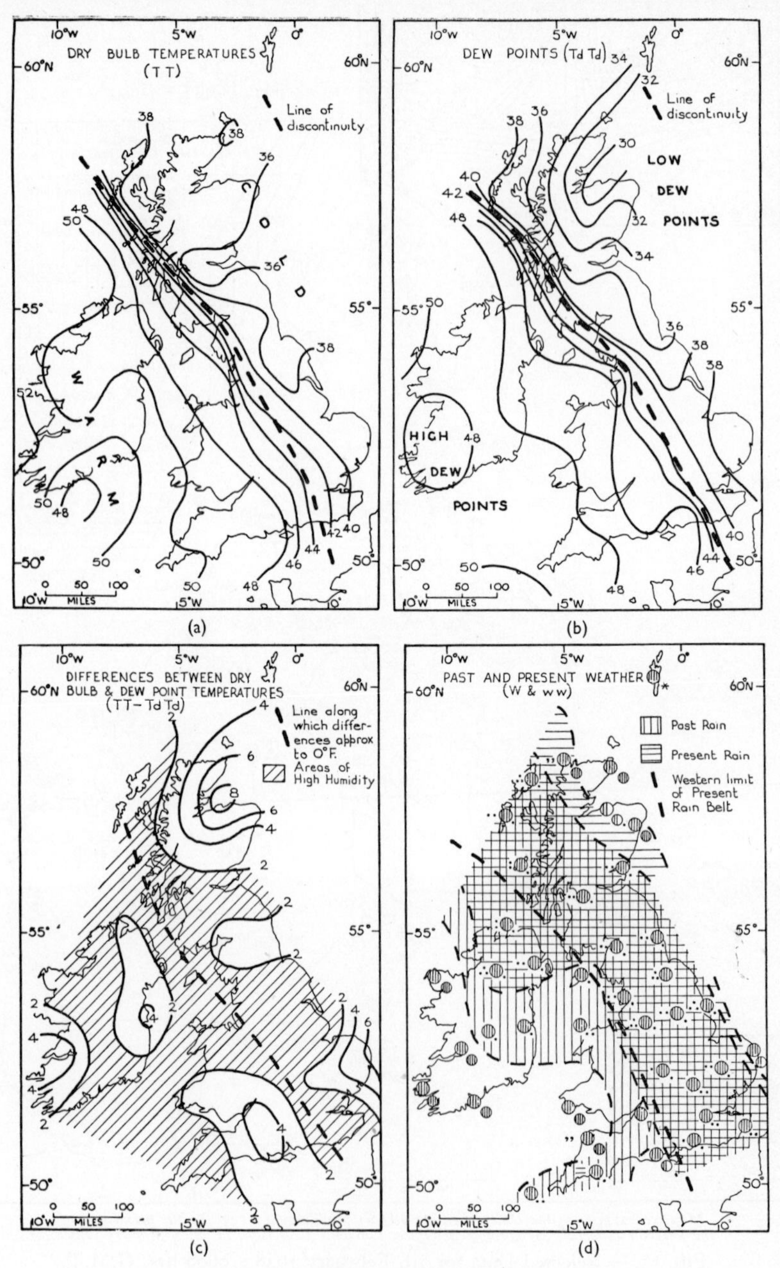

(a) (b) (c) (d)

FIG. 53 (*contd.*). — (*a*), (*b*), (*c*), (*d*)

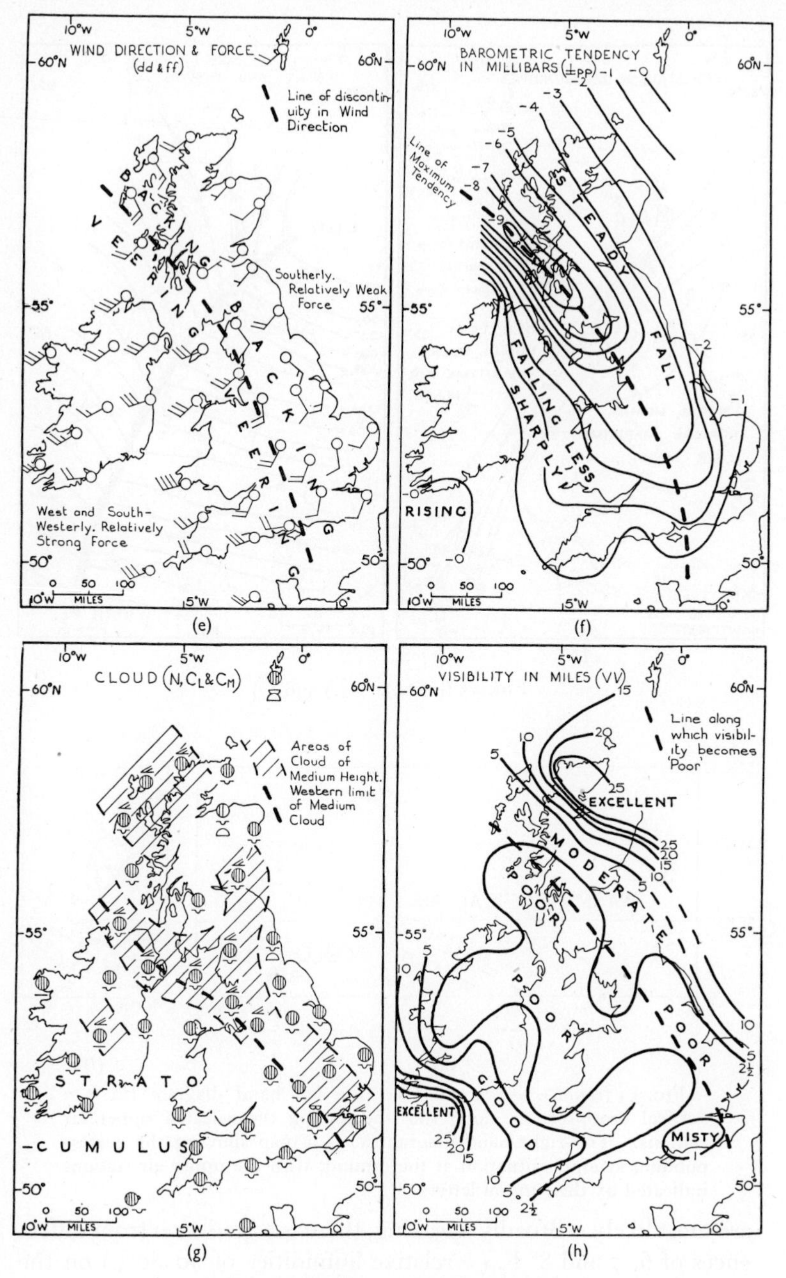

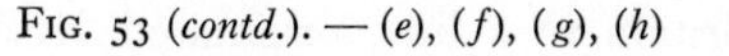
FIG. 53 (*contd.*). — (*e*), (*f*), (*g*), (*h*)

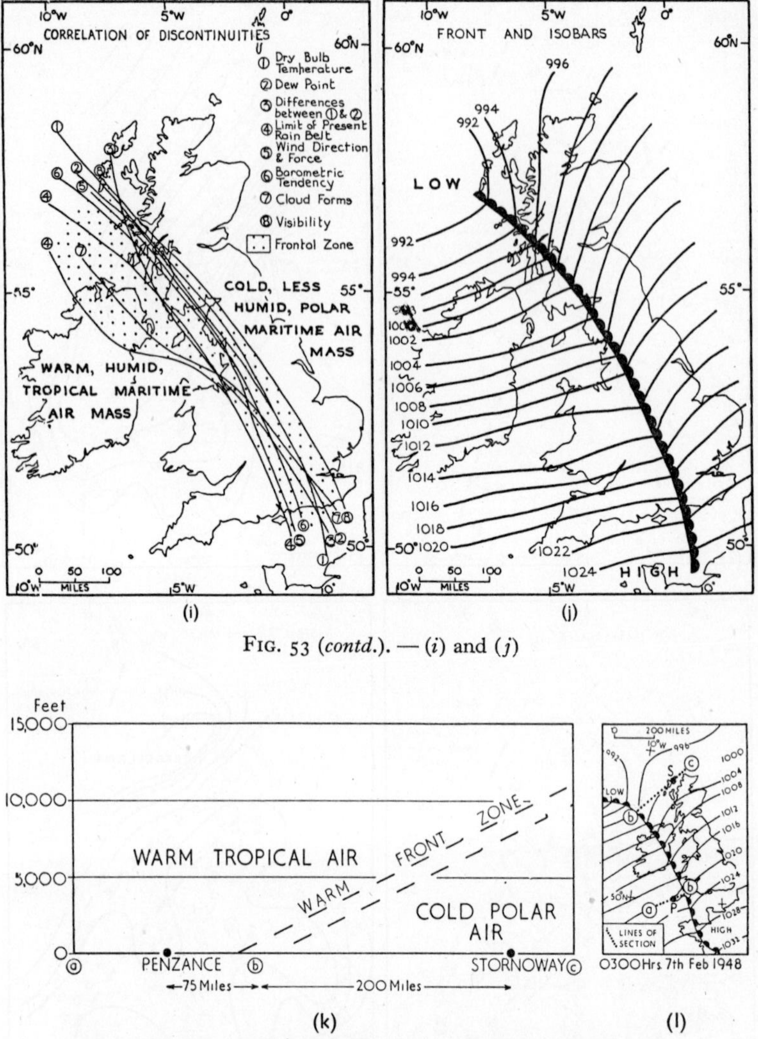

FIG. 53 (*contd.*). — (*i*) and (*j*)

FIG. 53 (*contd.*). — (*k*) and (*l*) — the left hand diagram (*k*) is a vertical cross-section along the line joining the selected upper air stations. The right hand diagram (*l*) is a map showing the corresponding synoptic situation at the ground, with the upper air stations indicated by their initial letters

are most likely. Broadly speaking, there is a gradation from differences of 6, 7 and 8° F. (=relative humidities of 70–80%) on the east coast of Britain to a line, orientated NNW.–SSE. through

Western Scotland, North-west England and Central and South-east England, where differences approximate generally to 0° F. (=relative humidity of 100%). The only exception to this pattern is an area on the Scottish Border, revealed by the data for Tynemouth and Silloth (3 degrees difference=89% relative humidity). Westwards of the line, the distribution of small and large differences is quite variable, being less than 2° F. (=relative humidity 93–100%) over much of Ireland and Cornwall and up to 4° F. (=relative humidity *c.* 86%) over South Wales, an area between Bristol and Southampton, and in extreme South-west Ireland. This general pattern would appear to suggest steadily increasing humidity broadly westwards from 70–75% relative humidity on the east coast of Britain to a belt of saturated air (100% relative humidity) which correlates well in position with the temperature and dew point discontinuities noted on maps 53*a* and 53*b*. The gradual rate of increase of humidity towards the frontal zone suggests a warm, rather than a cold, front. Further west the indiscriminate scatter of moist patches with drier patches is not unusual for warm sector conditions ; a tropical maritime air mass is already indicated here.

Fig. 53*d* shows the pattern of " present weather " and " past weather ". The most obvious feature is a continuous belt of " present rain " lying NNW.–SSE. across most of Scotland and England. Extreme North-east Scotland and the Gorleston area of East Anglia are as yet free from rain. The rain belt is some 200 to 300 miles wide and the rain falling in it is mostly *continuous*. Data for " past weather " show a wider (generally 300 miles or more) belt of rain covering the South-west Peninsula, Wales and Eastern Ireland. All these facts are consistent with the presence of a belt of warm front rain moving generally east-north-eastwards across the British Isles. The western limit of this rain belt, therefore, would indicate the position of the warm front on the ground (Fig. 53*d*). To the east lies the pre-frontal rain and its preceding cloudy skies. To the west lies the warm sector with its local mist, drizzle, overcast skies and, over Northern Ireland, heavy rain, which is probably explained by the proximity of the centre of the depression (Fig. 53*j*).

The map of wind force and direction (Fig. 53*e*) shows that over Scotland and Eastern England winds are generally southerly and light, whilst over Ireland, Wales and the South-west Peninsula they are generally west-south-west and relatively strong. The line of discontinuity between the two areas is quite well marked and indicates the location of the front very precisely. The winds over Eastern Britain have backed southerly and have mostly increased a little in advance of the front, and those over Western Britain have veered and increased. The backing and veering are quite orthodox but the backing is more usually accompanied by a more consistent increase in wind force. Similarly, the veer behind the front, in particular a warm front, is usually accompanied by a decrease in wind force.

In Fig. 53*f*, the *isallobars* [1] show a simple U-shaped pattern with barometric tendencies decreasing progressively outwards from a line NNW.–SSE. through South-west Scotland and England, which correlates well with the other lines of discontinuity already noted. To the east, in advance of the front, the negative barometric tendency increases as the front approaches, e.g. Gorleston and Felixstowe – 0·6 millibars ; West Raynham – 1·6 millibars ; Manchester and Elmdon – 4·6 millibars. To the west, behind the front, the negative tendencies decrease sharply especially over the North Channel ; then over Ireland in the warm sector the barometer is virtually steady, which is orthodox.

The distribution of cloud types and amount (Fig. 53*g*) displays NNW.–SSE. bands of alto-stratus and nimbo-stratus up to 150 and 200 miles in total width and lying across the Western Isles, the coastlands of the North Channel, the Isle of Man, North-west England, East Anglia and Kent. These clouds are typical of the rain area in advance of a warm front. To the west over much of Ireland, Wales and the South-west Peninsula, a continuous sheet of strato-cumulus, with some stratus, is coincident with the warm sector behind the warm front. The distribution of visibility (Fig. 53*h*) shows a NNW.–SSE. belt, corresponding to the frontal zone, which has " poor " [2] visibility. To the extreme east in advance of the front, visibilities are " excellent ", deteriorating westwards to " moderate " as the front approaches. To the west, behind the front, visibilities vary locally but are generally better than those of the frontal zone, but only in South-west Ireland

[1] i.e. lines of equal barometric tendency (see p. 28).
[2] See Fig. 24b, p. 34.

do they compare with those well in advance of the frontal zone.

The correlation of the several elements analysed is depicted on Fig. 53*i*. There is very close agreement indeed between the position of the various lines denoting a relatively wide frontal zone of discontinuity some 50–150 miles in width. To the west lies part of a warm, humid, Tropical air mass, to the east lies part of a cold, less humid, Polar-Maritime air mass. The data analysed appear to suggest that the front is moving eastwards. On Fig. 53*j*, the warm front has been drawn in ; it follows a slightly curving line through Tiree, the Clyde Estuary, the Solway Firth, the Lake District, East Lancashire, the Midlands and Sussex. Isobars inserted at intervals of 2 millibars reveal a centre of low pressure of less than 992 millibars located off Western Scotland, with higher pressures, up to 1024 millibars, over the English Channel. The isobars are angled quite sharply in the north near the centre of the depression, and less sharply in the south near its periphery.

Analysis of Previous Weather Charts

On Fig. 53, inset A shows the synoptic situation for midnight of Saturday, 7th February, six hours previous to the chart under examination. " Low H " appears to have been one of a series of " *secondary* " [1] depressions moving eastwards towards the British Isles. The " *primary* " [1] depression was centred over Southern Greenland. " Low H " was centred some 700 miles west of Scotland and the warm front in question lay across extreme Southeast Ireland and the Scilly Isles. Thus over most of the British Isles at this time pre-warm front weather was extensively represented.

Upper Air Data

It would be ideal if upper air details were available for 0600 hours for representative stations. Unfortunately, upper air ascents are made not at 0600 hours, but at 0300 hours and 1500 hours at most stations.[2] Data for 0300 hours are here taken (Fig. 53*k* and *l*), as a comparable, approximate position of the front at the ground at that time can be estimated from the Daily Weather Report of the 7th February, 1948. Penzance was about 75 miles behind the

[1] See pp. 6 and 214. [2] See p. 26.

warm front at 3.0 a.m. on the day in question, and Stornoway was about 200 miles in advance of the warm front. The upper air graphs show that the contrast in temperature at the ground, viz. Penzance 50° F., Stornoway 38° F., is continued up to 35,000 feet (266 millibars). The graph for Penzance passes entirely through Tropical-Maritime air which is generally stable throughout except below its layer of strato-cumulus, the base of which appears to have been at about 2,900 feet (900 millibars) at this time, where it is very moist with relative humidities approaching 90%, and only a small rise in temperature would make it unstable. Immediately above the cloud layer this air is remarkably dry[1] between about 4,000 feet and 10,000 feet, with relative humidities of less than 50%, after which it is very moist with relative humidities of almost 100%. The graph for Stornoway shows a very well marked inversion between 750 mbs. and 700 mbs.[2] which would appear to be the warm front zone, above which is stable Tropical-Maritime air with relative humidities of the order of 83% and below which is Polar-Maritime air with relative humidities of the order of 70% to 90%. Also shown is a strato-cumulus base at about 2,000 feet. Only a small rise in temperature at Stornoway would render the air unstable — it is, in fact, unstable between 2,800 feet and 4,200 feet.

Thus, combined evidence derived from surface synoptic data, past weather charts and upper air reports, has demonstrated conclusively the presence (over the British Isles at 0600 hours on 7th February, 1948) of a warm front with many standard "text-book" characteristics.

The Cold Front

The cold front may be defined as that zone of contact between a cold air mass and a warm air mass which are moving in such a direction as to cause the warm air to be undercut and elevated by the advancing cold air, thus causing a well marked fall in air temperature first at the ground and then progressively upwards through the atmosphere later. Weather changes due to the approach of the warm front find expression gradually at first in the upper atmosphere and then through successively lower layers until

[1] See p. 113, inset B.
[2] This is equivalent to a height range of 7,800 feet to 9,000 feet.

the front arrives at ground level. In contrast the approach of the cold front causes more rapid weather changes which are expressed in the lower atmosphere first. Figs. 54 and 55 illustrate diagram-

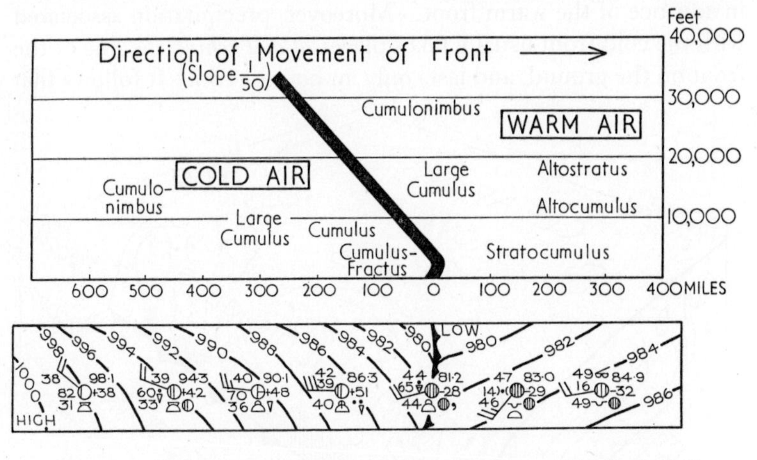

FIG. 54. — Diagrammatic Cross-Section through an Idealised Cold Front

Note : The Cold Front zone is shown in black. The upper diagram is a vertical cross-section ; the lower diagram is the corresponding horizontal synoptic distribution at the ground.

matically the structure of the ideal cold front and Fig. 51 tabulates the progression of weather phenomena associated therewith. It should be stressed that the action of the cold wedge undercutting the rear of the warm sector is vigorous, perhaps violent, and intermittent rather than continuous, all of which is in contrast to the situation at the warm front. The consequences of this are threefold : firstly, the plane of the cold front is on the average at an angle three times steeper to the ground than the warm front ; [1] secondly, the cold front moves more quickly than the warm front, eventually overtaking it and causing the depression to occlude ; and thirdly, the frontal zone of the cold front is usually much narrower than that of the warm front.

As the cold front approaches, the chief event is the backing and increasing of the wind with marked tendencies to squalliness (Fig. 51) ; a slight fall in atmospheric pressure also takes place as a rule. The alto-cumulus and alto-stratus of the warm sector

[1] See p. 103.

develop into heavy cumulus and cumulonimbus, and precipitation begins. Rain, snow, sleet, or hail, is of the heavy, intermittent, showery type in contrast to the steadier, continuous precipitation in advance of the warm front. Moreover, precipitation associated with the cold front usually takes places *at and behind* the line of the front on the ground, and lasts only an hour or two. It follows that

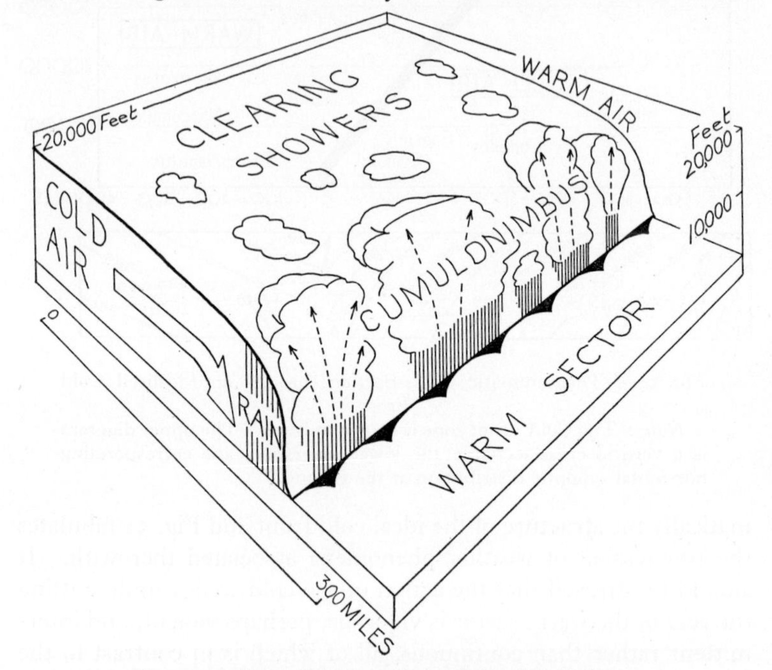

FIG. 55. — Block Diagram of an Idealised Cold Front

Note : The line representing the Cold Front on the ground has its identifying projections in black on the side towards which the front is moving.

cold front precipitation belts are usually relatively narrow — about 20 to 30 miles in width — and often discontinuous in both space and time. Temperature falls only slightly just before the cold front arrives and high humidities are maintained, but the passage of the front is signified by a sharp drop in temperature and in humidity, a sharp veer of the wind often with squally tendencies, and a sudden rise in atmospheric pressure. Again, in direct contrast to the warm front zone and the warm sector, the cold front zone is characterised by clouds with a marked *vertical* development — heavy cumulus and, ultimately, cumulonimbus. Conditions favourable to the development of thunder and lightning are often associated with cold front zones. Behind the cold front

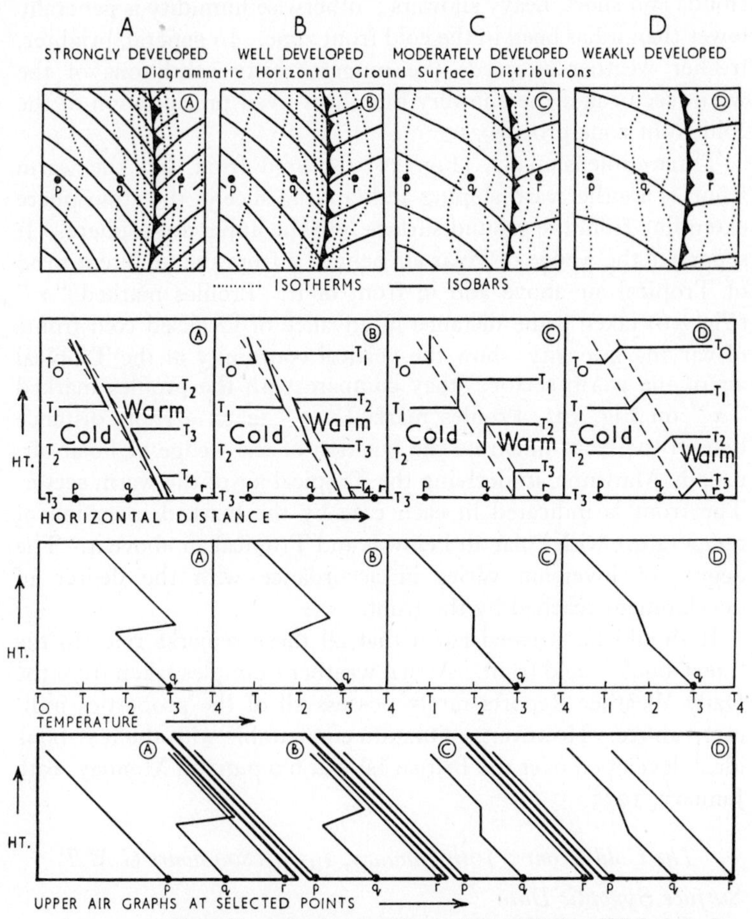

(*Adapted from Petterssen 1956*) *by permission of McGraw-Hill Book Co. Inc.*

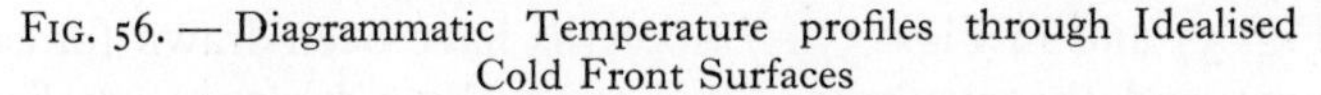

FIG. 56. — Diagrammatic Temperature profiles through Idealised Cold Front Surfaces

Note : The top set of four diagrams shows the horizontal distribution on the ground of the isobars and isotherms for cold fronts of different intensities. The next set of diagrams, immediately below, show the corresponding vertical distributions of temperature. The bottom two sets of diagrams shows corresponding upper air temperature graphs for positions *p*, *q*, and *r*, marked in all the diagrams.

after the main precipitation belt has passed, Polar air replaces Tropical air and visibility shows a marked improvement. Local instability is expressed in towering cumulus and cumulonimbus clouds and short, heavy showers ; otherwise humidity is generally lower than it has been in the cold front zone. In general, brighter, fresher weather succeeds the muggy, misty conditions of the warm sector and the showery but short-lived precipitation of the cold front zone proper.

Three-dimensionally, (Fig. 55) the cold front, like the warm front, is another vast, sloping and curving slice of the atmosphere extending from the ground surface into the upper atmosphere. It separates the wedge of Polar air behind it from the undercut mass of Tropical air above and in front of it. Profiles marked " *r* " (Fig. 56) taken some distance in advance of idealised cold fronts of varying intensity, show the vertical continuity of the Tropical air of the warm sector ; they compare with the profiles marked " *x* " on Fig. 52. Profiles marked " *q* " taken a short distance behind the front illustrate the position of the wedge of Polar air, usually Maritime, underlying the Tropical air of the warm sector. The front is indicated in each case by the marked inversion of temperature with Polar air below it and Tropical air above it. The degree of inversion varies in accordance with the degree of development reached by the front.

It should be stressed again that all these remarks refer to the " text-book " cold front. Actual weather examples taken from the Daily Weather Reports rarely possess all of the properties indicated above. However, a situation comparable with the text-book ideal developed over the British Isles at 6.0 p.m. on Monday, 10th January, 1955.

The Cold Front : 10th January, 1955, 1800 hours G.M.T.

Surface Synoptic Data

A selection of data for the above date and time has been plotted on Fig. 57 and in Figs. 57*a–j* isopleths have been drawn for each element and the resultant distributions have been regionalised. The distribution of air temperatures (Fig. 57*a*) is dominated by a close arrangement of the isotherms in an east-west belt across Southern Ireland, the North Wales coastlands, Lancashire and Yorkshire. North and south of this narrow zone of very steep

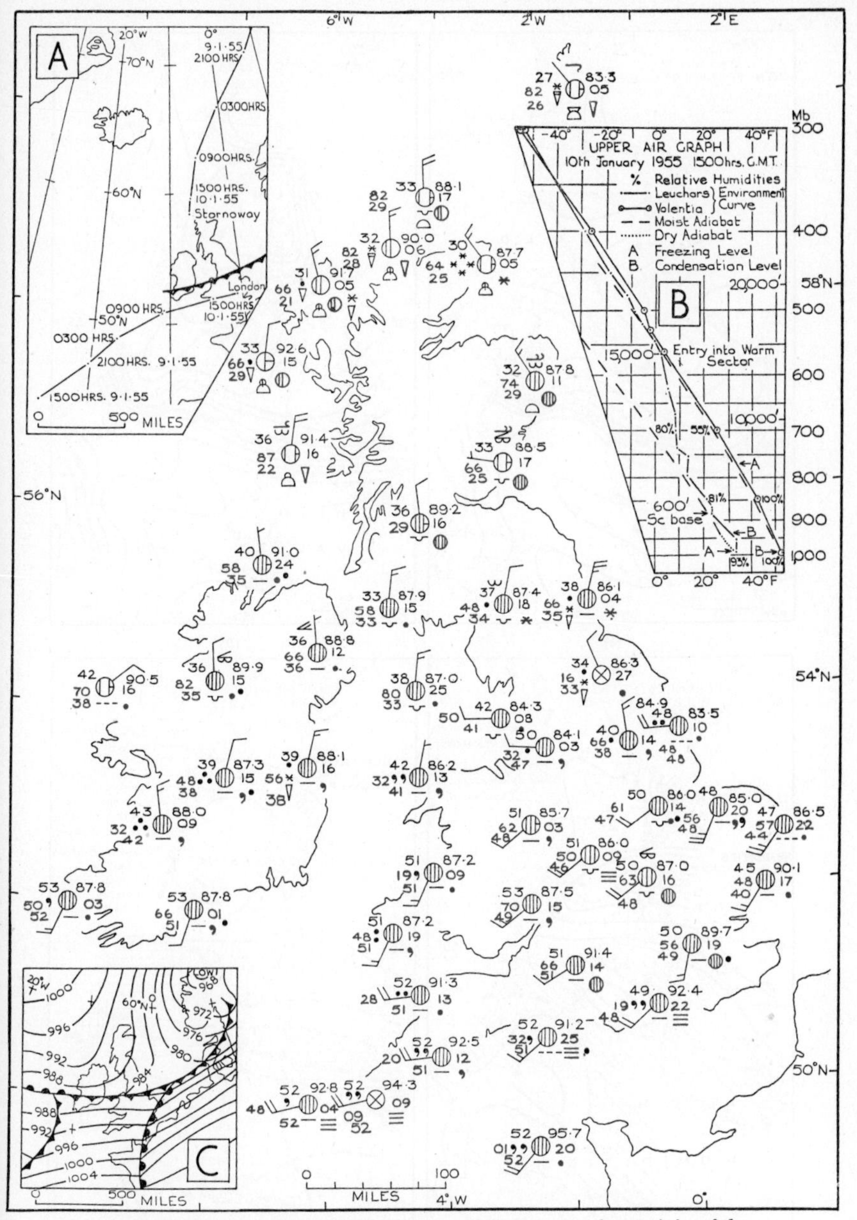

Maps redrawn from the Daily Weather Report 10th January 1955 by permission of the Director-General, Meteorological Office, London. Copyright H.M. Stationery Office.

FIG. 57. — Selected Data for 10th January 1955 : 1800 hrs. G.M.T.
The Cold Front
Inset A — Track map ; Inset B — Upper Air Graphs
Inset C — Isobars : 1800 hrs. G.M.T. 10th January 1955

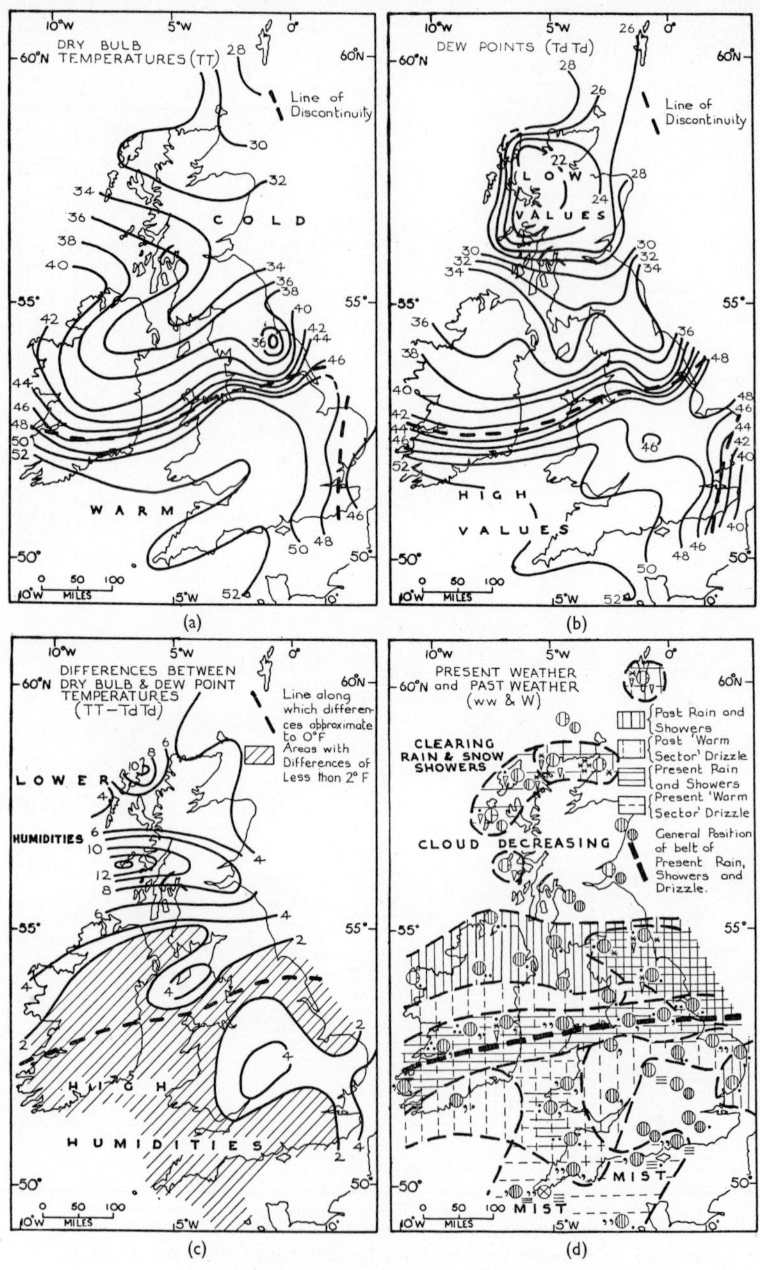

FIG. 57 (*contd.*). — (*a*), (*b*), (*c*), (*d*)

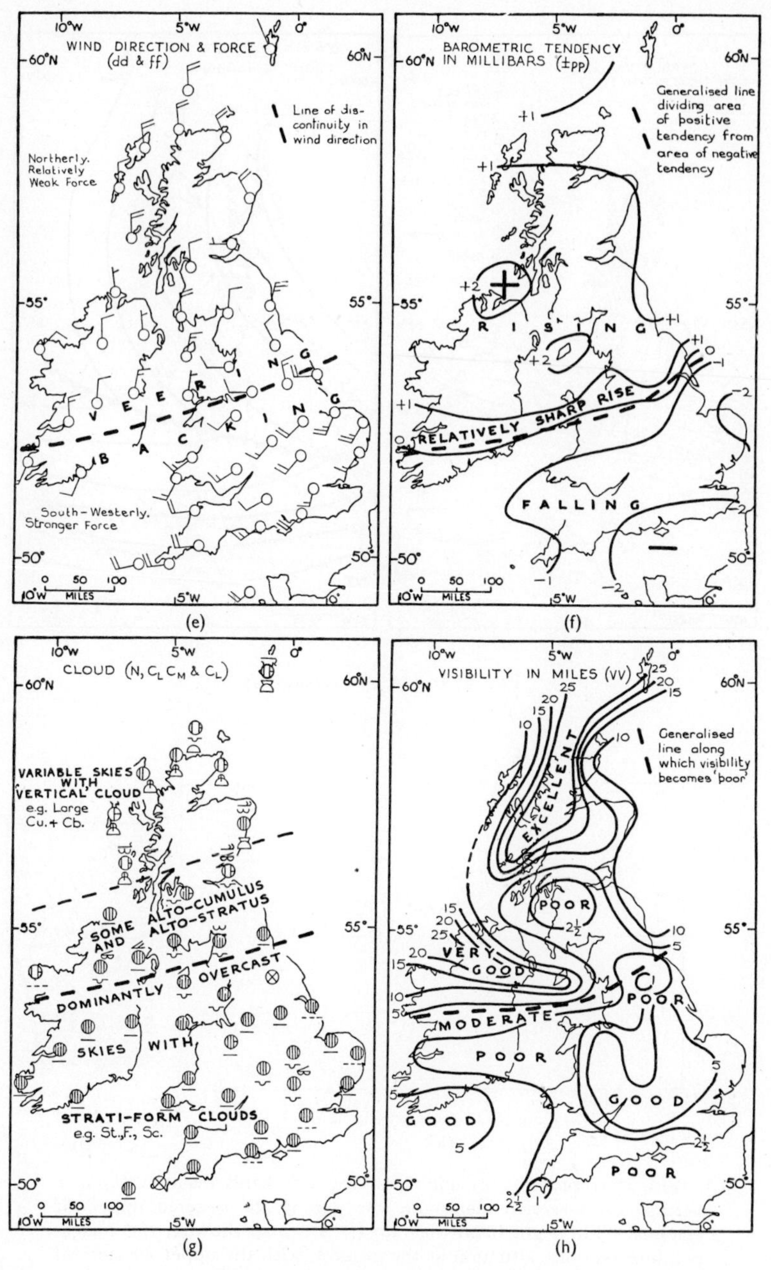

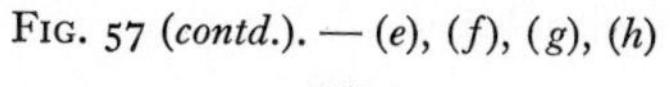

FIG. 57 (*contd.*). — (*e*), (*f*), (*g*), (*h*)

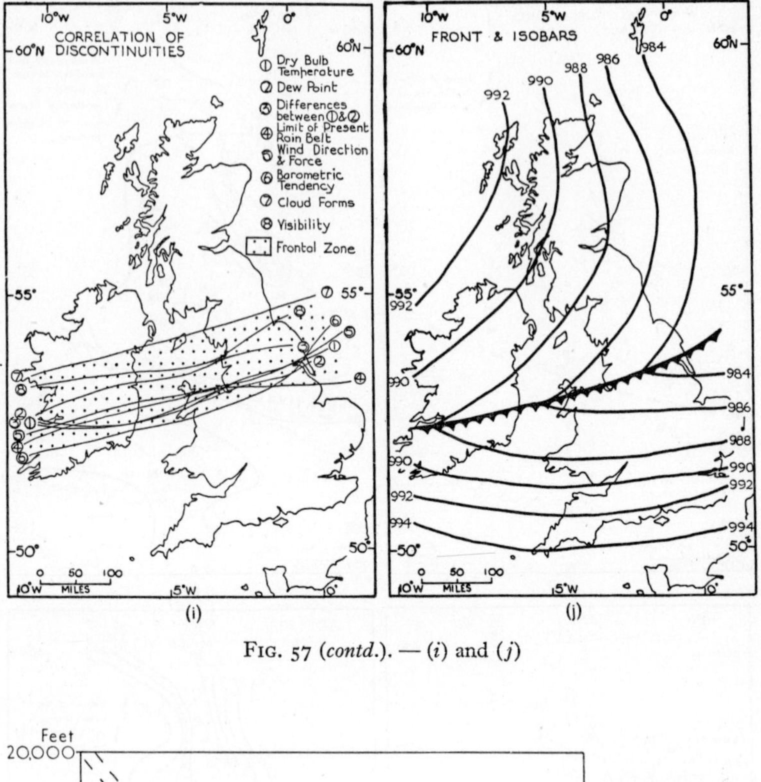

FIG. 57 (*contd.*). — (*i*) and (*j*)

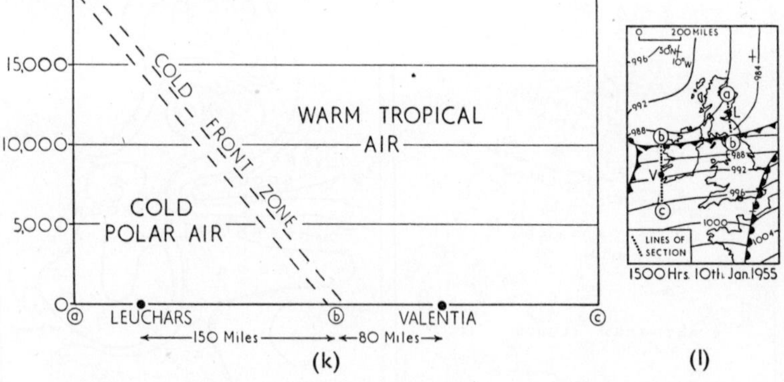

FIG. 57 (*contd.*). — (*k*) and (*l*) — the left hand diagram (*k*) is a vertical cross-section along the line joining the selected upper air stations. The right hand diagram (*l*) is a map showing the corresponding synoptic situation at the ground, with the upper air stations indicated by their initial letters

temperature gradient the isotherms are more widely spaced and less regular in pattern. Temperatures to the north of the zone are generally low, averaging about 36° F.; temperatures to the south are generally high, averaging about 50° F. The average means of daily maximum temperatures for January for the areas north of the zone is about 45° F., and for the areas to the south about 47° F.[1] Already then, temperature alone suggests the presence of cold, probably Polar, air over the northern parts of the British Isles and warm, probably Tropical, air over the southern parts, with a well marked discontinuity separating them.

The distribution of dew points (Fig. 57*b*) is broadly a repetition of that of temperature. A very clear east-west zone of closely aligned isopleths through approximately the centre of the British Isles divides a region of low dew points (average 35° F.) to the north from a region of high dew points (average 49° F.) to the south. Over East Anglia and Kent a smaller zone of transition, which is also suggested by the temperature distribution (Fig. 57*a*), may indicate perhaps a second and less well marked discontinuity. The distribution of differences[2] between temperature and dew point (Fig. 57*c*) shows a general twofold division between a northern area with relatively large differences ranging from 4° to 14° F. (= range of 60% to 90% relative humidity), and a southern area with relatively small differences ranging from 4° to 0° F. (= a range of 86 to 100% relative humidity) and in the south-west, 0° F. (= 100% relative humidity). The line dividing the two areas is not very clearly indicated but a continuous belt where differences approximate to 0° F. coincides with the zones of discontinuity already revealed on Fig. 57*a* and *b*. The difference between the average temperature and the average dew point for the areas of cold air to the north is 36° − 33° = 3° F. (= 89% relative humidity); for the area of warm air to the south it is 50° − 49° = 1° F. (= 96% relative humidity). Thus, the cold air to the north would appear to be less moist than the warm air to the south which is almost saturated.

The pattern of "past weather" (Fig. 57*d*) includes an east-west belt of rain and snow about 100 miles or more in width lying across Northern Ireland and Northern England. A second feature is a large area of drizzle with some mist lying immediately to the south

[1] Op. cit., p. 112, footnote 2.
[2] See Fig. 44, p. 100.

over the rest of Ireland, Wales and South-west England. Thirdly, in North and West Scotland *instability showers*[1] are locally represented. " Present weather " shows the main rain belt to have moved southwards to occupy a position identical with discontinuities already noted. The precipitation area has narrowed to less than 100 miles in places, and includes more drizzle ; an area of snow and rain showers has persisted over Southern Scotland and Northern England, and drizzle continues to affect South Wales and the South-west Peninsula. The precipitation reported at coastal stations may be due to orographic lifting of the air. In the north of Scotland, instability showers of rain, snow and hail also persist. " Past rain " at Gorleston and Felixstowe may be a further clue to the possible existence of a front in that neighbourhood. These patterns are consistent with the idea of a front lying east-west across the centre of the British Isles, and moving southwards. Since the cold air would be behind in this event, and the warm air in advance, a cold front is immediately indicated. This is corroborated by the drizzle and misty conditions typical of a warm sector to the south, and by the clearing showers typical of a cold sector composed of Polar-Maritime air to the north.

Wind direction and force (Fig. 57*e*) adds further evidence of a sharp discontinuity along a line joining the Humber, Mersey and Shannon estuaries. To the south of this line winds (immediately in advance of the cold front) are backing slightly from west-south-west to nearly south-west ; to the north of it, winds (immediately behind the cold front) are veering as much as 145° from south-west to north and even to north-north-east at some stations. The veering is accompanied by a decrease in force. The narrowness and sharpness of the frontal zone may be appreciated by comparing wind force and direction at the following pairs of stations : Spurn Head and Lindholme ; Aberporth and Holyhead ; and Valentia and Rineanna.

The isallobars (Fig. 57*f*) correlate very closely with lines of discontinuity already observed. A line from the Humber through North Wales and the south of Ireland divides an area of falling barometer to the south (in advance of the cold front) from an area of rising barometer in the north (behind the cold front). The closeness of the isallobars just north of this line indicates the

[1] See p. 55.

orthodox, relatively sharp rise in pressure immediately behind the cold front.

Fig. 57*g* shows that much of the British Isles south of a line Tynemouth — Blacksod Point at this time was overcast with extensive layer cloud (stratus, strato-cumulus and stratus-fractus, i.e. low cloud). The northern half of Scotland by contrast, had less cloud and it was of the heavy cumulus and cumulonimbus type, i.e. clouds of strong vertical development. Thus the passage of the cold front was accompanied by a succession of low cloud, then medium cloud and then clouds with marked vertical development. Visibility (Fig. 57*h*) was *good* or *very good* to the north in the Polar air behind the front, except for the district around Renfrew and Prestwick. The belt of " good " visibility immediately behind the cold front is very well marked. To the south visibility is " poor " in the frontal zone itself and " poor " in drizzle or rain in the warm sector; the Midlands constitute a major exception here, having no precipitation and fairly good visibility.

The very good correlation already anticipated in the course of the above analysis is revealed in Fig. 57*i*. The lines of discontinuity for the several elements are strikingly coincident with the two exceptions of visibility and cloud type. The line for visibility indicates the area of improvement in visibility behind the cold front; it is usual for such a line to coincide with the rear edge of the precipitation belt, as does this one (cf. Fig. 57*d*). The position of the line indicating the change in cloud type from stratiform to those with a marked vertical development is unusually far (some 250 miles) behind the position of the cold front on the ground.

It is possible that cumulus and cumulonimbus clouds were developed further south, but were invisible because of the thick stratus cloud and, therefore, not reported. In any event the cumulus and cumulonimbus clouds over Scotland have formed in Polar air away from the frontal zone itself. Fig. 57*j* shows the cold front lying east-west along a line joining the Humber, Mersey and Shannon estuaries, with the isobars angled very sharply across it. The front in fact extends across the North Sea from a depression over Southern Norway, which is partly occluded (Fig. 57 inset C). Some of the elements plotted and analysed (e.g. temperature and dew point) had suggested the possible existence of a front in East Anglia. As Fig. 57 inset C shows, the warm front from this depression lies across the East Anglian coast and Kent ; it is less well marked than the cold front.

Geostrophic Track Data

The identification of the air masses involved here may be facilitated by the use of a geostrophic wind scale (see pp. 51–53) and in Fig. 57, inset A, the paths by which these two air masses have reached Britain indicate conclusively that the warm, moist air over the south of the British Isles is Tropical-Maritime (T1), having come in from the south-west from sea areas off Spain between 30° and 40° W., Longitude ; and that the cold, less moist air over the north of the British Isles is Polar-Maritime (P1 or P2), having come in from the north-north-east from sea areas off Norway around 70° North Latitude and 10° East Longitude. Each of these tracks plotted on Fig. 57, inset A covered a period of about 24 hours.

Upper Air Data

In Fig. 57*k* and *l* upper air information for Leuchars at 1400 hours and for Valentia at 1500 hours on the 10th of January, 1955 has been plotted. Valentia, (surface air temperature of 53° F.) was in the warm sector at this time about 80 miles in advance of the cold front ; Leuchars, (surface air temperature of 34° F.) was in the cold sector some 150 miles behind the cold front. This temperature contrast is continued up to 15,000 feet (565 millibars) where the graphs for the two stations meet. At Valentia, a stratus cloud base was reported to be at 600 feet at noon and 700 feet at 1800 hours, and was presumably about this height at 1500 hours. The air was saturated, or nearly so, at the ground and up to about 12,000 feet (634 millibars) ; intermittent drizzle reported at 1800 hours was in all probability falling at 1500 hours also. The graph follows the wet adiabat very closely up to about 16,000 feet (550 millibars) ; the subsequent fall in evening temperatures would probably make the air stable in its lower layers. Now, at Leuchars the graph indicates a sequence of unstable layers and *isothermal*[1] *layers* up to about 8,000 feet (740 millibars), after which the air is

[1] An *isothermal layer* is a layer of the atmosphere within which temperatures remain steady. The fall of temperature with height ceases at the base, and is resumed at the top, of such a layer (Fig. 57 inset B).

stable. The entry into the warm sector would appear to be at about 15,200 feet (560 millibars), above which level the air is stable Tropical-Maritime in type.

The Occlusion and Types of Occluded Fronts

As previously explained,[1] the cold front of a depression moves more quickly than the warm front and eventually overtakes it. This means that contact is established at the ground between the Polar air originally behind the warm sector and the Polar air originally in front of it. The warm sector is thus elevated from the ground, first at its tip at the centre of the depression and then progressively outwards towards the edge of the depression. The warm and cold fronts gradually converge, and are replaced on the ground by a zone of contact and intermixture between the two Polar air masses. This zone of contact is termed an *occlusion*, or, alternatively, an *occluded front*. If the Polar air originally behind the warm sector is less cold than the Polar air originally in advance of the warm sector, a *warm front occlusion*, or, more simply, a *warm occlusion* is formed with the *less cold* air behind over-riding the *colder* air in front. The warm occlusion resembles in several ways the warm front. Alternatively, if the air originally behind the warm sector is colder than the air originally in advance of the warm sector, a *cold front occlusion* or, more simply, a *cold occlusion* is formed with the *colder* air behind undercutting the *less cold* air in front. The cold occlusion has some features similar to those of the cold front. The accompanying diagrams and table (Figs. 45, 58, 60, 61, 63 and 64) illustrate the structure of the occluding depression and the pattern of the warm and cold occlusions. Let us examine in more detail an example of an *occluding depression*. Three types of data will be analysed: first, horizontal distributions of meteorological conditions at the ground surface; second, evidence of geostrophic tracks of air samples to the British Isles, and third, upper air graphs for selected stations.

The Occluding Depression: 12th November, 1954, 0600 hours G.M.T. Surface Synoptic Data

Selecting first of all the dry bulb temperatures of air from the data plotted on Fig. 59, it is at once apparent that a narrow wedge of

[1] See p. 106.

Summary of Occlusion Characteristics Idealised Sequences

Element	*In advance*	*At the passage*	*In the rear*
	THE WARM OCCLUSION (cf. Warm Front)		
PRESSURE	Falling markedly.	Fall arrested (or markedly decreased).	Rising sharply (or fall much decreased).
WIND	Backing and slightly increasing.	Veer, sometimes sharp.	Probably backing.
TEMPERATURE	Rising slightly.	Slight rise.	Little change.
HUMIDITY	Increasing	Saturated or nearly so.	Decreasing.
CLOUD	Cs, As, increasing.	Nb, Cb.	Cb, decreasing.
WEATHER	Moderate to heavy rain.	Tending to cease.	Clearing showers.
VISIBILITY	Deteriorating.	Poor in rain.	Improving to good.
	THE COLD OCCLUSION (cf. Cold Front)		
PRESSURE	Falling markedly.	Fall arrested (or markedly decreased).	Rising sharply (or fall much decreased).
WIND	Backing and slightly increasing.	Veer, sometimes sharp.	Probably backing.
TEMPERATURE	Falling slightly.	Slight fall.	Little change.
HUMIDITY	Increasing.	Saturated or nearly so.	Decreasing.
CLOUD	Ci, As, increasing	Nb, large Cu, Cb.	Cb. descreasing.
WEATHER	Heavy rain showers near the front.	Heavy rain showers or rain continued for a short time.	Clearing Showers.
VISIBILITY	Deteriorating.	Poor in rain.	Improving to very good.

FIG. 58. — Occlusion Characteristics : A Summary of Idealised Sequences (Table)

relatively warm air extends northwards over Wales and the Irish Sea, within which temperatures are of the order of 50° to 57° F. To the east of it over Northern and Central England there is less warm air with temperatures of about 46° to 48° F. To the north over Scotland and to the west over Ireland there is distinctly colder air with temperatures in the region of 37° to 42° F. The zones of sharp temperature change are indicated by the thick, broken lines on the map. This general pattern is reproduced on the dew point distribution (Fig. 59*b*). A narrow wedge of higher dew points (50°–56° F.), coinciding with the wedge of higher temperatures, thrusts northwards and is flanked by an area of lower dew points (43°–49° F.) over Northern and Central England, and even lower dew points (34°–39° F.) over Scotland and Ireland. A pattern of discontinuities is shown similar to that in Fig. 59*a*. Fig. 59*c* indicates the distribution of humidity. A large area of moist air (relative humidities 93–100%) is situated over the Midlands, Lincolnshire, Norfolk, the South-West Peninsula, South Central England, Wales and eastern Irish Sea and its coastlands. Humidities decrease westwards and north-eastwards from these areas, e.g. differences[1] between temperature and dew point of 6° to 11° over Ireland (= relative humidities of 80 to 65%), and of 3° to 9° (= relative humidities of 70 to 90%) over Scotland. Just off Western Scotland, however, another, but much smaller, area of relatively moist (relative humidity 93 to 96%) air exists. Frontal zones possibly associated with this humidity distribution are indicated on the map (Fig. 59*c*). The evidence so far suggests the presence of relatively warm, moist air in a narrow warm sector flanked on both sides by colder, less moist air ; the air to the west is rather colder and drier than that to the east.

Data for " past weather " (Fig. 59*d*) reveal an area of rain and drizzle with some showers, over England (except the extreme east coast), Wales, Ireland and the Western Isles. Skies were generally overcast in the precipitation area with perhaps partly clouded skies at some stations reporting showers. The pattern of " present weather " shows the precipitation area to have extended over most of England and Wales and western Scotland. A zone of moderate to heavy, continuous rain extends from Benbecula and Tiree, through West Freugh and Silloth, to Manchester and Elmdon, Mildenhall and West Raynham. To the west of the precipitation area, Ireland has rapidly clearing skies (Collinstown two eighths ; Aldergrove one eighth cloud amounts) and local instability showers, e.g. Castle Archdale, all of which suggests post-cold front weather. The precipitation area itself would indicate the general eastward movement of the " weather system " and the coalescing

[1] See Fig. 44, p. 100.

of warm sector drizzle with warm front rain and cold front rain.

In Fig. 59*e* winds have backed from south-west to southerly and strengthened somewhat in Northern England and Scotland, e.g. Spurn Head, Lindholme, Manchester, Squires Gate, Stornoway. Over the Midlands, e.g. Cottesmore, Cranfield, etc., winds have veered west-south-westerly, decreasing at first and then freshening. Along a line from the Isle of Man to Pembrokeshire winds have backed slightly to the south-west and freshened again, e.g. Holyhead and Pembroke. Over Ireland, a marked veer to the west and north-west with a decrease in force, is in evidence. The zones of discontinuity in wind direction indicate the positions of the three frontal zones, the first extending from Benbecula (where a calm would perhaps suggest that the centre of the depression is nearby) to West Freugh, whence the second continues southwards between Wales and Ireland and the third continues to the Mersey estuary, thence curving eastwards to Norfolk.

The most striking feature of the distribution of barometric tendency (Fig. 59*f*) is a north-south belt of closely aligned isallobars through Eastern Ireland. Centrally through this belt passes the boundary between positive tendencies to the west and negative tendencies to the east. This boundary is an indication of the position of the cold front. A line joining places of greatest fall in barometric tendency, e.g. Prestwick, Manchester and Cranfield, perhaps indicates the position of the warm front. In between the two suggested frontal zones, the warm sector stations show relatively large falls in the barometer with the largest fall occurring at the tip of the warm sector, e.g. Prestwick –6·0 millibars, and not in the area showing the lowest barometric reading, i.e. the Western Isles off Scotland. This may be a result of the depression moving *quickly* and also occluding *quickly*. The isallobars certainly indicate that the cold front is moving relatively quickly eastwards.

The distribution of cloud types (Fig. 59*g*) has two main divisions; firstly, Ireland is dominated by cumuliform cloud with marked vertical development, and skies are only partly clouded. Secondly, the rest of the British Isles is dominated by layer cloud, especially stratus and stratocumulus, with bands of altocumulus and nimbostratus lying NNW.–SSE. across the Midlands, Norfolk, the Welsh Border country, South Lancashire, the Isle of Man and the western coastlands and islands of Scotland.

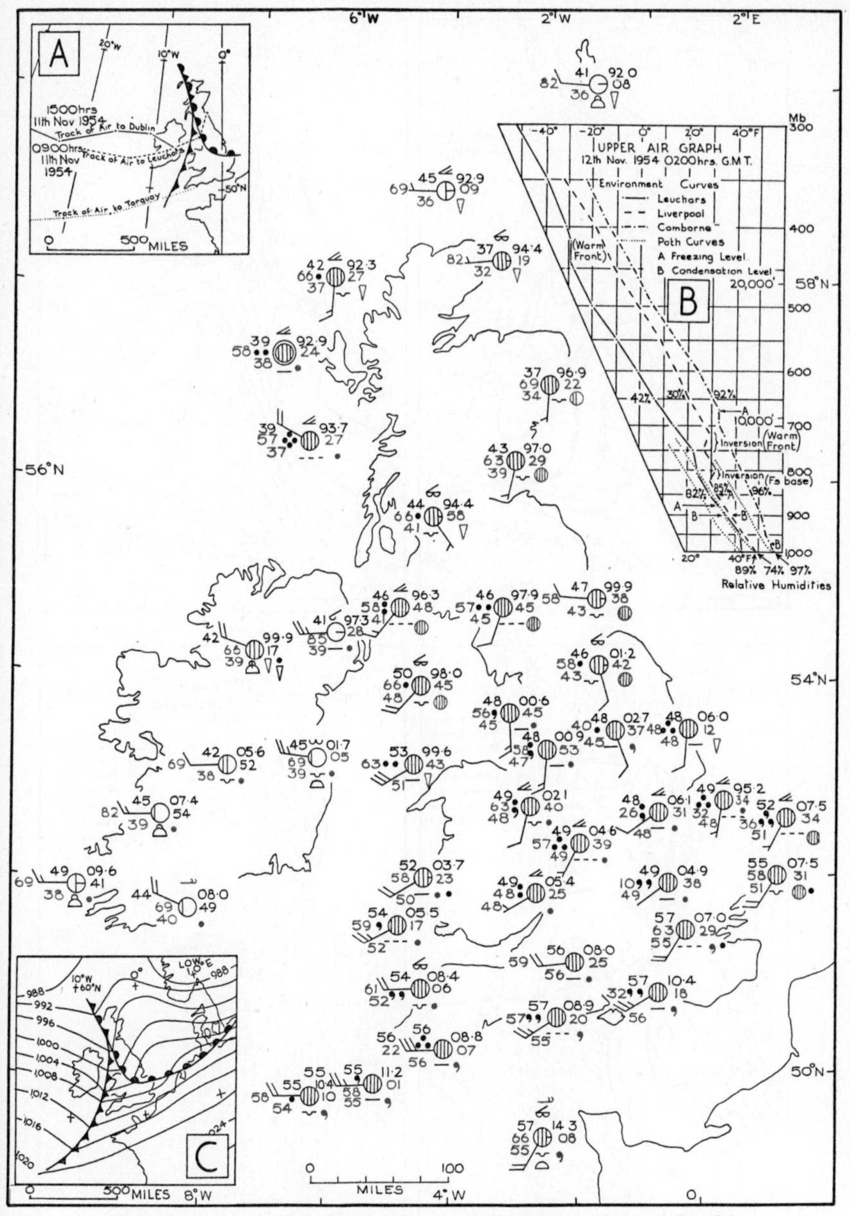

Maps redrawn from the Daily Weather Report 12th November 1954 by permission of the Director-General, Meteorological Office, London. Copyright H.M. Stationery Office.

FIG. 59. — Selected Data for 12th November 1954 : 0600 hrs. G.M.T.
The Occluding Depression
Inset A — Track Map ; Inset B — Upper Air Graphs
Inset C — Isobars : 0600 hrs. G.M.T. 12th November 1954

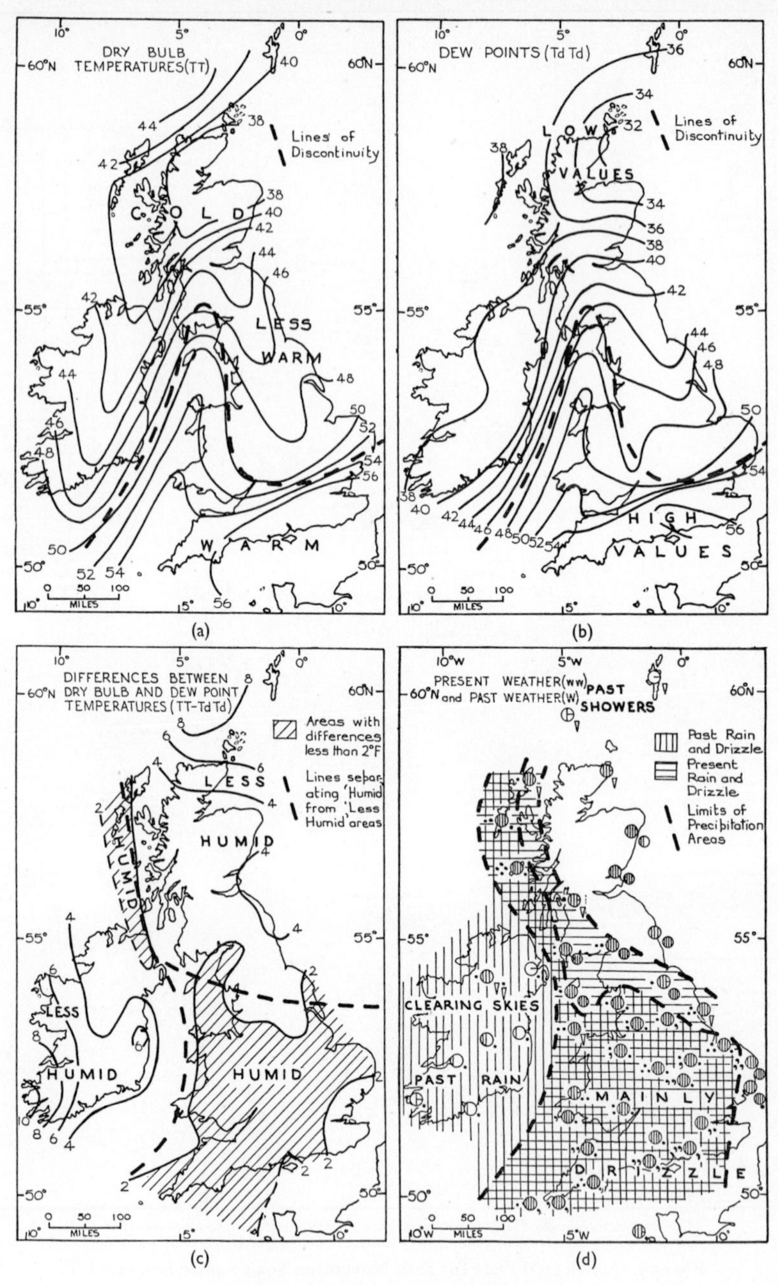

FIG. 59 (*contd.*). — (*a*), (*b*), (*c*), (*d*)

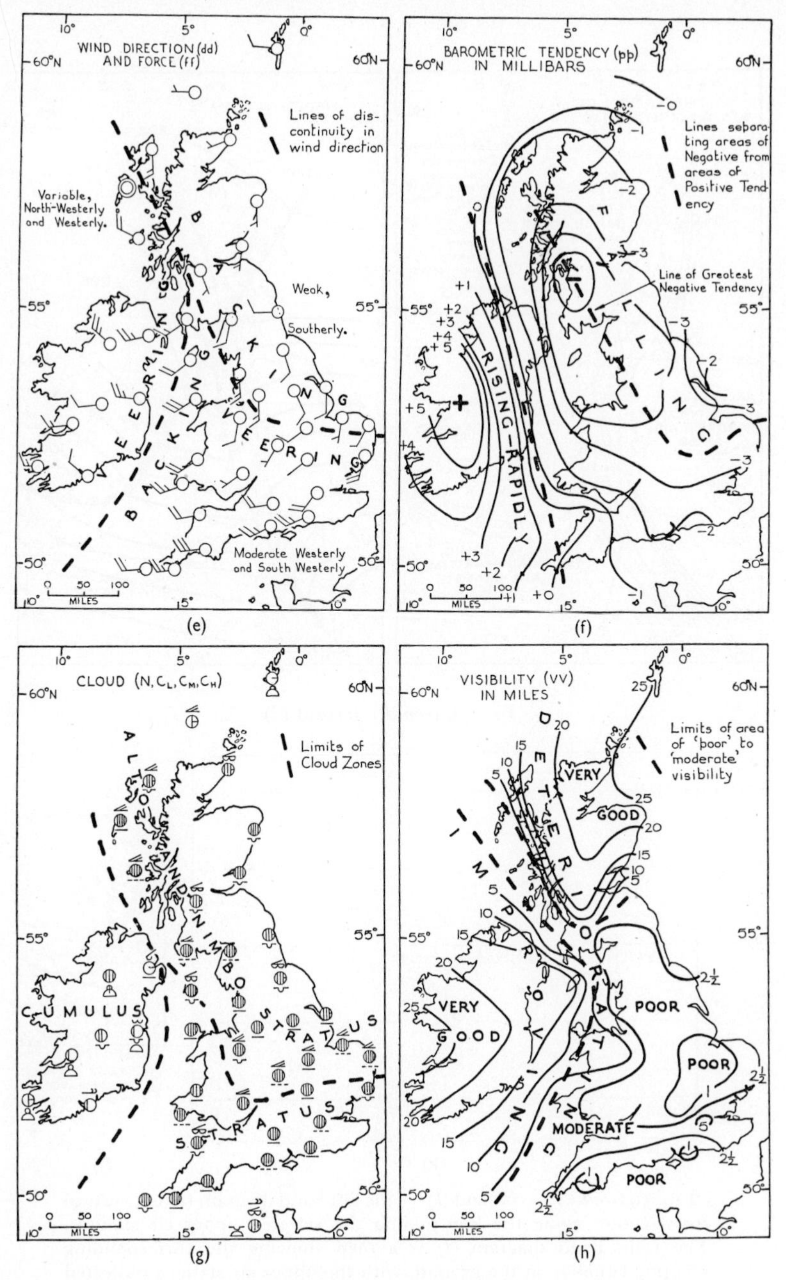

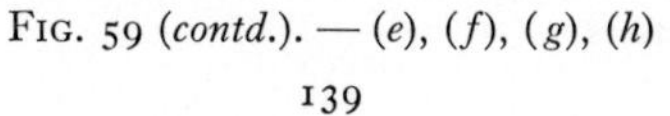
FIG. 59 (*contd.*). — (*e*), (*f*), (*g*), (*h*)

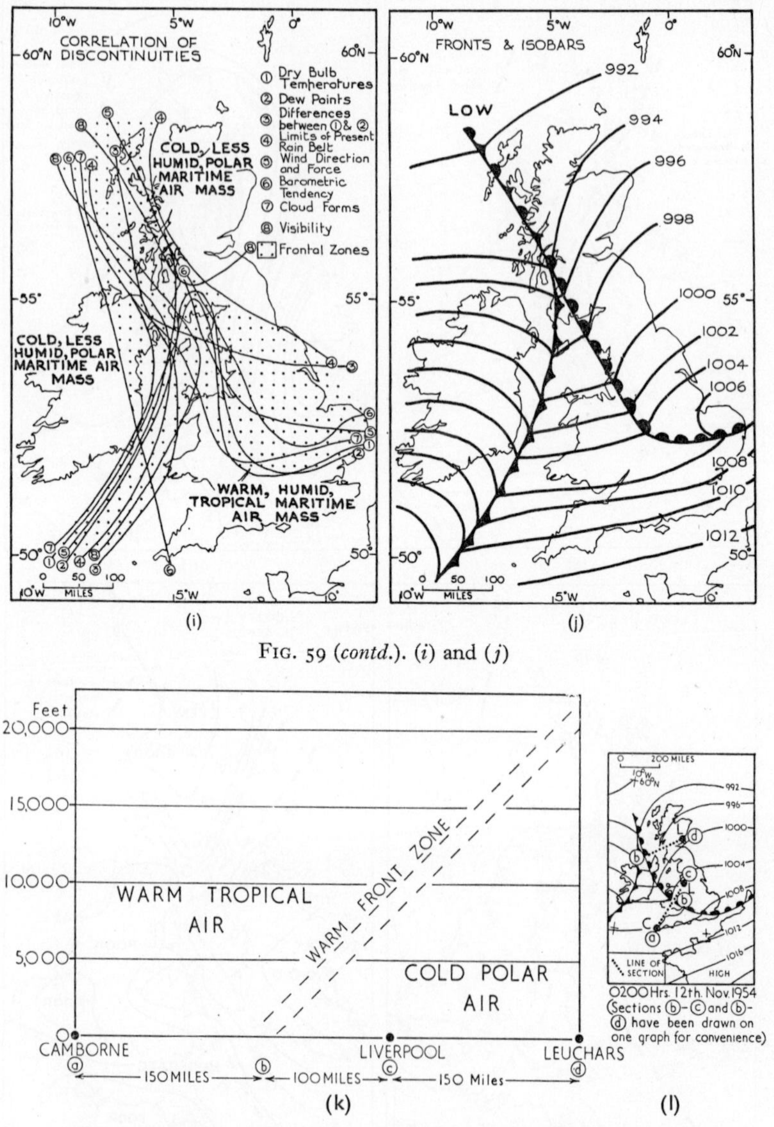

FIG. 59 (*contd.*). (*i*) and (*j*)

FIG. 59 (*contd.*). — (*k*) and (*l*) — the left hand diagram (*k*) is a vertical cross-section along the line joining the selected upper air stations. The right hand diagram (*l*) is a map showing the corresponding synoptic situation at the ground, with the upper air stations indicated by their initial letters

These clouds are typical of the area in advance of a warm front. A narrow zone of "poor" visibility (Fig. 59*h*), generally coincident with these bands, widens southwards in the shape of a triangle, based on the south coast of England, in which visibilities, although mostly under 2½ miles, range from about 1,000 yards to about 5 miles. East of this triangle over South Scotland and North-east England visibility is somewhat better (3 to 5 miles) and "very good" (20 miles or more) over the centre and north of Scotland. To the west, over Ireland, visibility improves rapidly to about 20 miles also. These facts are consistent with the presence of a narrow and diminishing warm sector over the eastern part of the Irish Sea, Wales and the south and west of England with conditions typical of those in advance of a warm front to the east and conditions typical of those behind a cold front to the west.

The correlation of these elements on Fig. 59*i* is broadly indicative of the frontal zones shown on Fig. 59*j* which also shows the isobars at intervals of 2 millibars. The warm front curves from Norfolk to Manchester and thence north-north-westwards towards Glasgow after which it is joined by the cold front to form an occlusion which continues north-north-westwards to a point west of Stornoway where the lowest pressure of 992·3 millibars was reported. The cold front curves south and then south-south-west through the Irish Sea and along St. George's Channel. Isobars are appropriately straight in the warm sector and suggest an eastward movement of the depression as a whole,[1] as did the isallobar pattern (Fig. 59*f*). Evidence for the existence of the occluded front is afforded by the narrowness of the warm sector, the overlap of the discontinuities off the west of Scotland (as revealed by the various elements plotted), and the occurrence of a rain belt and high humidity in the same area, especially the heavy, continuous rain reported at Tiree, (Fig. 59*d*).

Geostrophic Track Data

The geostrophic wind scale has been employed in Fig. 59, inset A to show the tracks followed by the air masses involved in the weather situation just analysed in terms of its horizontal surface distributions. The air in the warm sector, which has been shown

[1] A depression with a warm sector tends to move along a line parallel to the isobars in the warm sector.

to possess the normal properties of Tropical-Maritime air (T1) (viz. relatively high temperatures and dew points, high humidities and overcast skies, drizzly or rainy weather with low, layer-cloud bases and poor visibility), appears to have come in from the west-south-west through the Western Approaches. The air behind the cold front has arrived from a position almost due west from Ireland, and, being relatively cold, with variable skies and clearing showers and good visibility etc., must be classified as Polar-Maritime (P5) which has followed a relatively southerly track over the Atlantic. Cold air in advance of the warm front appears to have come in from due west over the Atlantic and probably also had a " Polar-Maritime " source (P5?).

Upper Air Data

Upper air data (Fig. 59, inset B) for Camborne, Leuchars and Liverpool at approximately 2 a.m. reveal the contrast in temperature and humidity conditions *inside* the warm sector, e.g. at Camborne, about 150 miles behind the warm front at this time, and *outside* the warm sector, e.g. at Liverpool, which at this time must have been some considerable distance, about 100 miles or so, in advance of the warm front at the ground. The inversion in the graph for Liverpool at about 8,000 feet possibly indicates the height of the warm front above Liverpool at this time. Below the front is another inversion about 6,000 feet which probably coincides with the belt of stratus-fractus cloud reported at nearby stations about this height two hours previously at midnight. Below 800 mbs. is stable, Polar air, probably rendered stable by nocturnal cooling. Above the warm front is stable Tropical air. The graph for Camborne shows stable Tropical air up to an isothermal layer[1] at about 10,000 feet (685 millibars) ; thereafter it is slightly unstable to about 18,000 feet (500 millibars) and then stable again. The graph for Leuchars, well in advance (*c.* 250 miles) of the warm front at this time shows stable Polar air to about 1,000 feet (960 millibars) (again probably caused by nocturnal cooling) ; thereafter it is unstable up to about 4,000 feet (860 millibars), and then, above this, stable. At 21,000 feet (450 millibars) an isothermal layer suggests the effect of weak frontal zone. The acceptance of this suggestion would require a relatively steeply inclined warm

[1] See p. 132, footnote 1.

front zone (Fig. 59*k* and *l*, and cf. Fig. 49). Note that freezing and condensation levels for Leuchars and Liverpool, both in the cold section of Polar air in advance of the warm front are approximately comparable at about 4,000 feet (860 millibars) and 2,000 feet (930 millibars) respectively. At Camborne, however, in the warm sector of Tropical air, a freezing level at 10,500 feet and a condensation level at 600 feet were reported.

The Full Occlusion: Warm Type

The full occlusion of the *warm* type (Figs. 60, 61 and the Table in Fig. 58) involves the juxtaposition at and near the ground of two Polar air masses, *the air in the rear being less cold than the air in advance* of the front formed between the two air masses. Since Maritime air is normally warmer than Continental air *in winter*, this type of occlusion is more likely to develop at that season. The *cold occlusion* is in fact comparatively rare but is most likely to develop *in summer* when air from the Continent might well be warmer under certain circumstances than air from the Atlantic. The approach of the warm occlusion is heralded by the appearance of layers of cirrostratus, followed by altostratus, nimbostratus and stratus-fractus and associated rain. Pressure falls markedly, winds

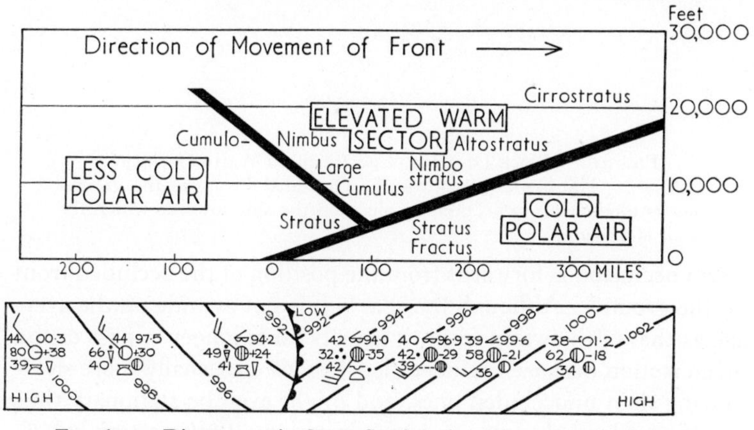

FIG. 60. — Diagrammatic Cross-Section through an Idealised Warm Occlusion

Note: The frontal zones associated with the Warm Occlusion are shown in black. The upper diagram is a vertical cross-section; the lower diagram is the corresponding horizontal synoptic distribution at the ground.

back and increase slightly, humidity increases till the air is saturated, temperature rises slightly nearer the front and visibility deteriorates especially in rain. The rain belt is usually about 100 to 200 miles in width and occurs generally *in advance* of the front for the simple reason that the orientation of the structure of the

FIG. 61. — Block Diagram of an Idealised Warm Occlusion
Note : The line representing the Occluded Front on the ground has its identifying projections in black on the side towards which the front is moving.

warm occlusion is forwards from the position of the occluded front on the ground. Although the rain belt is not as wide on the average as that of the warm front, it usually takes longer to pass over a given station because occluded depressions are usually more slow-moving than unoccluded ones, and might even be stationary thus causing prolonged, continuous precipitation. Precipitation, which may be sleet or snow if it is cold enough, is associated with two processes, firstly, the continued elevation of the warm sector and the continued intermixture of the Tropical air of the warm sector with the underlying Polar air masses, and secondly, the interaction of the two Polar air masses themselves near the ground below the warm sector. Precipitation is usually more intense and prolonged when the two Polar air masses have considerable differences in temperature and/or humidity. It will be noted that the approach of the warm occlusion is accompanied by a weather sequence which resembles in many ways that preceding a warm front. At the passage of the warm occlusion, however, there is only a slight rise in temperature in contrast to the marked rise at the warm front. Moreover, heavy cumuliform clouds, including the spectacular cumulonimbus, accompany, or may replace, the stratiform cloud just in advance of the warm occlusion, but like the warm front, precipitation tends to moderate and cease at the passage of the front. The air is still very moist at this stage and the visibility poor. Conditions behind the warm occlusion differentiate it still more from the warm front, simply because a cold Polar air mass occurs behind the occluded front in contrast to the warm Tropical air of the warm sector behind the warm front. Indeed the weather sequence behind a warm occlusion has more in common with the weather sequence behind a cold front. As a rule pressure rises sharply behind the warm occlusion, or, if it continues to fall, the fall is markedly decreased; winds veer, often sharply, immediately after the passage of the front, and later may back a little; cloud is still of the vertical type but skies tend to clear and only local instability showers occur; humidity decreases but temperature shows little change after the slight rise at the passage of the front; visibility improves to "very good" and the weather generally is brighter and improved.

"Text-book" warm occlusions possessing the standard characteristics described above are probably even rarer than "text-book" warm or cold fronts. Nevertheless, occlusions in general are more frequent over the British Isles than simple warm and cold fronts [1] and one of the best examples in recent years of a warm occlusion occurred at noon on the 7th November, 1955. The following analysis of this weather situation includes three sections: first, an examination of the horizontal distributions of ground surface weather conditions; second, a consideration of geostrophic tracks for air samples at selected stations, and third, an interpretation of upper air data for selected stations.

[1] See pp. 106 and 120.

The Warm Occlusion: 7th November, 1955, 1200 hours G.M.T.

Surface Synoptic Data

The most conspicuous feature about the horizontal distribution of dry bulb temperatures (Fig. 62*a*) is a minor zone of discontinuity extending from the North Channel across Southern Scotland and North-east England and then along the Yorkshire coast towards the Wash. To the south of this zone, temperatures are generally between 56° F. and 60° F.; to the north of it they are generally between 52° F. and 50° F. Outside the zone, isotherms are mostly irregular and rather widely spaced.

A similar, but less conspicuous, zone of minor discontinuity appears in the dew point distribution (Fig. 62*b*), with relatively low values (47°–51° F.) to the north and relatively high values (53°–56° F.) to the south. Fig. 62*c* shows that differences[1] between dry bulb and dew point temperatures are less than 2° F. in an east-west zone lying across Northern Ireland, where it is narrow, Northern England and Scotland, where it is wider. Relative humidities in this zone range from 93 to 100%. Northwards and southwards from this zone relative humidities decrease progressively to about 86% over the Outer Hebrides and about 80% over the South-west Peninsula. It is noticeable that the southern limit of the humid zone coincides approximately with the zone of discontinuity already noted in the air temperature and dew point distributions. Thus, evidence so far examined, indicates the presence of a zone of discontinuity separating one type of air mass over Scotland from another type of air mass over Southern Ireland, Wales and Central and Southern England.

The position and extent of the belt of "present" rain and showers (Fig. 62*d*) correlate fairly well with the zone of high humidity just differentiated above. It is a wide belt (from 120 to 220 miles from north to south), however, suggesting association with a warm front or a warm occlusion rather than with a cold front or a cold occlusion. Reference to the extent of "past rain and showers" shows that the precipitation area has moved northwards. Thus, the southern edge of the "present" precipitation area may indicate the position at the ground of a warm front or a warm occlusion. The belt of "present showers" south of the main precipitation area, and the decreasing cloudiness in the extreme south, strongly suggest conditions more characteristic of

[1] See Fig. 44, p. 100.

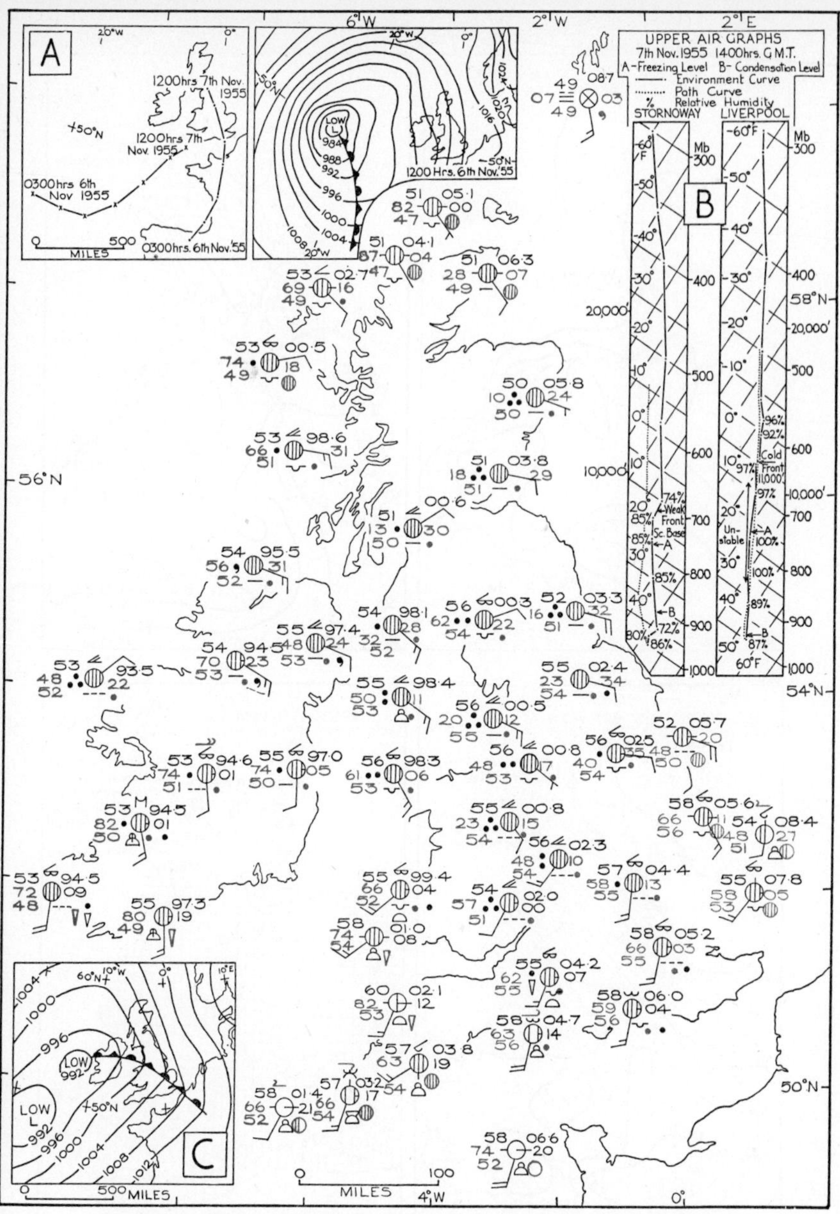

Maps redrawn from the Daily Weather Reports of 6th November 1955 and 7th November 1955 by permission of the Director-General, Meteorological Office, London. Copyright H.M. Stationery Office.

FIG. 62. — Selected Data for 7th November 1955 : 1200 hrs. G.M.T.
The Warm Occlusion
Inset A — Track Map and Previous Synoptic situation
Inset B — Upper air graphs
Inset C — Isobars : 1200 hrs. G.M.T. 7th November 1955

Note: The orientation of the upper air graphs is due to the limitations of space and for the sake of clarity. The graphs for Stornoway and Liverpool have been drawn separately, and the temperature axis of the graph is inclined instead of being horizontal as in other similar types of diagram.

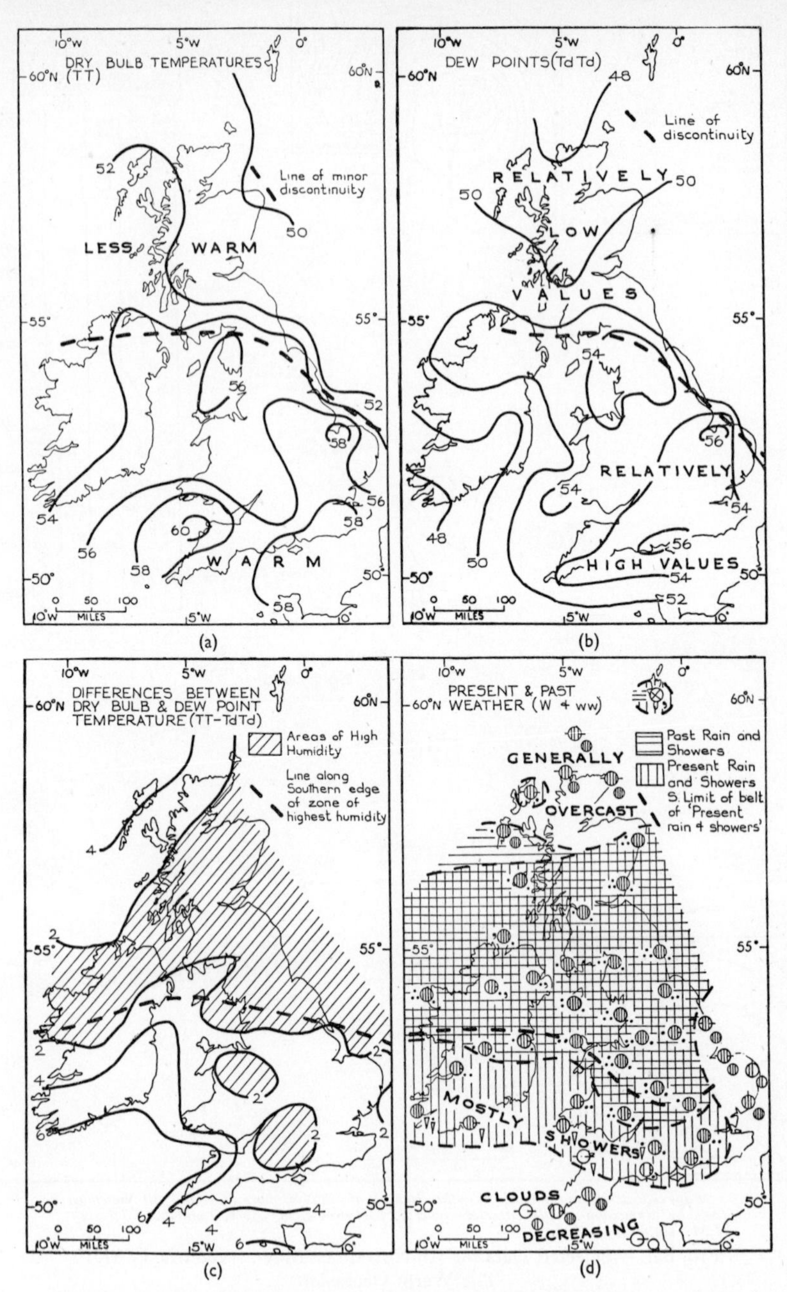

N.B. Fig. 62(*d*) — the upper two symbols in the key should be interchanged.

FIG. 62 (*contd.*). — (*a*), (*b*), (*c*), (*d*)

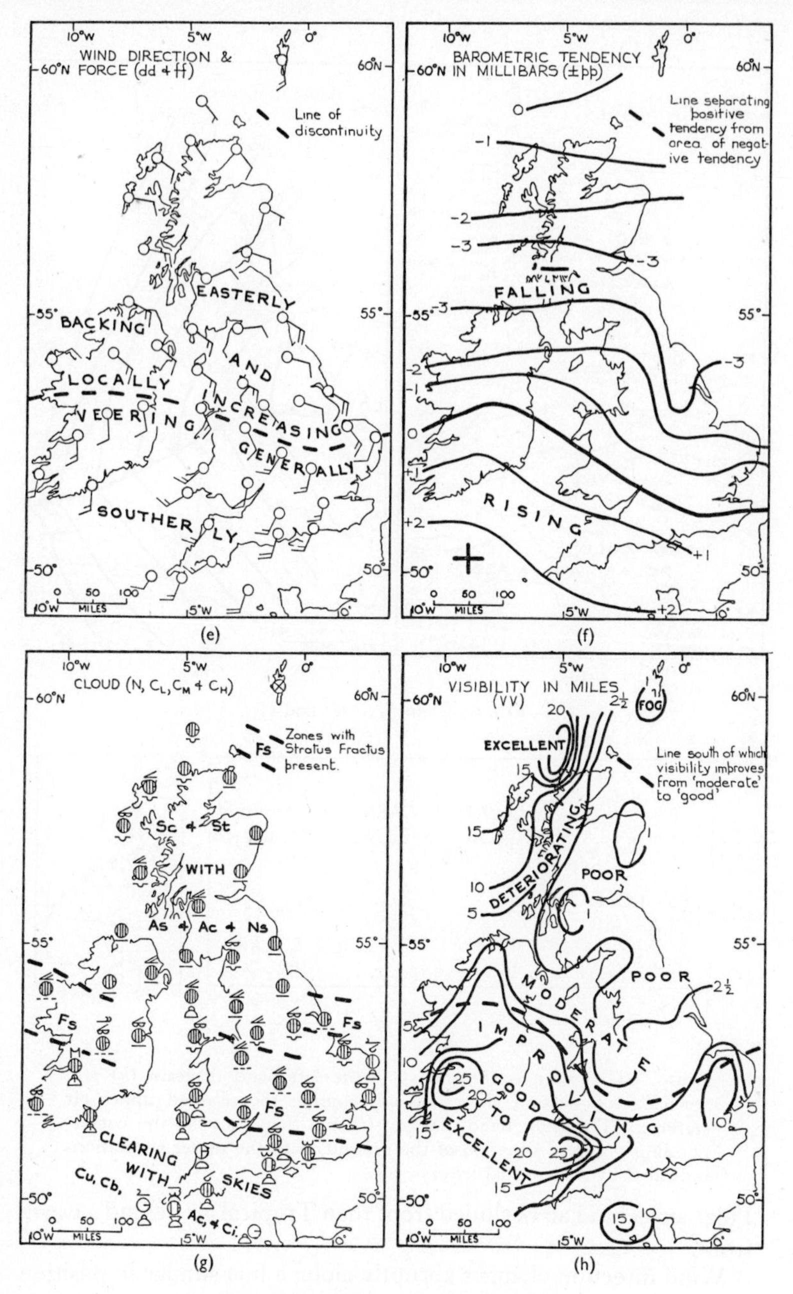

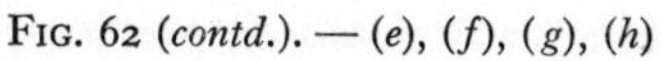
FIG. 62 (*contd.*). — (*e*), (*f*), (*g*), (*h*)

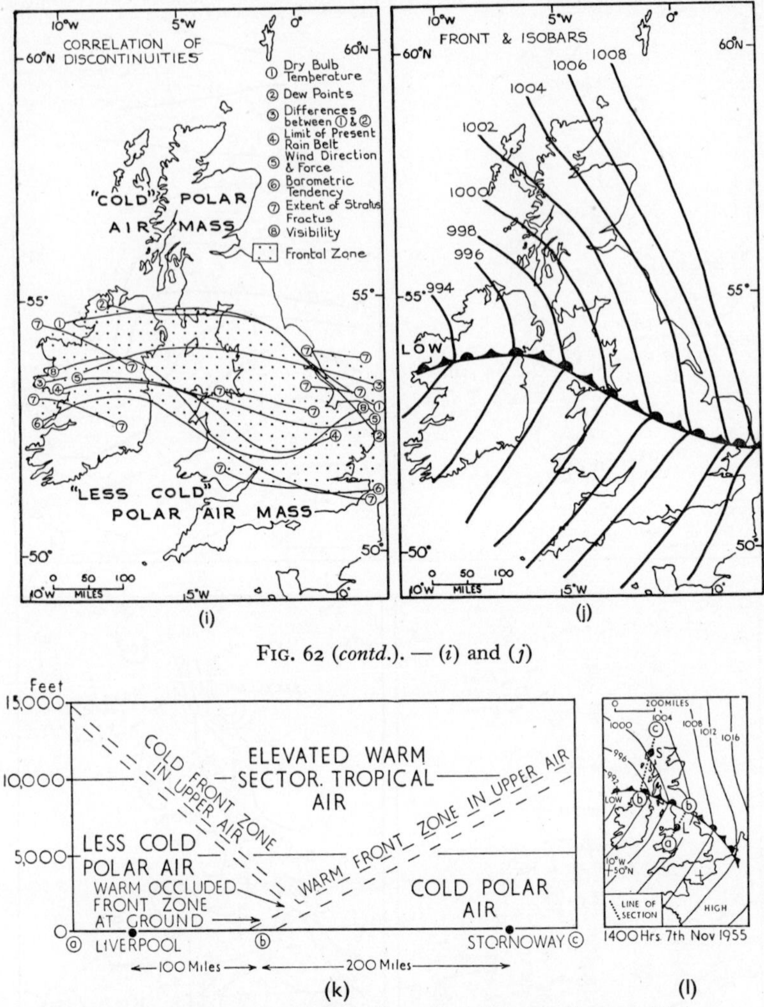

FIG. 62 (*contd.*). — (*i*) and (*j*)

FIG. 62 (*contd.*). — (*k*) and (*l*) — the left hand diagram (*k*) is a vertical cross-section along the line joining the selected upper air stations. The right hand diagram (*l*) is a map showing the corresponding synoptic situation of the ground, with the upper air stations indicated by their initial letters

Polar air behind an occluded front than Tropical air behind a warm front.

Wind direction changes abruptly along a line similar in position to the discontinuity already noted on previous maps (Fig. 62*a*, *b*, *c*). Evidence from Fig. 62*d* suggested a *northward* movement of this weather system. The winds, light to moderate and south-easterly or easterly over Northern Scotland, are backing more consistently easterly and strengthening over Northern Ireland, Southern Scotland and Northern England. Then, along an east-west line passing centrally through Ireland and thence through Holyhead and Shawbury to Gorleston, the winds veer sharply to southerly and ultimately south-westerly, sometimes decreasing but generally strengthening over Southern England.

The isallobaric pattern (Fig. 62*f*) is very simple and regular. Isallobars aligned east-west represent a north-south gradation which may be divided into a major area of *positive* tendency over Southern Ireland, South Wales and Southern England, and a major area of *negative* tendency over the remainder of the British Isles. The line of division between these areas is coincident with discontinuities noted previously over Ireland but further to the south of discontinuities previously noted over Wales and England (Figs. 62*a*, *b*, *c* and *e*). The progressive fall in the barometer in the north of the British Isles is suggestive of the approach from the south of a warm front or a warm occlusion. The immediate rise in barometer in the south of the British Isles, however, is more typical of conditions behind a warm occlusion rather than behind a warm front which is usually followed by the steady or slightly falling barometric tendencies of the warm sector.

Cloud cover (Fig. 62*g*) was extensive everywhere except in the South-west of England and Southern Ireland where cloud was decreasing in amount and was dominantly large cumulus and cumulo-nimbus, associated locally with clearing showers (Fig. 62*d*). Therefore Polar air is again indicated. Bands of " bad weather cloud " — stratus fractus — across Central Ireland, North Wales and Central England are suggestive of the frontal zone itself which also has much stratus, stratocumulus, altostratus altocumulus and nimbostratus clouds which extend northwards with the " present " rain and showers belt (Fig. 62*d*).

Visibility (Fig. 62*h*) is " poor " to " moderate " in an area over Northern Ireland, Northern England and Southern Scotland which is generally coincident with the belt of " present " rain and showers (Fig. 62*d*) and the belt of highest humidity (Fig. 62*c*). To the north and south of this area visibilities are " good " to "excellent". This pattern is consistent with the idea, already mooted, of a broad frontal zone lying across Northern Ireland, Northern England and Southern Scotland. Other evidence (e.g. Fig. 62*d*) suggests a northward movement of the frontal zone; therefore visibilities are deteriorating just north of the zone and improving just south of it (Fig. 62*h*).

The correlation of these several discontinuities is shown on (Fig. 62*i*). A relatively wide frontal belt extends approximately east-west across Central and Northern England, Wales, the Irish Sea and Northern Ireland. Its width, from about 120 to about 220 miles, and its general continuity, tend to identify it as a warm occlusion zone rather than a cold occlusion zone which is usually much narrower (often less than 50 miles) and discontinuous. A warm occlusion is indicated rather than a simple warm front because the weather conditions *behind* the frontal zone over Southern Ireland, South Wales and South-west England suggest the presence of Polar air and not "warm sector" Tropical air. Cloud amounts are decreasing and not being maintained; vertical cloud is becoming increasingly dominant, not layer cloud; humidity is decreasing and not being maintained; there are local clearing showers and no drizzle; the barometer is rising progressively not remaining steady or falling slightly. On the other hand, however, temperatures are being maintained and are also increasing locally. In fact temperatures of 56°–60° F. at noon in early November in these areas are much higher than average, the mean daily *maximum* temperatures for these areas are about 49°–53° F.[1] This, contrary to other evidence, would indicate Tropical air, not Polar air. Similarly temperatures over Scotland (viz. 50°–54° F.) in advance of the frontal zone are higher than the mean daily maxima (viz. 46°–48° F.) for that area. How can these high temperatures be reconciled with other evidence that Polar air is in occupation on either side of the frontal zone which has been marked in with the isobars on Fig. 62*j*?

Geostrophic Track Data

Fig. 62, inset A shows the tracks followed by samples of air to Glasgow and Lizard between 0300 hours on 6th November, 1955 and 1200 hours on 7th November, 1955, and the weather situation

[1] Climatological Atlas op. cit., p. 112, footnote 2.

at 12 hours on 6th November in the eastern North Atlantic. The position (50° N., 25° W.) and extent of occluded Low *L* at noon on the 6th November were such as to cause Polar air (P7), coming from source regions in the Greenland area, to reach latitudes as low as 30° N.–40° N., before moving eastwards and then northwards across Portugal and the Bay of Biscay to the British Isles. The Polar air must inevitably have been warmed a great deal *en route* through sub-tropical latitudes, and hence the relatively high temperatures over the British Isles at 1200 hours on 7th November, 1955. Thus, reference to geostrophic track data and previous weather situations support the suggestion that Polar air (P7), warmed in transit,[1] was in occupation north and south of the east-west frontal zone previously identified by correlation of discontinuities (Fig. 62*i*). Reference to cloud data for 0000 hours and 0600 hours in the Daily Weather Report for the 7th of November shows that very cloudy conditions persisted over much of the British Isles. This would reduce greatly the overnight loss of heat by radiation and provide further explanation of the unusually high temperatures at 1200 hours on 7th November, 1955.

Upper Air Data

In Fig. 62, inset B and Figs. 62*k* and *l* upper air data for 1400 hours for Stornoway, which was some 200 miles in advance of the warm occlusion at the ground at that time, and Liverpool, which was some 100 miles behind the warm occlusion at the ground at that time, show evidence of the structure of the occlusion system. At Stornoway, a minor discontinuity is suggested at about 8,500 feet (725 millibars); this would appear to be the base of strato-cumulus cloud reported at the station and also the entry into the elevated warm sector, by this time so modified as to be scarcely distinguishable from the Polar air beneath it which has been subjected to much warming.[1] Below this minor discontinuity the modified Polar air was generally slightly unstable; above it the modified Tropical air was generally stable. The marked inversion near the ground below 1,000 feet (960 millibars) is difficult to explain except perhaps in terms of a temporary local sea mist (which was not reported at the synoptic hours) (cf. Lerwick). Now, at Liverpool a clear inversion at 11,000 feet (660 millibars)

[1] See pp. 48 and 56.

would indicate the entry into the warm sector, giving a steeper inclination to the cold front aloft in the upper air than the preceding warm front (Fig. 62*l*). Below the inversion the air, being modified Polar, was generally slightly unstable and very humid; above it the air, being modified Tropical was only just stable (in fact, unstable between 14,200 feet and 15,200 feet, i.e. 560 millibars and 585 millibars) and very humid. It is unreasonable to expect differentiation in terms of humidity in air masses of such complex history as these.

The evidence consulted both at the ground and in the upper air and that relating to past weather situations as well as the present weather situation under review, has revealed the discontinuity identifiable as a warm occlusion with " cold " Polar and in advance of it to the north and " less cold " Polar air to the south. The purely *relative* significance of such labels as " cold ", " less cold " is thus admirably illustrated.[1] These much modified Polar air masses were associated with warm, and not cold, conditions over the British Isles on 7th November, 1955. In terms of the origins and classification of the weather system to which they belong, however, they are *Polar* air masses (P7).

The Cold Occlusion

It has already been noted that the *cold occlusion* is a comparatively rare phenomenon which is more liable to develop over the British Isles during the summer months than at any other time of the year. In July and August for example, Polar air reaching Britain via Central and Northern Europe is more likely to be relatively warmer than Polar air reaching Britain across the Atlantic from the north-west for the first has crossed a relatively warm land mass, whilst the second has traversed an ocean which is relatively cool at this time of year.

The *full occlusion of the cold type* (Figs. 63 and 64) involves the juxtaposition at and near the ground of two Polar air masses, the *air in the rear* being *colder* than the *air in advance* of the front formed between them. The approach of the cold occlusion is normally indicated by the appearance of bands of cirro-stratus and cirro-cumulus cloud succeeded quickly by altostratus, nimbostratus and then thick and heavy cumulus clouds, culminating in

[1] See p. 112, footnote 1.

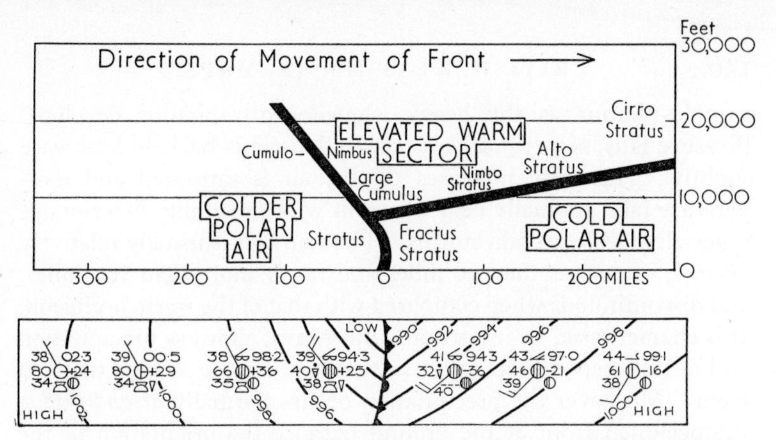

FIG. 63. — Diagrammatic Cross-Section through an Idealised Cold Occlusion

Note : The frontal zones associated with the Cold Occlusion are shown in black. The upper diagram is a vertical cross-section ; the lower diagram is the corresponding horizontal synoptic distribution at the ground.

FIG. 64. — Block Diagram of an Idealised Cold Occlusion

Note : The line representing the Cold Occluded Front on the ground has its identifying projections in black on the side towards which the front is moving.

cumulo-nimbus as the heavy, showery precipitation develops. Pressure falls, sometimes very markedly, winds back and increase slightly. Humidity increases till the air is saturated and temperature falls gradually near the front whilst visibility deteriorates especially locally in rain storms. The rain belt is usually relatively narrow, often less than 50 miles and rarely more than 100 miles, and discontinuous when compared with that of the warm occlusion. It is characterised by interrupted but heavy, showery precipitation and in this respect resembles the rain belt associated with the cold front. Moreover the precipitation occurs normally *at and behind* the occluded front at the ground because the orientation of the structure of the cold occlusion is backwards from the position of the front on the ground (Figs. 63 and 64). Two factors may cause a prolongation of the heavy rain associated with the passage of a cold occlusion: firstly, the occlusion is liable to move slowly across the British Isles, and secondly, the two Polar air masses involved may possess such adequate contrasts in temperature and humidity as to cause unusually heavy precipitation.

The actual passage of the cold occluded front is recognised by a marked decrease in the rate of fall of the barometer, or, more ideally, by an immediate rise in the barometer. Winds veer sometimes sharply and perhaps decrease a little. Temperature continues to fall slightly. Heavy showers develop from thick, vertically developed cloud, and visibility is poor in showers.

The weather sequence in the rear of the cold occlusion resembles that in rear of the cold front. Pressure rises often very sharply. The marked veer in winds just at the passage of the front is followed by a gradual backing, and, after the shower belt, humidity decreases, cloud decreases, visibility improves and a bright, invigorating type of weather develops with sunny periods and local clearing showers, i.e. weather usually associated with Polar-Maritime air. Cold occlusions exhibiting all the features outlined above are certainly very rare. One of the best examples to develop in recent years occurred at 6.0 p.m. on the evening of the 14th August, 1953. As in previous analyses reference will now be made to (*a*) horizontal distributions of surface data, (*b*) past weather situations, and (*c*) upper air information for selected stations.

The Cold Occlusion : 14th August, 1953, 1800 hours G.M.T.
Surface Synoptic Data

The distribution of air temperatures (Fig. 65*a*) shows a general gradation from high temperatures (70° F. or more) over South-east England to lower temperatures (50°–60° F.) over Ireland, Western Scotland and the Western Isles. This is partly explained by the fact that South-east England by 6 p.m. on 14th August, 1953 had had, and was still having in the extreme south east, a sunny day. At 0600 hours (Fig. 65, inset A) the occlusion had only just reached Ireland and at 1800 hours on the 13th August, 1953 it was some 200 miles further west. Much more cloud (Fig. 65*g*) had kept temperatures down over the west. None the less the simple, regular north-south trend of the isotherms over Western Scotland and Ireland is possibly suggestive of a minor discontinuity between two air masses. The dew point distribution (Fig. 65*b*) is generally a repetition of the temperature distribution just described but only in the pattern of the isopleths, and not in their values. Over south-east England dew points are as low as 50° F. in places, and they are low again (52°–54° F.) in North-west Ireland. Intervening is a belt of high dew points (56°–60° F.) extending accross Eastern Ireland, the North Channel, Western Scotland and the Western Isles. Fig. 65*c* reveals more directly the regional contrasts in humidity. Outstanding is the interrupted zone of small differences[1] between temperature and dew points, viz. high relative humidities, of 95% or more, over the east of Ireland and the Western Isles. This zone is flanked to the west by increasingly large differences, and to the east by extremely large differences, e.g. 20° F. or more, over South-east England. As Fig. 65, inset A and later analyses will demonstrate, the weather system under examination is moving eastwards. Thus, humidities were increasing along the western coastlands of Great Britain and decreasing in Western Ireland and off the Outer Hebrides. Relative humidities over Eastern England were as low as 55–60% locally, and as low as 47% at West Raynham.

The " present " and " past weather " map (Fig. 65*d*) shows very conclusively that the temperature gradation, the zone of high dew points and of high humidities are all associated with belts of

[1] See Fig. 44, p. 100.

"past" and "present" rain. A north-south belt of rain some 100–150 miles wide was reported in "past weather" over much of Ireland, the North Channel and the Western Isles. In "present weather", this belt was reported as occupying a north-south zone narrower in width (50–100 miles) and shorter in length, extending over the west coast of Scotland and the east coast of Ireland. Eastern England and Eastern Scotland had had, and locally were still having, sunshine, but the overcast skies of Western Britain were extending eastwards.

Wind direction (Fig. 65*e*) over the eastern part of Great Britain varied around the south point, and wind strength ranged between "light" and "moderate". However, over the western part of Great Britain, wind direction became more consistently south or thereabouts, and wind strength more consistently "moderate". This represents the pre-frontal zone where winds were backing and increasing. To the far west, at Benbecula and over Western and Central Ireland, there was some evidence locally of slight veer in wind direction to south west and/or of slight decrease in strength to "light". This post-frontal zone of veer and decrease in wind direction and force is, however, less consistently clear than the pre-frontal zone of backing and increasing.

Barometric tendencies (Fig. 65*f*) were surprisingly small, suggesting perhaps that the occlusion was rather slow moving (Fig. 65, inset A), but a north-south zone of maximum fall does appear over the western coasts of Scotland and the eastern coasts of Ireland thus correlating with the discontinuities already noted. To the east and west of this zone the barometer is falling very slightly.

The cloud distribution (Fig. 65*g*) reveals north-south bands of cirrus, cirrostratus and cirrocumulus over Eastern Scotland and much of England and Wales. These increase in amount and merge westwards into lower and thicker cloud, dominantly stratiform, but with some large cumulus. Then in the extreme west over Western Ireland, cumuliform clouds dominate. This general pattern is compatible with the idea of a frontal zone lying north-south approximately between Great Britain and Ireland, and moving generally eastwards.

The distribution of visibility (Fig. 65*h*) brings out an elongated north-south area of only "moderate" visibility over Western Scotland and North-east Ireland, which correlates in position with

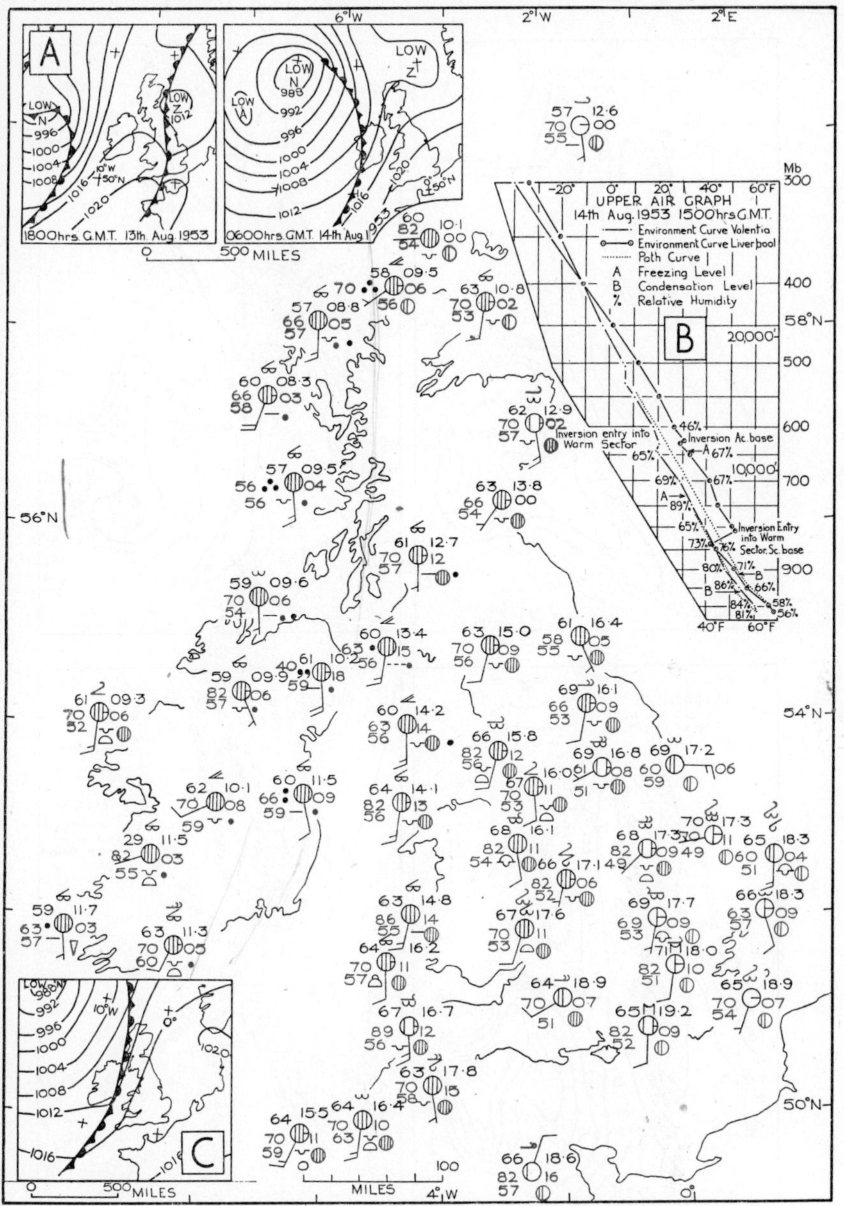

Maps redrawn from the Daily Weather Reports of the 13th August 1953 and the 14th August 1953 by permission of the Director-General, Meteorological Office, London. Copyright H.M. Stationery Office.

FIG. 65. — Selected Data for 14th August 1953 : 1800 hrs. G.M.T.
The Cold Occlusion
Inset A — Previous synoptic situations
Inset B — Upper Air Graphs
Inset C — Isobars : 1800 hrs. G.M.T. 14th August 1953

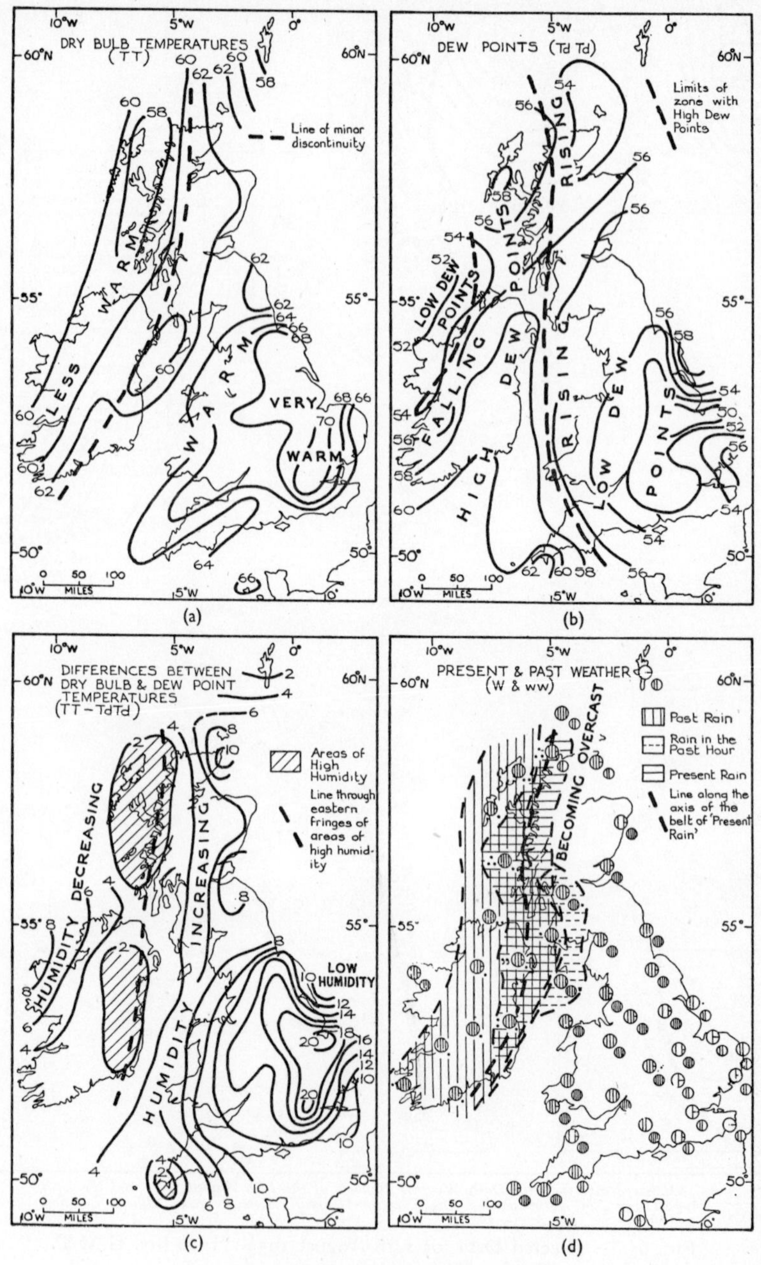

FIG. 65 (*contd.*). — (*a*), (*b*), (*c*), (*d*)

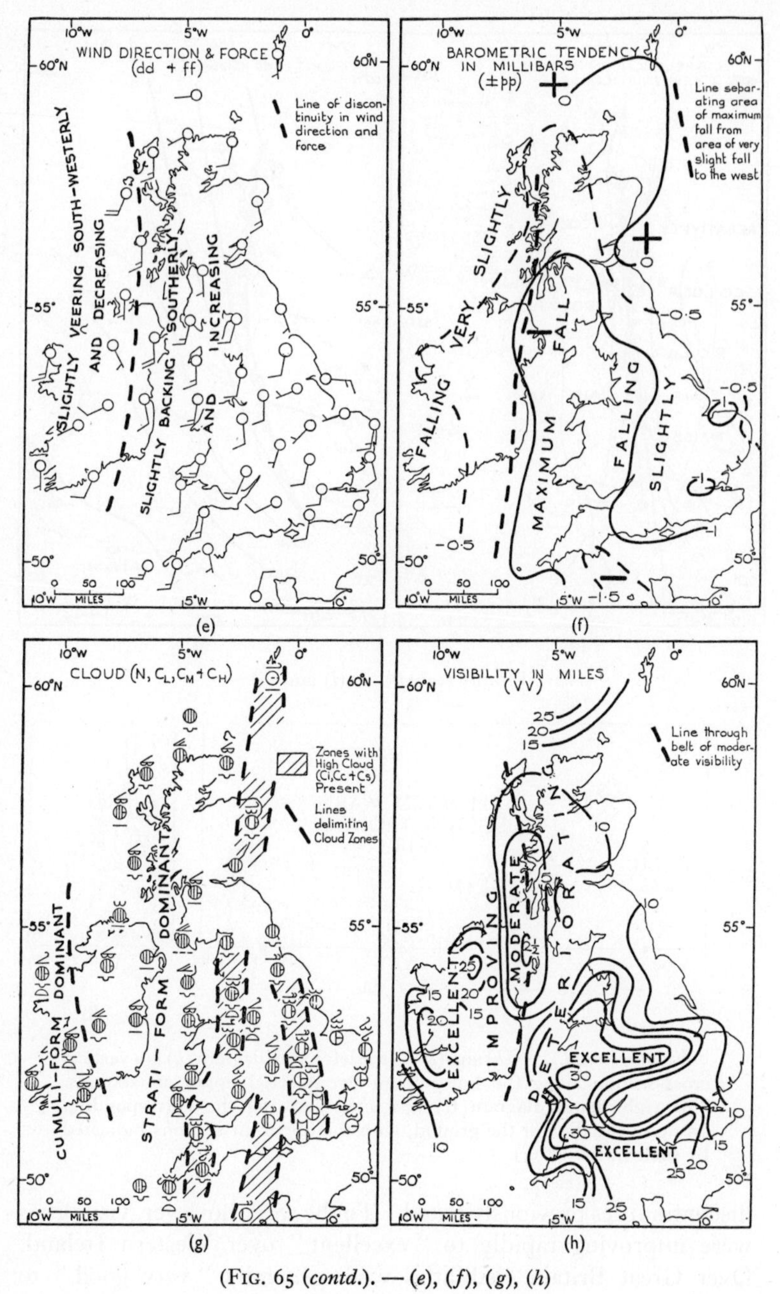

(Fig. 65 (*contd.*). — (*e*), (*f*), (*g*), (*h*)

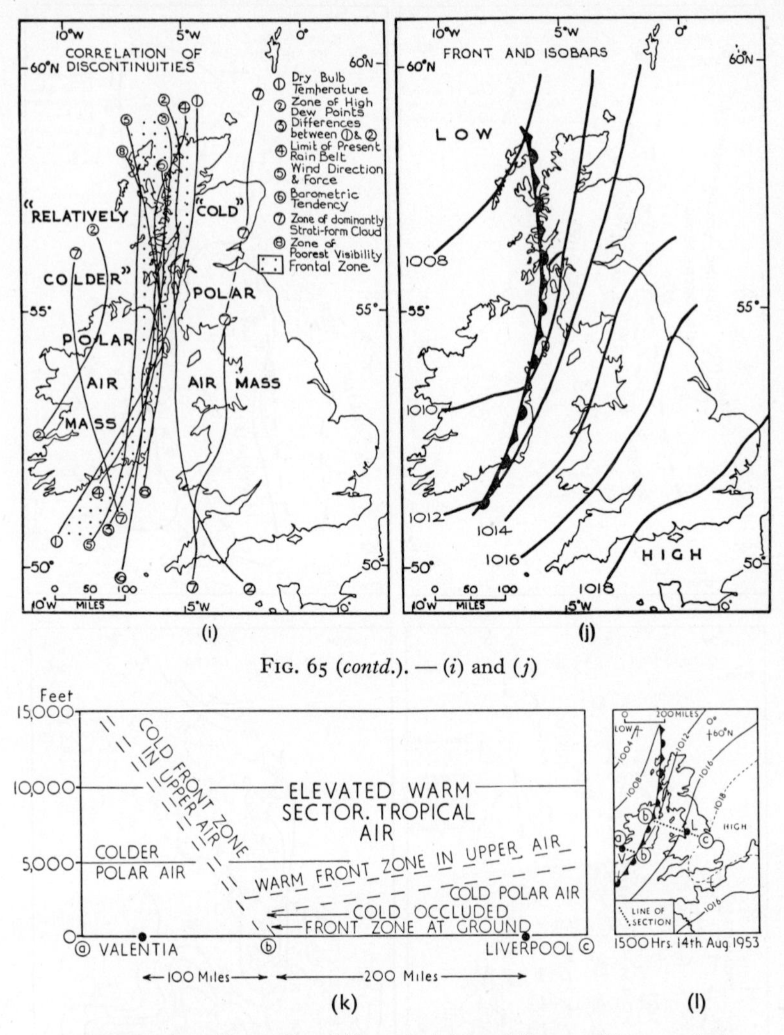

(i) (j)

FIG. 65 (*contd.*). — (*i*) and (*j*)

(k) (l)

FIG. 65 (*contd.*). — (*k*) and (*l*) — the left hand diagram (*k*) is a vertical cross-section along the line joining the selected upper air stations. The right hand diagram (*l*) is a map showing the corresponding synoptic situation at the ground, with the upper air stations indicated by their initial letters

discontinuities previously noted. To the west, however, visibilities were improving rapidly to " excellent " over Western Ireland. Over Great Britain visibilities were generally " very good " to

" excellent " but over the Bristol Channel, Cardigan Bay and the Irish Sea they were deteriorating as the front approached.

The correlation of discontinuities on Fig. 65*i* shows the presence of a narrow, north-south frontal zone along the western coastlands of Scotland and the eastern coastlands of Ireland. The only lines which do not pass within this zone, viz. No. ② — limits of zone of high dew points, and No. ⑦ — limits of zone of dominantly stratiform cloud, can justifiably be ignored since in this particular instance each of the two elements concerned revealed a wide zone affected by the front rather than a narrow discontinuity associated with the front proper. Two Polar air masses are indicated, the one to the west of the frontal zone being relatively " colder " than the other one to the east of it.

Finally, in Fig. 65*j*, the eastward moving cold occlusion is marked in together with the isobars at 2 millibar intervals. The isobars are relatively widely spaced and over South-east England pressure is high (1,018 millibars) in association with an anticyclone over North-west Europe. The occluded front is attached to a low pressure system centred near Iceland (Fig. 65 inset C).

Preceding Synoptic Situations

In Fig. 65, inset A, two simplified maps show the synoptic situations at 0600 hours on 14th August, 1953 and 1800 hours on 13th August, 1953. *Low N*, a secondary depression, has moved slowly northwards from a position 55° N., 20° W. and its occluded front has swung eastwards and north eastwards towards Ireland. By 0300 hours on 14th August, 1953 (Fig. 65*l*), the occluded front was located centrally across Ireland. *Low N* was filling in *slowly* by this time and moving eastwards equally *slowly*. Polar air behind the occluded front appears to have come from the neighbourhood of South Greenland (P5), and that in advance of the front has obviously been affected by a longer sojourn at relatively lower latitudes over the North Atlantic and is consequently warmer (P7). Despite *Low N's* having reached this post-mature stage of development, the discontinuity at the line of the occluded front was well preserved as has been revealed in the analyses of horizontal distribution of surface data above.

Upper Air Data

In Fig. 65*k* and *l*, and in Fig. 65 (inset B), upper air data for 1500 hours on 14th August, 1953 for Liverpool, at that time some 200 miles in advance of the cold occlusion at the ground, and Valentia, at that time 100 miles behind the cold occlusion at the ground, indicate the presence of a warm sector aloft at 4,250 feet (840 millibars) at Liverpool and at 11,500 feet (645 millibars) at Valentia. Reference to Fig. 65*k* will show how these data enable the reconstruction of the vertical profile of the frontal system in existence at this time. The steeper slope of both the cold front in the upper air and the cold occlusion at the ground is in contrast to the gentler slope of the warm front in the upper air. The inversion at Liverpool, which marks the entry into the warm sector, also may coincide with a layer of stratocumulus, or large cumulus, cloud which was reported at adjacent stations at 1200 hours and 1800 hours. Temperatures are generally higher, freezing level higher, humidities generally lower and condensation level higher for the Liverpool graph than for the Valentia graph. These contrasts suggest that Polar air in the rear of the occlusion is *relatively moister* as well as being *relatively* " colder " than the Polar air in front of the occlusion. Polar air at Liverpool is generally unstable ; but the Tropical air above the frontal inversion at 11,500 feet is sometimes unstable and sometimes stable. Polar air at Valentia is for the most part only just stable whereas the Tropical air above the frontal inversion is very stable. It is evident from the data examined that a slow moving, but well developed, cold occlusion system possessing many standard features affected weather over the British Isles at 1800 hours on 14th August, 1953, with the exception of South-east England where anticyclonic conditions extended from a high pressure centre over Europe (Fig. 65, inset C).

The Bent-Back Occlusion

Sometimes when a deep depression occludes quickly the occluded front may be turned back at the centre of the depression thus producing the *bent-back occlusion* (Fig. 66*j*, p. 170). The end of the occluded front becomes detached from the centre of the depression and ultimately begins to move in a direction opposite to that in which it originally moved. The *bent-back* portion then swings round anticlockwise (in the Northern Hemisphere) within the mechanism of the depression to a position some distance behind *either* the remainder of the occluded front, *or* the remainder of the original cold front, should it still be active. At this stage of development a depression is *post-mature.* Ultimately the intermixture of the Polar and Tropical air becomes so extensive that discontinuities lose their identity, and isobaric patterns tend to be universally smooth and more or less circular in plan with no angular portions. This constitutes the final " frontless " stage of the depression to be examined later at the end of this chapter (see pp. 174–181).

To recognise the existence of a " bent-back " portion in an occluded front it is obvious that the isobaric pattern would assist if discontinuities do not terminate at the centre of the depression but pass through it or round it, following curving paths. Other standard features indicating the presence of the bent-back portion in the Polar air behind the occluded front would be the orthodox, pre-frontal back, and post-frontal veer, in wind direction ; local development of precipitation with associated high humidities and abundant cloud, often of the " bad weather " type, e.g. stratus-fractus ; locally inferior visibility ; and pre-frontal fall, and post-frontal rise, in pressure. After the bent-back portion of the occlusion passes through, a general improvement in the weather normally takes place : the barometer rises, cloud decreases and brighter weather perhaps with clearing showers becomes established.

It is not often that an occlusion reaches the " bent-back " stage over the limited area of the British Isles, so as to demonstrate these standard features. However, a good example occurred on the 3rd September, 1954 at 6.0 a.m. The following analysis conforms to the general pattern of the previous ones.

The Bent Back Occlusion : 3rd September, 1954, 0600 hours G.M.T.

Surface Synoptic Data

The temperature distribution (Fig. 66*a*) shows an area of highest values (58°–64° F.) over England and Wales, grading westwards towards rather lower values (53°–58° F.) over Ireland, and northwards to still lower values (44°–54° F.) over Scotland. The gradations are gentle ones, which would be quite compatible with the idea of a post-mature depression, but there is a suggestion of a restricted warm sector over Central and Southern England.

The distribution of dew point values (Fig. 66*b*) confirms this regional pattern very closely. The area of highest dew points over

England, suggesting again the existence of a warm sector, is rather better defined with more precise discontinuities along its fringes. The rise in dew points in Western Ireland is the first hint of a south-westward continuation of the discontinuity passing along the northern edge of the supposed warm sector.

On Fig. 66*c* the distribution of humidity[1] reveals strong evidence for a curving discontinuity extending from Yorkshire across the Lake District to Northern Ireland, and then south-westwards and southwards to South-west Ireland. To the north is consistently humid air with relative humidities between 93% and 100%. To the south, a subdivision may be made between air over England, with relative humidities varying very much locally from 86% to 100%, and air over West Wales, Cornwall, Cardigan Bay, the Bristol Channel, St. George's Channel and South-east Ireland, where relative humidities are relatively low, ranging from 74% to 93%. This pattern suggests the presence of three different types of air over the British Isles at this time (1) consistently moist air to the north probably affected by a major frontal zone along its southern edge ; (2) variably moist air to the south-east, suggesting the variable humidity not uncommonly associated with warm sectors ; and (3) less humid air to the south-west being affected on its western flank by the incoming edge of the aforementioned major frontal zone which already resembles in pattern and character, that of the bent-back portion of an occluded front.

" Present " and " past weather " details (Fig. 66*d*) confirm this pattern admirably. An east to west belt of rain and drizzle, some 200–250 miles wide (suggesting a *warm* rather than a *cold* occlusion) reported in " past weather " across Ireland, the Irish Sea, North Wales, Northern England and Southern Scotland was reduced considerably in width to about 100–150 miles in "present weather". At the same time it appears to have moved northwards, swinging north-westwards with the anticlockwise mechanism of the depression. In both " past " and " present weather ", a small but significant extension southwards of the rain belt over Western Ireland was reported. Here the relative position of the " past " and " present " rain areas suggests the eastward movement of the bent-back portion of the major occluded front. Over South-eastern and Eastern England much mist and overcast skies with

[1] See Fig. 44, p. 100.

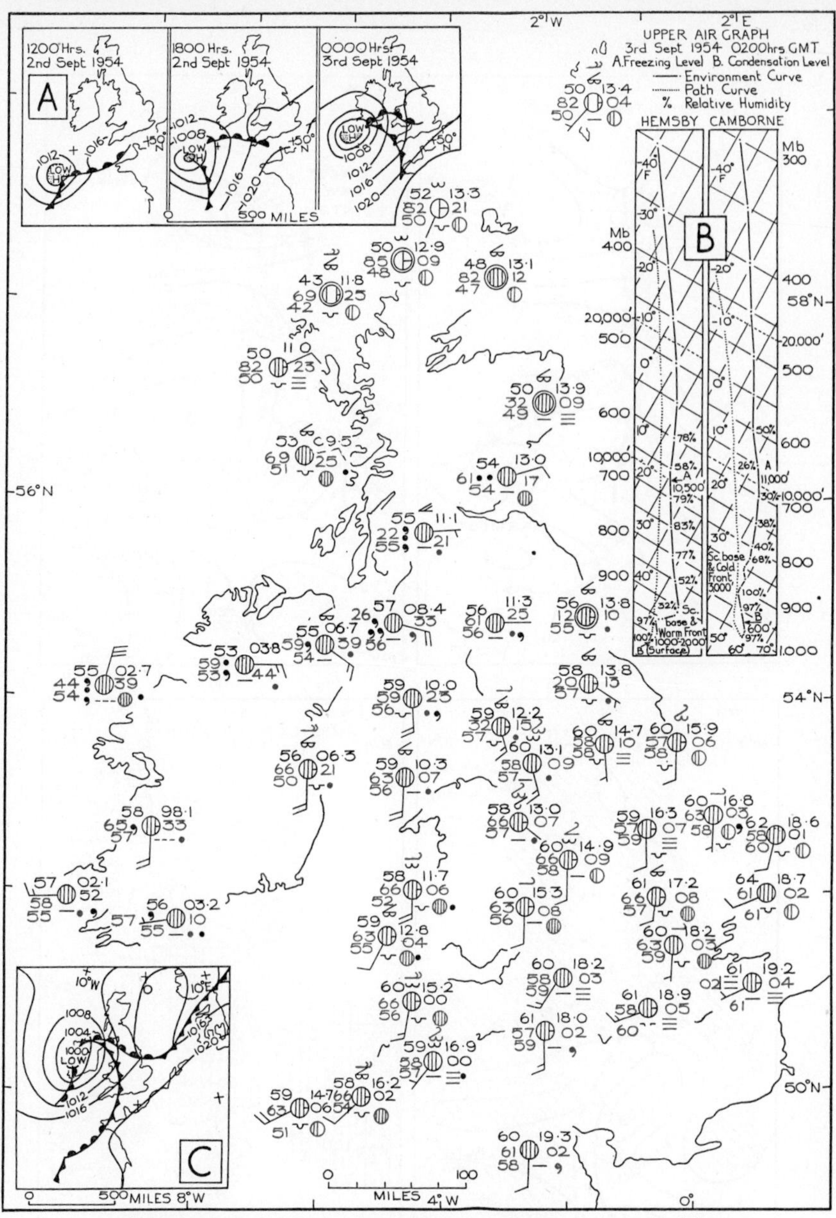

Maps redrawn from the Daily Weather Reports of 2nd September 1954 and 3rd September 1954 by permission of the Director-General, Meteorological Office, London. Copyright H.M. Stationery Office.

FIG. 66. — Selected Data for 3rd September 1954 : 0600 hrs. G.M.T.
The Bent-Back Occlusion
Inset A — Previous Synoptic Situations
Inset B — Upper Air Graphs
Inset C — Isobars : 0600 hrs. G.M.T. 3rd September 1954

Note : The orientation of the upper air graphs is due to the limitations of space and for the sake of clarity. The graphs for Camborne and Hemsby have been drawn separately, and the temperature axis of the graph is inclined instead of being horizontal as in other similar types of diagram.

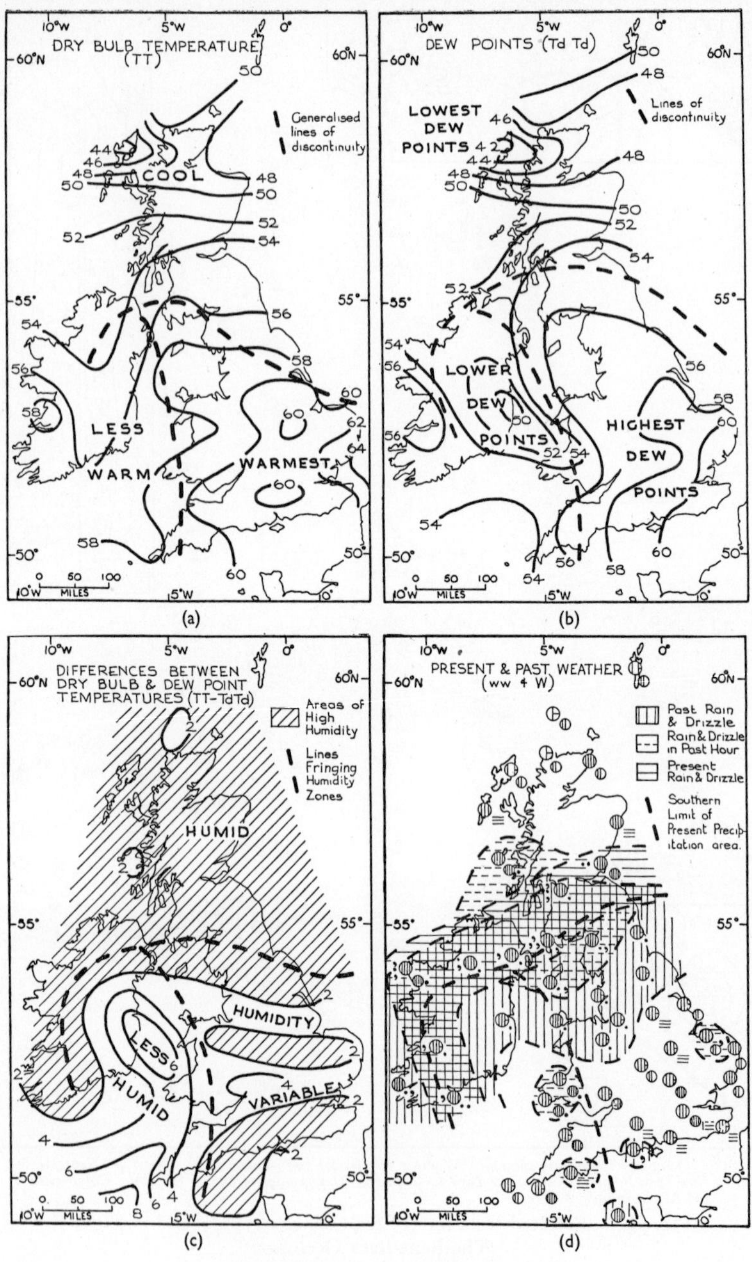

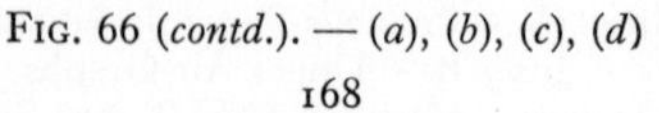

FIG. 66 (*contd.*). — (*a*), (*b*), (*c*), (*d*)

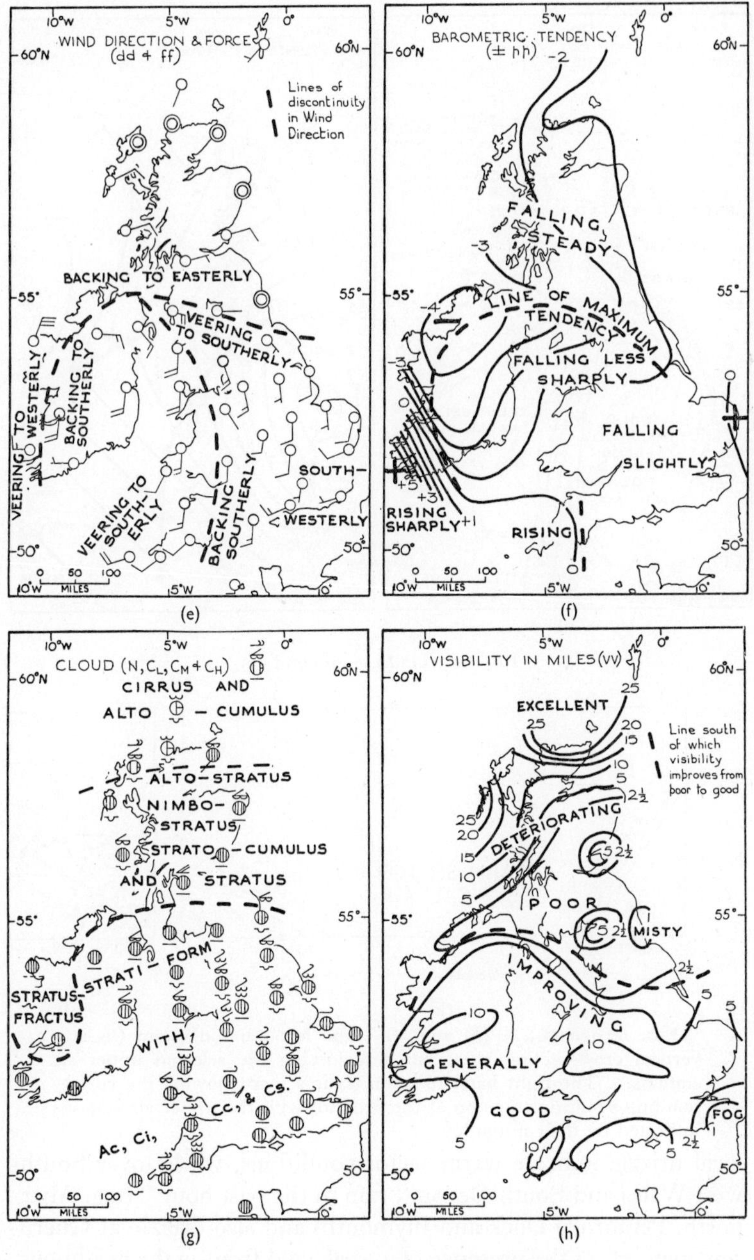

FIG. 66 (*contd.*). — (*e*), (*f*), (*g*), (*h*)

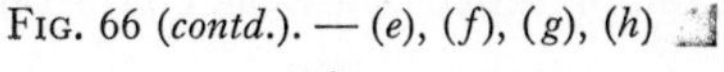

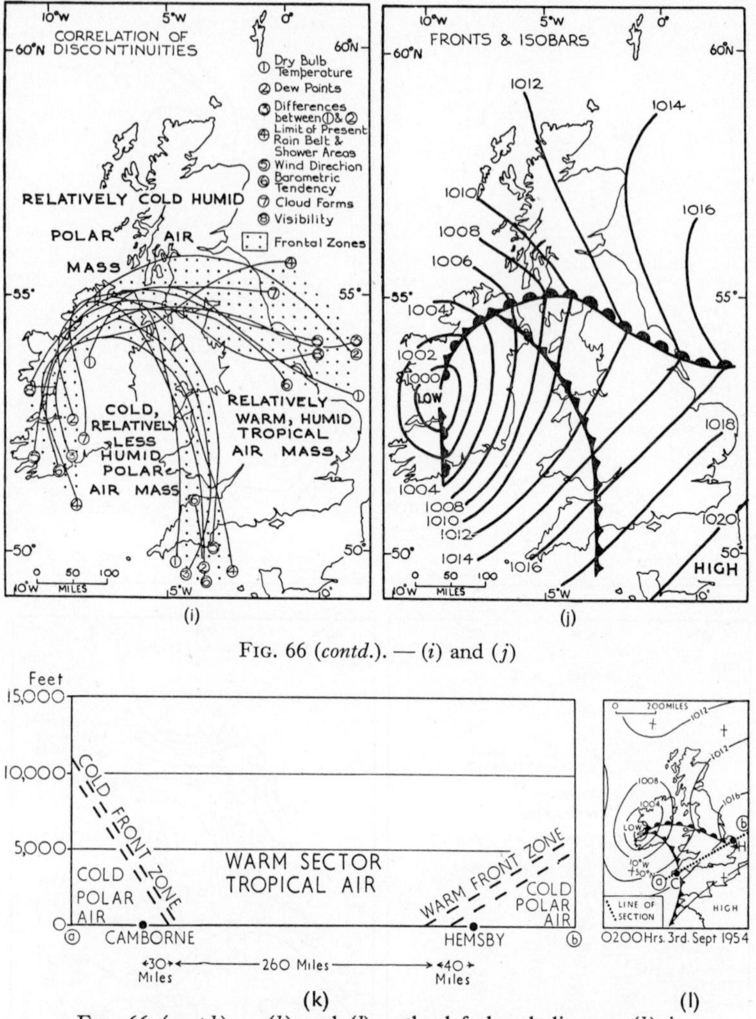

FIG. 66 (*contd.*). — (*i*) and (*j*)

FIG. 66 (*contd.*). — (*k*) and (*l*) — the left hand diagram (*k*) is a vertical cross-section along the line joining the selected upper air stations. The right hand diagram (*l*) is a map showing the corresponding synoptic situation at the ground, with the upper air stations indicated by their initial letters

local drizzle indicate warm sector conditions, whilst over South-west Wales and South Devon " rain in the past hour " (e.g. Aberporth, Pembroke Dock and Plymouth) and also drizzle at Guernsey, may reflect the presence of a weak cold front in the neighbourhood. Over the north of Scotland relatively clear skies were becoming overcast and mist was developing as the main rain belt approached.

The division of the wind distribution (Fig. 66*e*) into zones of " backing " and " veering ", and zones of " steady direction " confirms the presence of three discontinuities, two flanking the warm sector over England and one representing the occluded front over Northern Ireland which becomes the bent-back occluded front over Western Ireland. The discontinuity over Wales and the South-west Peninsula is the least distinctive of all. Over Scotland, in advance of the warm occluding front, winds are light and several calms are reported. Later references to the isobaric pattern will explain this point. Otherwise winds are " light " to " moderate " becoming " strong " only at Blacksod Point in North-west Ireland behind the occluded front.

The map for barometric tendency (Fig. 66*f*) provides further confirmation of these discontinuities. The line of maximum negative tendency follows a curving path along the warm front, the warm occlusion and the bent-back portion of the warm occlusion, i.e. from Yorkshire via Northern Ireland to South-west Ireland. In advance of this line in the north over Scotland, the barometer was falling steadily ; to the south of it over England and Wales, there is a large area where the barometer was falling only slightly, viz. the warm sector ; to the extreme west and south-west, at Valentia and in Cornwall, the barometer was rising very rapidly especially at Valentia, strongly suggesting post-frontal conditions which, in the light of all evidence available, must refer to the bent-back portion of the warm occlusion.

The north-south progression of cloud amounts and types (Fig. 66*g*) over North and Central Scotland indicates pre-frontal conditions. Over Western Ireland, Blacksod Point and Rineanna reported stratus fractus cloud which suggests a possible correlation with the area of the bent-back occlusion, Otherwise the rest of Ireland, England and Wales were generally overcast with strati-form cloud dominant below much altocumulus and cirrus clouds.

The distribution of visibilities (Fig. 66*h*) also confirms previous patterns. " Excellent " visibilities over the extreme north of Scotland are succeeded southwards by " moderate ", then " poor " ones as the major frontal zone is reached. To the south of the major frontal zone, visibility improves to "moderate" in the south-east, but with some fog, and to "good" in the south-west behind the cold front. There is perhaps a slight suggestion in the visibility distribution over Western Ireland of the presence of the bent-back occlusion.

The correlation of these discontinuities on Fig. 66*i* is consistent and clear. Three frontal zones emerge — (i) the warm front extending from North-east England to Northern Ireland where it is joined by (ii) a cold front extending from the South-west Peninsula across Wales and the Isle of Man, and (i) and (ii) together become (iii) the occluded front which continues north-westwards a little before bending back over Western and South-western Ireland. Relatively warm, humid, Tropical air occupies the warm sector over England; relatively cold, humid Polar air occupies the pre-frontal zone over Scotland and cold, relatively less humid, Polar air occupies the zone in the south-west between the cold front and the bent-back portion of the occluded front. The frontal system and isobars (Fig. 66*j*) reveal a depression, relatively shallow (of less than 1,000 millibars) and probably filling in, centred near the mouth of the River Shannon in the west of Ireland. Its warm occluded front is bent back and points southwards independently of this centre. The weakness of the cold front is evidenced in the straightness of the isobars across it; in contrast, the warm front and the occluded fronts are quite well marked. The widely spaced isobars over Scotland confirm the frequency of calms reported there.

Past Synoptic Situations

Inset A, Fig. 66 shows the progress of Low "H" from a position some 350 miles off South-west Ireland at 1200 hours 2nd September, 1954, when it was not occluded, to a position just off Valentia at 0000 hours 3rd September, 1954, when it was starting to occlude. Tropical-Maritime air in the warm sector appears to have moved north-eastwards from the sea off Portugal (T1 or T2). The Polar-Maritime air behind the cold front appears to have come southwards from sea areas off South-west Iceland reaching as far south as 45° N. before turning eastwards and north-eastwards to the British Isles (P5). As a result of its southerly track this air was warmed considerably in contrast to the Polar air in advance of the warm front which appears to have remained in much higher latitudes.

Upper Air Data

In Fig. 66, inset B and Fig. *k* and *l*, upper air information for 0200 hours on 3rd September, 1954 for Hemsby and Camborne has been plotted. At Hemsby, some 40 miles in advance of the warm front at this time, the entry into the warm sector would appear to be represented by the marked inversion and the stratocumulus layer from 1,000 feet up to 2,000 feet (i.e. 960 millibars to 930 millibars). Below the inversion relative humidities are high (93–97%) in the Polar air, and there is an unstable layer between about 300 feet and 1,000 feet (i.e. 975 millibars and 960 millibars). Just above the inversion and the cloud layer relative humidities are very low (32%) [1] but increase in the Tropical air above to 83% at about 8,000 feet (740 millibars), after which they decrease again. Condensation level is at the surface and freezing level at 10,500 feet. Now at Camborne, estimated at some 30 miles behind the cold front at 0200 hours on 3rd September, 1954, an isothermal[2] layer and stratocumulus layer at about 3,000 feet (900 millibars) would suggest a weak cold front zone, more steeply inclined than the warm front zone just identified at Hemsby. Previous analyses of horizontal surface distributions indicated the relative sharpness of the discontinuity at the warm front compared with the weakness of the discontinuity at the cold front. At Camborne, the Polar air below the cold front zone is very humid (97–100% relative humidities) and unstable. The Tropical air above the cold front zone is generally stable but remarkably dry (68–26% relative humidities) which may be explained by the weakness of frontal zone itself and the degree of intermixture which has taken place between the adjacent air masses. Condensation level is at 600 feet (800 millibars) and freezing level at 11,000 feet (660 millibars) (cf. Hemsby).

Thus Polar-Maritime air, apparently, was in occupation in advance and in the rear of a warm sector, containing relatively dry Tropical air, which is much more clearly differentiated at the warm front than at the cold front.

In conclusion the examination of the several types of data have

[1] See p. 24.
[2] See p. 132, footnote 1.

demonstrated the presence over the British Isles at 0600 hours on 3rd September, 1954, of a bent-back occlusion possessing many standard characteristics.

The Frontless, Decayed Depression

At the final stage of its life cycle a depression assumes a relatively homogeneous character as discontinuities lose their sharpness and ultimately disappear completely. The depression becomes a centre of revolving, mixed Polar air at the surface with the remains of the warm sector held above it and becoming gradually assimilated into the general circulation of the atmosphere (Fig. 45). The depression is usually filling in at this stage, i.e. atmospheric pressure is rising at the centre; furthermore, the barometric gradient may sometimes be decreased resulting in a slackening of winds, and the system as a whole moves more slowly. Alternatively, the low pressure may be maintained at the centre with associated strong winds. The isobaric pattern is more or less concentric and winds flow slightly inwards and anticlockwise (in the Northern Hemisphere) across them. The weather associated with this final " frontless " stage will obviously vary from depression to depression, depending on the history of the depression concerned and its rate of decline. Generally speaking, the weather is relatively cool for the time of year, locally humid and showery, perhaps rainy, with blustery winds of moderate force, much cloud of both the large cumulus and stratus type (stratus-fractus being quite characteristic) and with variable, but generally improving, visibility.

It is important to avoid confusing the frontless decayed depression with the " Polar depression " [1] which also constitutes a vortex of Polar air. The Polar depression develops, however, *at birth* as a vortex of Polar air within a Polar air mass. It is relatively small in extent but may cause heavy and continuous rain. Precipitation due to an old, frontless, warm-sector depression is perhaps more scattered and less violent, although exceptions to generalisation, of this nature are numerous in practice.

The following analysis of an example of a frontless, decayed depression at 0600 hours on 3rd May, 1954, proceeds in the same general way as for previous examples.

[1] See p. 216, Chapter 6.

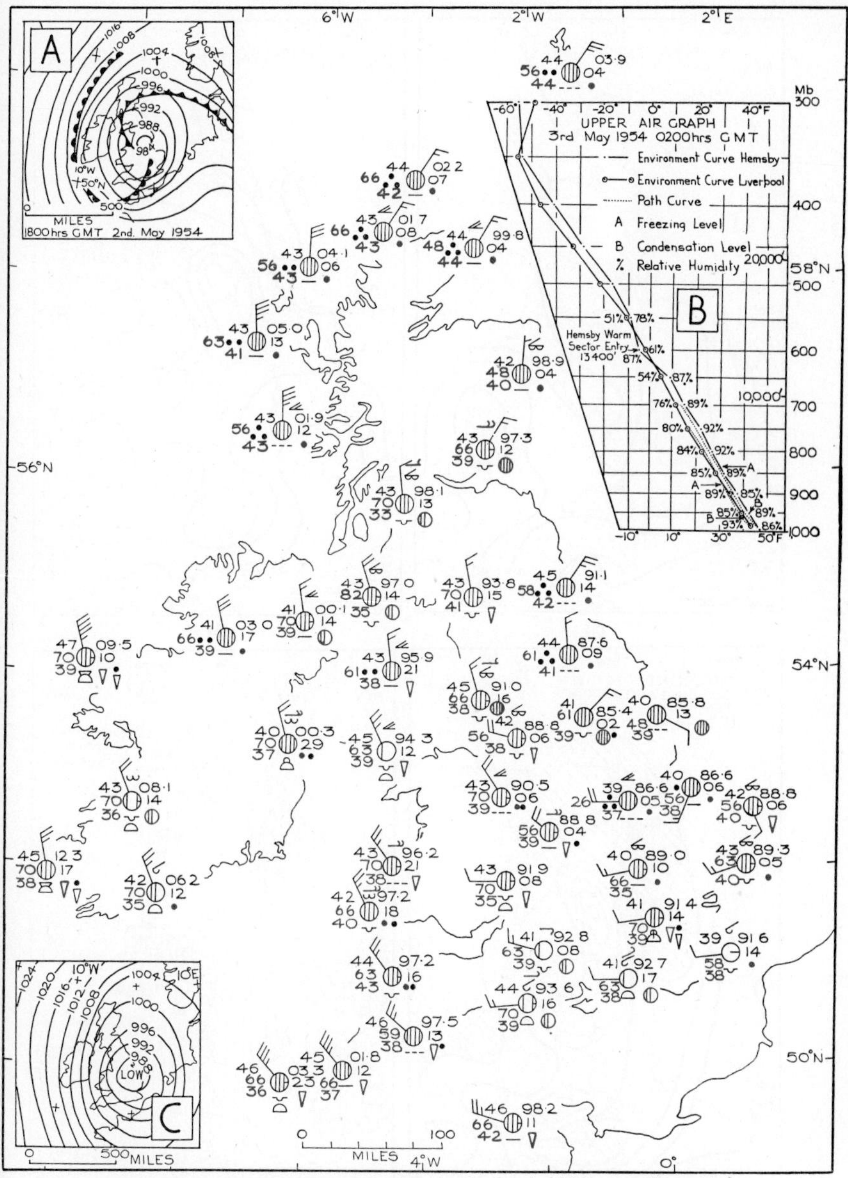

Maps redrawn from the Daily Weather Reports of 2nd and 3rd May 1954 by permission of the Director-General, Meteorological Office, London. Copyright H.M. Stationery Office.

FIG. 67. — Selected Data for 3rd May 1954: 0600 hrs. G.M.T.
The Frontless, Decayed Depression
Inset A — Previous synoptic situation
Inset B — Upper Air Graphs
Inset C — Isobars: 0600 hrs. G.M.T. 3rd May 1954

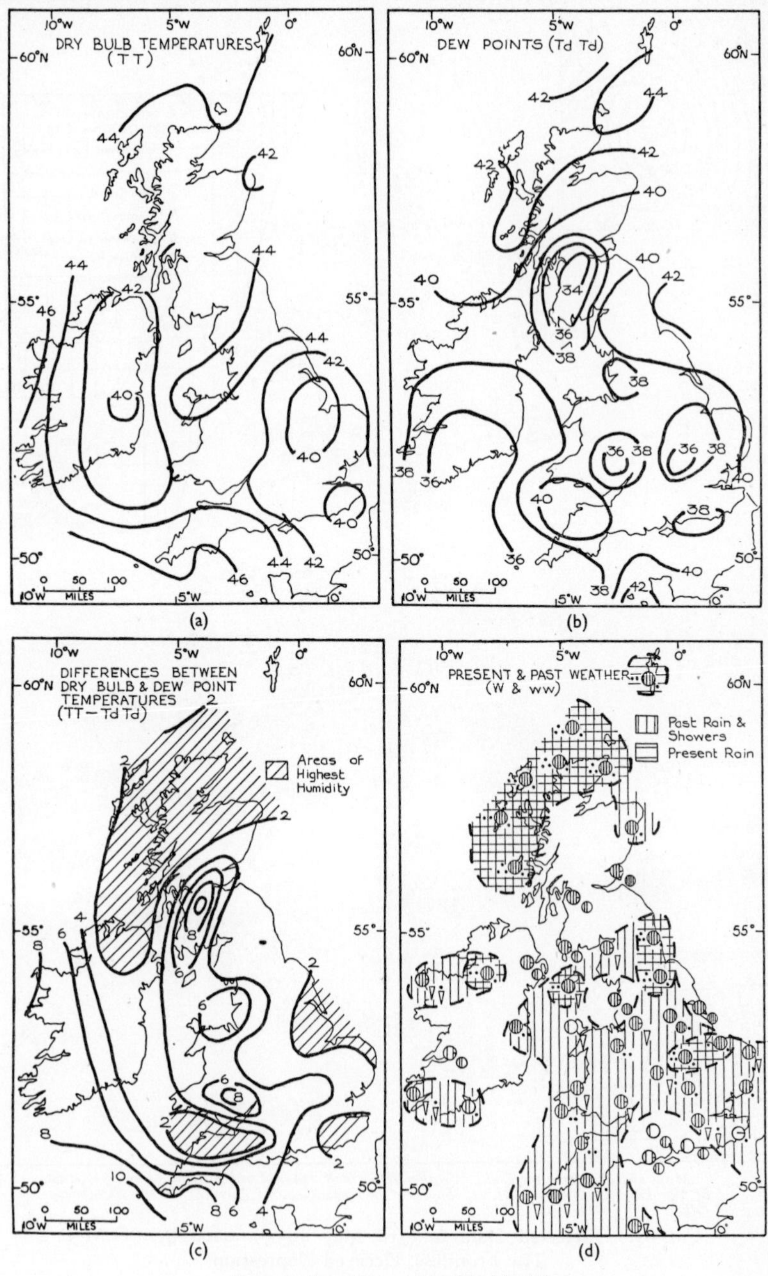

FIG. 67 (*contd.*). — (*a*), (*b*), (*c*), (*d*)

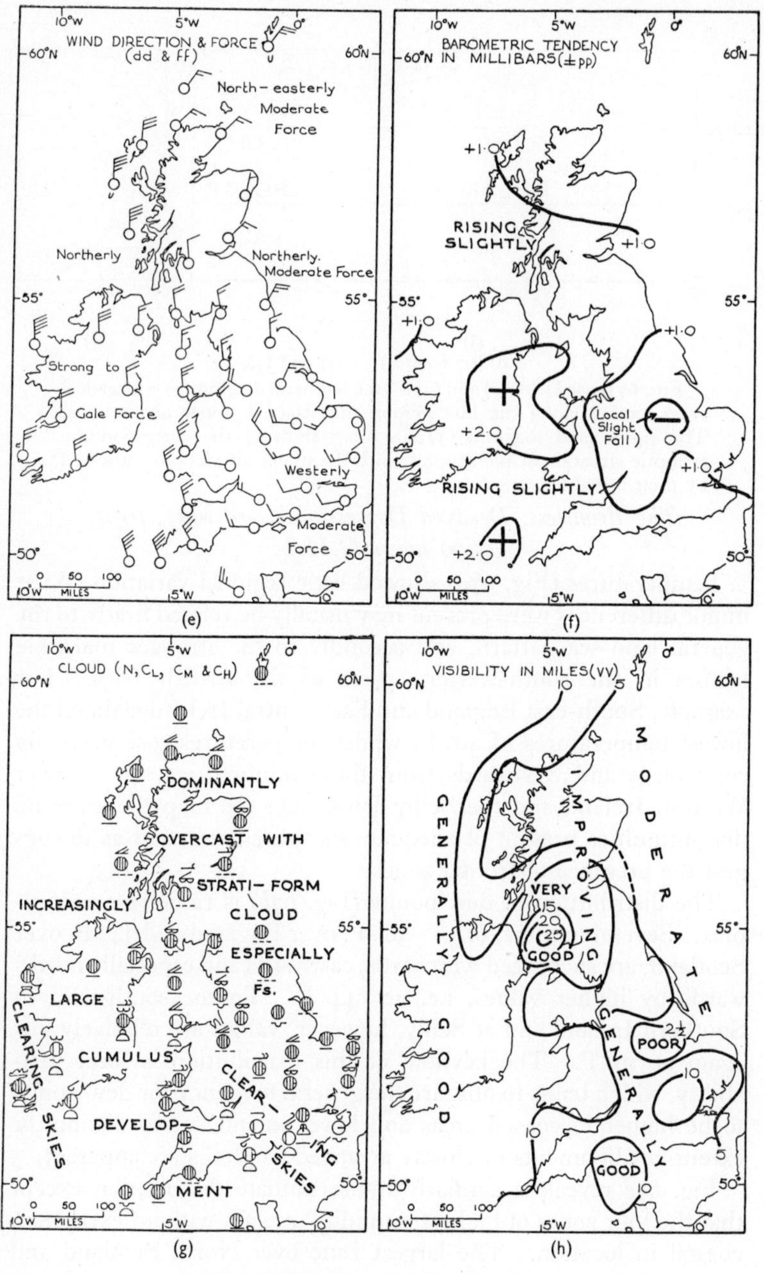

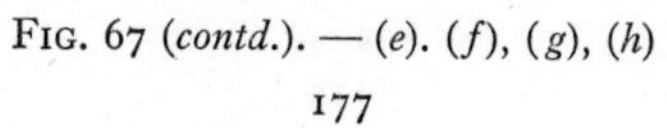

FIG. 67 (*contd.*). — (*e*). (*f*), (*g*), (*h*)

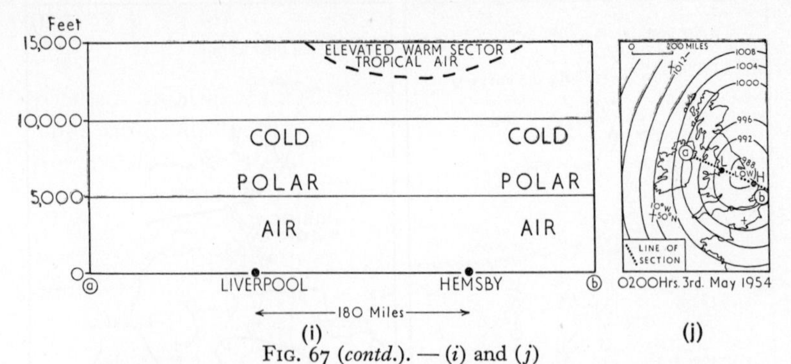

FIG. 67 (*contd.*). — (*i*) and (*j*)

FIG. 67 (*contd.*). — (*i*) and (*j*) — the left hand diagram (*i*) is a vertical cross-section along the line joining the selected upper air stations. The right hand diagram (*j*) is a map showing the corresponding synoptic situation at the ground, with the upper air stations indicated by their initial letters.

The Frontless, Decayed Depression : 3rd May, 1954, 0600 hours G.M.T.

Temperatures (Fig. 67*a*) showed little regional variation. What minor differences were present may usually be related firstly to the general land-sea pattern, and secondly to the stronger maritime factors in the south-western parts of the British Isles. For example, South-east England and East-central Ireland claimed the lowest temperatures of 40° F. whilst temperatures rose generally coastwards and westwards from these minima, e.g. 46° F. over Western Ireland and the Scilly Isles. On the map there are no discontinuities present of adequate sharpness or extent as to suggest the presence of frontal zones.

The distribution of dew points (Fig. 67*b*) is rather more complex. Several minima, of 36°–38° F. over England and 34° F. over Scotland, are succeeded westwards, eastwards and especially northwards by higher values, i.e. 40°–44° F. To the south-west in Southern Ireland and at Scilly, however, values are relatively low again at 36° F. The keynote of this distribution is local variability, which tends to obscure the general tendency for dew points to be higher in coastal areas and lower inland. No distinct or extensive alignments of closely arranged isopleths are apparent.

Fig. 67*c* reveals a similarly indiscriminate distribution except that the four zones of highest humidity[1] are all, without exception, coastal in location. The largest zone over North Scotland and

See Fig. 44, p. 100.

Northern Ireland is associated with relative humidities of 93–100% and, as will appear later, is explicable in terms of onshore northerly winds and orographic uplift. Similarly, onshore winds were affecting the Lincolnshire and North Devonshire coasts which report similarly high humidities. Over Wales, much of England and Western Ireland relative humidities were lower, in the order of 73–93%.

The pattern of "past weather" (Fig. 67*d*) reveals extensive shower and rain areas over many parts of the British Isles including nearly the whole of England and Wales, Northern Scotland and Western Ireland. This precipitation, though extensive, was essentially showery and localised, except in North-west Scotland and the Western Isles where continuous rain was reported in " present weather". Elsewhere, however, " present weather " data show that the shower and rain areas were much reduced in time and space, only Tynemouth, Dishforth, Ronaldsway, Castle Archdale, Cottesmore and West Raynham reporting precipitation at the time of observation. Alternatively, some districts had generally less overcast conditions with no precipitation, e.g. the Hampshire area, Central Ireland and Central Scotland. The character of these precipitation distributions is compatible with the idea of local pockets of instability in Polar air, accentuated on the coasts by orographic lifting usually where winds were onshore.

Winds (Fig. 67*e*) were generally northerly, " moderate " to " strong ", becoming " gale force " over western peninsulas. Exceptional, however, were the westerly winds of " moderate " force over South-east England. Onshore winds, e.g. on north-facing coasts in the west of the British Isles, may be correlated frequently with high humidity and precipitation areas shown in Figs. 67*c* and 67*d*. Considering the wind pattern as a whole, the air flow was generally in a semi-circular, anticlockwise direction, first north-easterly, then north, then north-westerly, and then westerly round a centre in Lincolnshire which was obviously the centre of the depression. Outwards from this centre wind force increased but there were no lines of consistent discontinuity in the broad semi-circular flow.

Barometric tendency distribution (Fig. 67*f*) shows pressure to have been rising slightly everywhere, except at Cottesmore in the vicinity of the centre of the depression where a slight fall was reported. Collinstown reported the maximum rise of 2·9 millibars. The generally greater rises in the barometer over the west of the British Isles as compared with the east suggest a general eastward movement of the depression as a whole.

So far as cloud conditions (Fig. 67*g*) are concerned much of Ulster and Great Britain, excluding the south-east of England, was dominantly overcast with extensive stratiform cloud especially stratus-fractus. Elsewhere, i.e. over Eire and South-east England, cloud amounts were smaller and convectional cumulus cloud with marked vertical development was tending to replace the stratus-cloud.

The visibility map (Fig. 67*h*) shows a gradation from "moderate" to "poor" in eastern Britain, to generally good over Ireland. Some local variety intruded into this general pattern, e.g. "excellent" visibilities over South-west Scotland. Visibility improved generally outwards from the centre of the depression where it was poorest (less than 2½ miles), and was improving generally as the depression moved eastwards.

In summary, for 6.0 a.m. on this morning in early May, the horizontal distributions of the weather elements suggest that no frontal systems were present but that mixed Polar air circulating round an old "low" centred over Lincolnshire was bringing relatively cold, blustery weather, with much cloud and local showers, prolonged in places. The average daily *minimum* temperatures for the British Isles for May fall between 42° F. and 48° F.[1]; at 0600 hours on 3rd May, 1954, temperatures were between 40° and 46° F. i.e. relatively cold.

Past Synoptic Situations

Inset A, Fig. 67, shows the synoptic situation in the British Isles area at 1800 hours on 2nd May, 1954. The depression under examination, Low "S", was a little deeper (less than 984 millibars) at this time and the frontal system, although becoming less strong, was marked in on the map. By 0600 hours on 3rd May, 1954, Low "S" (inset C, Fig. 67) had moved a little to the east over Lincolnshire, had filled in slightly and its frontal system had been dissolved into the circulation of the depression.

Upper Air Data

On Fig. 67, inset B, *i* and *j*, upper air details for 0200 hours at Hemsby and Liverpool on 3rd May, 1954 are instructive. At

[1] Op. cit., p. 112, footnote 2.

Hemsby, situated in the centre of the depression, evidence perhaps for the entry into the elevated warm sector may be found at 13,400 feet (600 millibars). Below this level is Polar-Maritime air, sometimes just stable, sometimes just unstable, and with relative humidities of 86% to 92%. Above this level in the warm sector, relative humidities are slightly lower (78%–87%) but temperatures, at specific heights are, relatively speaking, a little higher. At Liverpool, however, some 200 miles west from Hemsby and therefore some 200 miles from the centre of depression there is no evidence of a warm sector aloft. Throughout the graph, the Polar air is generally just stable and relative humidities decrease from 93% at the ground surface to 80% at 6,700 feet (750 millibars) and 51% at 15,700 feet (550 millibars). Only at the centre of the depression then is the warm sector distinguishable aloft.

In conclusion, the data examined have shown that at 0600 hours on 3rd May, 1954 over the British Isles, a frontless decay depression was established, which possessed many standard features.

Chapter 5

THE ANTICYCLONE

The *anticyclone* is in many ways the opposite of the depression discussed earlier.[1] It appears on the synoptic chart as a series of concentric isobars enclosing an area of *high* atmospheric pressure, i.e. high relative to the atmospheric pressure of surrounding areas. At the centre of an average *well-developed* anticyclone located over the British Isles the barometric pressure, when reduced to sea level, seldom exceeds 1,030 millibars. Should pressure be of this value the anticyclone is said to be *intense*, that is, reference is made to the actual barometric pressure at the centre and not to the *barometric gradient* which is usually slight. Thus an intense anticyclone is usually a large one. Those in which there is a general rise in pressure are said to be *building up*, or are *increasing in intensity* or, more simply, *intensifying*. Those in which barometric pressure is falling are said to be *giving way*, or to be *decreasing in intensity*, or, more simply, *declining*. Small anticyclones are comparatively rare ; they are insignificant features of the synoptic chart and in this respect they differ from the depression, the smallest of which is very often the most active.

Anticyclones may be sub-divided into two main classes :

1. *Semi-permanent or Seasonal Stationary Type*, which forms in sub-tropical high pressure belts and is persistent, though in the winter it tends to merge with the cold type of anticyclone prevalent at this time of year over land masses. In summer it is discernable at sea level only over the oceans for over the land it is replaced by low pressure areas. This type of anticyclone also develops over northern continents in winter. It is normally a shallow formation (not above 6,000 feet in depth) and is most pronounced and persistent in the Asiatic (Siberian) High where the barometric pressure sometimes exceeds 1,050 millibars. These two areas, the Sub-Tropical High pressure belt and the Asiatic High pressure area

[1] See pp. 4–9.

constitute source regions for Tropical-Maritime and Polar-Continental air masses respectively.

2. *The Temporary or Migratory Type* appears at intervals in temperate latitudes when it interrupts the continuity of the normal cyclonic activity. Those which form within the depression series often assume the shape of a wedge, anchored to the Sub-Tropical High, located between the individual depressions (Fig. 47). They are formed entirely within the cold air between adjacent warm sectors. Often behind the last member of a cyclone family (Fig.

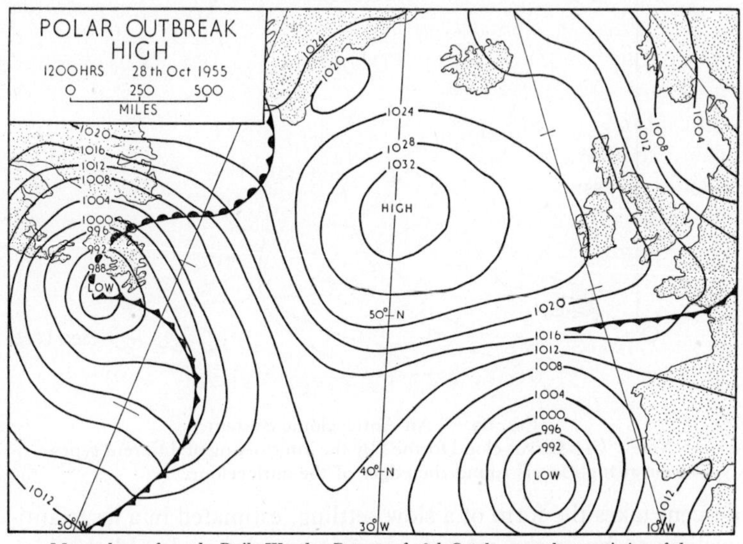

Map redrawn from the Daily Weather Reports of 28th October 1955 by permission of the Director-General, Meteorological Office, London. Copyright H.M. Stationery Office.

Fig. 68. — Polar Outbreak High

68) masses of cold air are drawn southwards to lower latitudes. This is known as an *outbreak of Polar air* (*Polar Outbreak High*). Because of heating from the underlying surface and subsidence aloft the original temperature contrasts diminish so that after a period of two to three days the new " high " has acquired the properties characteristic of the Sub-Tropical High.

The surface winds circulate round the high pressure centre in a *clockwise* direction in the Northern Hemisphere (Buys Ballot's Law).[1] At the surface, due to friction with the ground, the wind

[1] *Vide infra*, p. 216, footnote 1.

has an outward component across the isobars and consequently there is a surface outflow of air from the system (Fig. 69). If the high pressure system is to persist for days, as it does on numerous occasions, then this surface outflow must be compensated by inflowing air at high altitude which then subsides (Fig. 69).[1] The

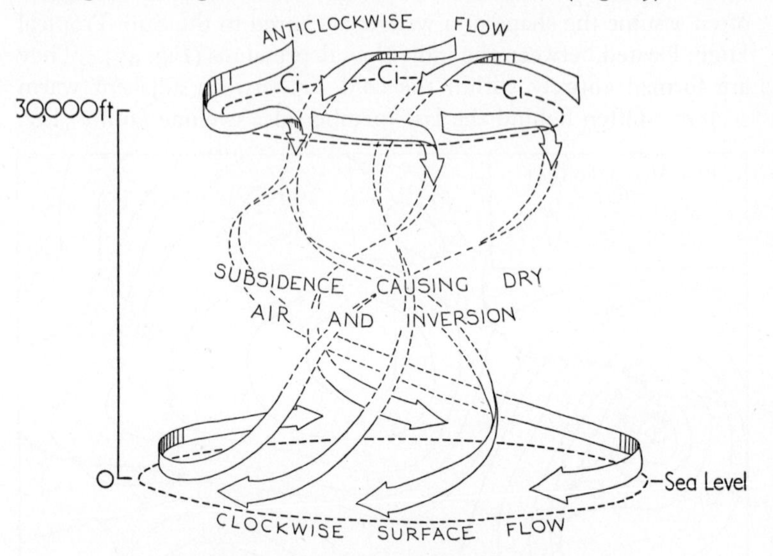

FIG. 69. — An Anticyclonic System
Note : Ci = Cirrus cloud formed by the intermixing of different types of air at high levels round the edges of the anticyclone.

descent takes the form of a slow settling, estimated in a large anticyclone to be at the rate of 300 feet per day ; should the high pressure centre be intensifying then the more usual rate of descent is in the order of 3,000 feet per day. As has already been noted [2] descending air is warmed adiabatically thus creating conditions where any precipitation is extremely unlikely except for drizzle

[1] Brunt, D. and Douglas, C. K. M. have shown (Mem. Roy. Met. Soc. v. III No. 22, 1928) that in areas of *rising* barometric pressure the winds are blowing apart laterally, i.e. they are areas of *divergence.* This deficiency can be made good only by air descending from above. Alternatively, in areas where the barometric pressure is *falling* the winds are coming together laterally, i.e. these are areas of *convergence.* The air is forced to rise so that continued convergence of moist air is inevitable associated with cloud and rain, e.g. in a depression, whilst divergence is normally associated with clear skies, e.g. in an anticyclone. (See Weather Map M.O. 595 H.M.S.O. 1956, pp. 60–1.)

[2] See pp. 19–21.

at coastal stations. Also, as a direct consequence of the adiabatic warming, the air becomes very stable. This stability, due to the subsidence, is counteracted to some extent by any heating of the air from below. However, in those regions where the air is cold, the effects of the subsidence in the upper air and the cooling of the air from below are likely to reinforce each other to render the stratification of the air stable in the extreme, which hinders the transfer of properties upwards by turbulence. On the other hand, great stability favours horizontal (lateral) mixing so that horizontal homogeneity is produced in air masses originating in anticyclonic regions. There is always this tendency towards homogeneous conditions should an anticyclone persist for any length of time, the conditions tending to spread outwards from the centre of high pressure.

Whilst depressions show a fair degree of uniformity in their patterns of formation, growth and decay, the anticyclones are far more irregular in their behaviour as well as in shape — they often appear as sluggish,[1] passive systems filling in the gaps between the more active cyclonic systems. The movement of the high pressure centre is generally towards the area of greatest positive barometric tendency, though very often anticyclones are stationary for a considerable period and meteorological stations under their influence report little or no change in barometric readings between one synoptic hour and the next.

So far, the anticyclones discussed have been subdivided into *Stationary* and *Migratory* types. It may be useful to consider another type of subdivision based upon whether the high pressure system is *warm* or *cold*. In the *warm type* the air in the troposphere is warmer than usual and there is an excess of air at high levels. This type of anticyclone extends to great heights and is likely to persist longer and to move more slowly than the cold anticyclone. In the *cold type* the high pressure is due to low temperatures and dense air at surface levels, and the formation is relatively shallow. Temporary, warm anticyclones, which occur mainly in summer, can be extensions of the permanent subtropical " high " but more

[1] Compare the rate of movement of " High L " (0600 hours, 11th May, 1950 — inset map A, Fig. 72) which moved some 500 miles in 5 days, with that of " Low H " (1200 hours, 2nd September, 1954 — See inset map A, Fig. 66), which moved 300 miles in 12 hours.

common is the warm anticyclone which evolves by a process of gradual change, due to adiabatic and surface heating, from a temporary cold anticyclone.

It is sometimes erroneously stated that anticyclones are always accompanied by fine weather. Almost any conditions may develop in an anticyclone though dry, quiet weather predominates. *From the point of view of weather* associated with high pressure systems, the migratory types of anticyclones in temperate latitudes (those systems affecting the British Isles) may be subdivided into two classes — those accompanied by *clear skies* and those in which the sky is *overcast*. The former are more frequent in summer, the latter in winter. It is interesting to note that Belasco found that anticyclones in general covered the British Isles 20% of the time during the period 1938–49, that is, they are only half as frequent as frontal conditions (Fig. 31).

" Clear Sky " Anticyclone

In *summer* the light winds and clear skies permit intensive solar and terrestrial radiation (radiation weather). Day surface temperatures rise to high levels over land but since subsidence aloft leads to stability and frequently to an inversion at some 2,000–3,000 feet above the earth's surface, no convective clouds are formed, except perhaps temporarily during the middle of the day when fair weather cumulus may appear. Nights are cool since the earth's surface loses heat freely through the clear atmosphere ; ground mists and fogs are frequent but they are usually dissipated soon after sunrise. During the day visibility is only moderate due to the accumulation of dust haze and smoke beneath the inversion.

In *winter* the clear sky anticyclone permits prolonged and intense radiation at night causing sharp frosts which are white if the air is cooled below its dew point. Fogs form frequently and there is a likelihood of a prominent inversion at the surface. Solar heating of the earth during the day is often able to disperse the fog by early afternoon but sometimes such fog persists throughout the day, in which case the temperature rises little above the low temperatures of the preceding night.

It will be seen that diurnal effects are the main features of the " radiation " weather of these " clear sky " anticyclones. Large diurnal ranges of temperature are characteristic and land and sea breezes are prominent on coasts due to marked differential heating of land and sea and the relatively large scope allowed by a weak anticyclonic circulation for the development of local winds.

The Cloudy Anticyclone

The inversion layer, due to subsidence, which is characteristic of most anticyclones is located normally at 2,000–3,000 feet above the ground. However, in an anticyclone which is building up, this inversion also intensifies and settles at a lower height day by day. Frequently the location of the inversion is marked by a continuous layer of stratocumulus cloud so that the weather may remain cold, dull and foggy for days. Above the inversion layer there is usually bright sunshine which is partly responsible for the *anticyclonic gloom* at the ground surface below the inversion. Again, visibility during the day is only moderate due to the accumulation of dust haze and smoke beneath the inversion. The stratocumulus cloud is not formed by large scale ascending air currents as is cumulus cloud, nor is any forced continuous rise of warm air over cold air involved, as at the warm front. The layer owes its origin to the local elevation of air caused by the turbulent [1] motion of the wind. The base of the cloud is usually at *c.* 2,000 feet, and the top at *c.* 5,000 feet. When closely examined (especially from above in an aircraft) stratocumulus cloud is found to have a cellular pattern due to the air rising in some places, falling in others.

In view of the frequency with which fog is associated with anticyclonic conditions it is pertinent at this stage to note its characteristics and modes of formation. Fog is defined as occurring *when the horizontal visibility is less than 1,100 yards.* Visibilities between 1,100 yards and 2,200 yards are described as *mist* or *haze* (Fig. 24*b*). *Mist,* due chiefly to the water droplets[2] in the atmosphere, is associated with *high* relative humidities ; *haze* is due to the accumula-

[1] See p. 56, footnote 1.

[2] In industrial areas, however, dust and smoke particles may be as important. Such mixed clouds are usually called "*smog*". It has been estimated that in the London smog of December 1952, which covered 450 sq. miles at 400 feet altitude for 4 days, smoke particles entered and left the fog at the rate of 1,000 tons per day, maintaining about 380 tons in the air all the time. Meethan, A. R. (1955) "*Know Your Fog*" Weather. Vol. 10, pp. 103–5.

tion of dust[1] or smoke particles in air of *low* relative humidity.

When air is cooled below its dew point condensation takes place. A limited portion of the air is cooled by contact with a cold land or sea surface and this cooling is diffused through the air by turbulent mixing. Light winds are admirable for the second part of the process as strong winds diffuse the cooling through too great a volume of air so that it becomes ineffective.

The formation of *radiation fog* involves the proximity of moist air to a land surface cooled by radiation through a clear sky at night. First, the lowest layers of air become cooled below their dew point and fog begins to form. Further cooling by radiation from the fog particles causes the fog to increase in thickness. Though the height of the fog may vary it is usually within the limits 500–1,000 feet, and above it there are clear skies. This type of fog occurs most frequently in autumn and winter when the night radiation period is long and the air is damp. Furthermore, the heating power of the sun is usually insufficient to disperse the fog during the day in winter. Consequently, winter fogs may persist for several days. Land fogs occur in anticyclones and ridges of high pressure due to the light winds and clear skies associated with such pressure systems. "*Warm front*" *fogs* occur due to the mixing of cold and warm air on the two sides of the front. *Sea fogs*, which may be blown inland over coastal districts, are caused by warm damp air passing over a cold sea surface. As the temperature of the sea is only slightly affected by solar heating by day and by radiation at night the occurrence of sea fog depends neither on time of day nor state of the sky. All that is necessary is that the temperature of the sea surface must be lower than the dew point of the air above it, for when the air is cooled below its dew point condensation and fog result. Similarly, fog may form in warm air moving over a cold *land* surface, e.g. in winter when a long spell of cold weather is followed by the arrival of mild, moist air usually from the west.

Having described in general terms the major characteristics of anticyclones and associated weather conditions the examples which follow have been chosen (from the British Daily Weather Reports) to illustrate the various types of anticyclone which affect

[1] Typical figures for London are: on a clear day 300 particles per cu. cm. of air; on a foggy day 60,000 particles per cu. cm. of air. *ibid* footnote 2, page 187.

Britain's weather. In previous chapters concerned with air masses and fronts the analysis and recognition of the selected synoptic situations involved a *primary* consideration of air temperature, air humidity, direction of air movement and associated general weather conditions. Atmospheric pressure as such was of *secondary* importance. However, the *initial* recognition of anticyclones *must* take into immediate account the values and distribution of atmospheric pressure which is normally high in relation to that of the surrounding regions. Upper air graphs in previous examples were important in revealing conditions of stability or instability within a given air mass and the height and width of frontal zones, etc.; for anticyclones they now provide valuable evidence of inversion levels and associated phenomena, which are used to demonstrate the degree of development attained by the anticyclone and also, together with data on general weather conditions, help to identify the type of anticyclone present. As with the air masses the anticyclones are areas of " continuity " so that plots of the various elements which make up the weather will be studied not only for the weather in itself, but also to confirm that " discontinuities " on a large scale are not present.

" Clear Sky " Anticyclone: Winter
19th January, 1953, 0600 hours G.M.T.

As can be seen from Fig. 70 inset map C pressure was high over the British Isles ranging from 1,036·9 millibars at Collinstown to 1,025·3 millibars at Lerwick. The whole of the British Isles (except the area north of a line joining Tynemouth to Benbecula and the extreme tip of the South-west Peninsula of England) had barometric pressure higher than 1,034 millibars, and in many areas, higher than 1,036 millibars. The isobars shown on Fig. 70, inset C, are relatively widely spaced (N.B. at intervals of 4 millibars) and roughly circular in pattern. Pressure was falling slowly except in Southern England and the Midlands where it was rising slowly (Fig. 70*a*). Winds (Fig. 70*b*) were generally light, flowing clockwise round the centre of the " high " which was marked by an area of calms.

The temperature/height graph (inset B, Fig. 70) constructed for 1500 hours at Liverpool, 19th January, 1953, shows that at the surface the air was at its dew point (viz. dry bulb temperature

35° F., dew point temperature 35° F.). The air was stable and the stability was increased by the presence of an inversion from 1,000 millibars to 973 millibars (950–2,300 feet approximately). The dry air aloft, so typical of anticyclones, was well marked for though the relative humidity at the surface up to 940 feet was 100% at the top of the inversion it was 70% and at 3,700 feet it was only 32%. The dryness of 40–50% relative humidity is maintained until dew point observations cease at 400 millibars (24,000 feet). Note also that the condensation level was at the surface and that the freezing level was at 950 feet.

The isotherms on Fig. 70*c* form a roughly circular pattern about two centres of low temperature (below 28° F.) which are rather elongated and lie over Yorkshire, the Midlands, the Severn Estuary and Ireland; excessive cooling over land the previous night is indicated. The temperature range of the map is from 25° F. (Cranfield) to 47° F. (Dyce) and though the greater part of England, South Wales and Ireland had temperatures below 32° F. it is significant that coastal areas had high temperatures — 43° F. at Scilly, 41° F. at Valentia and Blacksod Point — indicating the slower rates of cooling at coastal stations. Over Scotland temperatures were above 36° F. and rose northwards to 42°–45° F. In other words the discontinuities generally follow the coasts and would not therefore be associated with the presence of fronts.

The pattern of the dew point isopleths (Fig. 70*d*) is essentially the same as that of the isotherms with two minima, viz. 26°–28° F. over England and less than 24° F. over Ireland. Coastal areas of the South-west Peninsula and Western Ireland again have high values as does the north of Scotland.

The isopleths of the difference[1] between dry bulb and dew point temperatures (Fig. 70*e*) show a generally simple pattern of widespread small differences, i.e. high relative humidity. With the exception of Dyce (difference 9° F.; relative humidity 71%) and a few other coastal areas, most of the stations reported differences of 1° F. (i.e. relative humidity 96%), and an extensive belt covering the Lake District, the Isle of Man, North Wales, the Midlands and the London area reported relative humidities of 100%. This belt shows some overlap with the area of low temperatures (Fig. 70*c*) noted previously over England. Isolated areas of saturated

[1] See Fig. 44, p. 100.

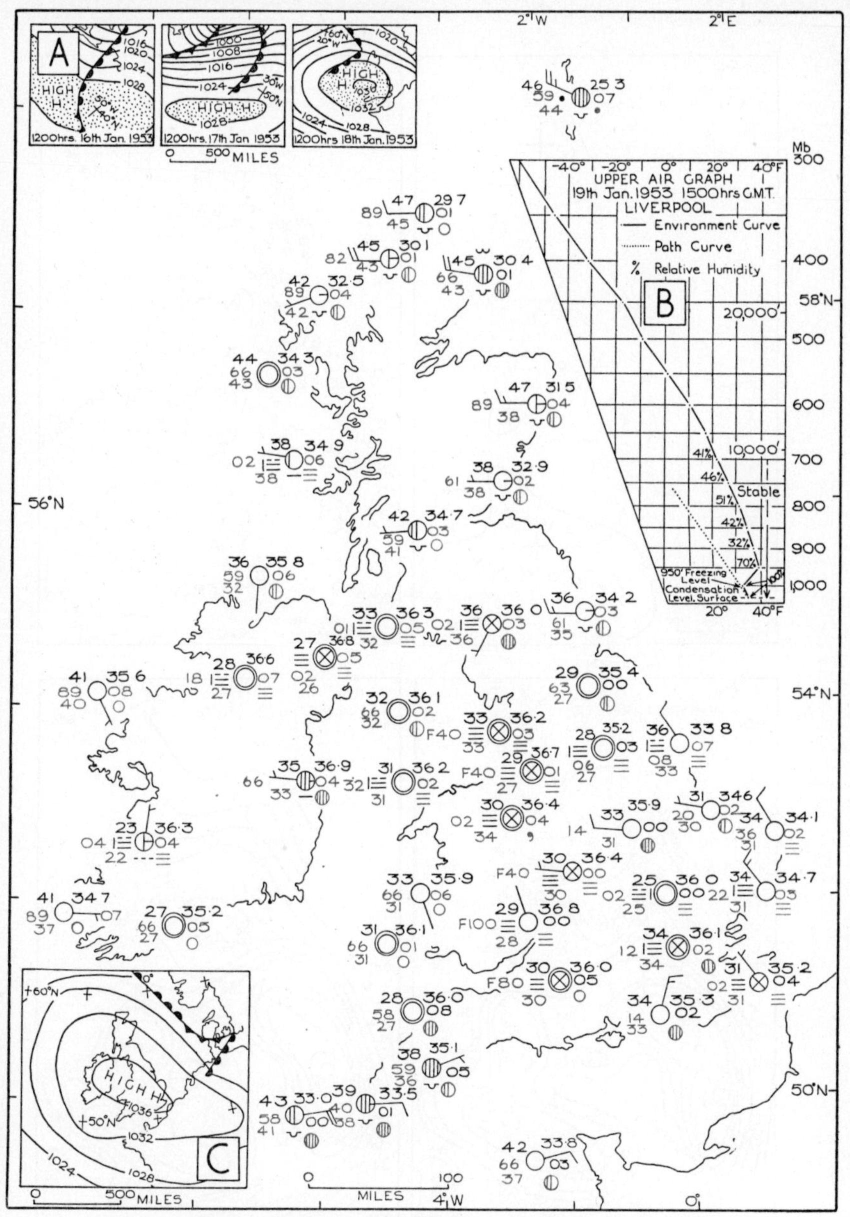

Maps redrawn from the Daily Weather Reports of 16th January 1953, 17th January 1953, 18th January 1953 and 19th January 1953 by permission of the Director-General, Meteorological Office London. Copyright H.M. Stationery Office.

FIG. 70. — Selected Data for 19th January 1953 : 0600 hrs. G.M.T.
The Clear Anticyclone — Winter
Inset A — Previous synoptic situations
Inset B — Upper Air Graph
Inset C — Isobars : 0600 hrs. G.M.T. 19th January 1953

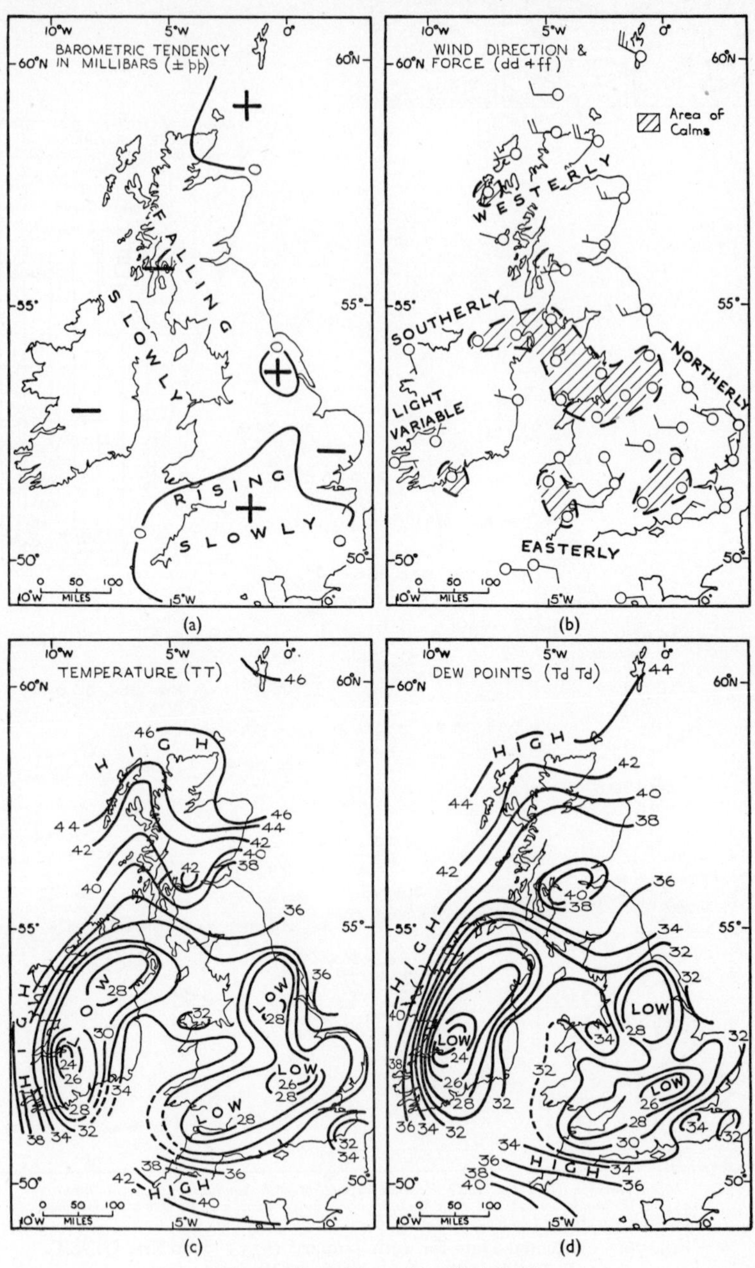

FIG. 70 (*contd.*). — (*a*), (*b*), (*c*), (*d*)

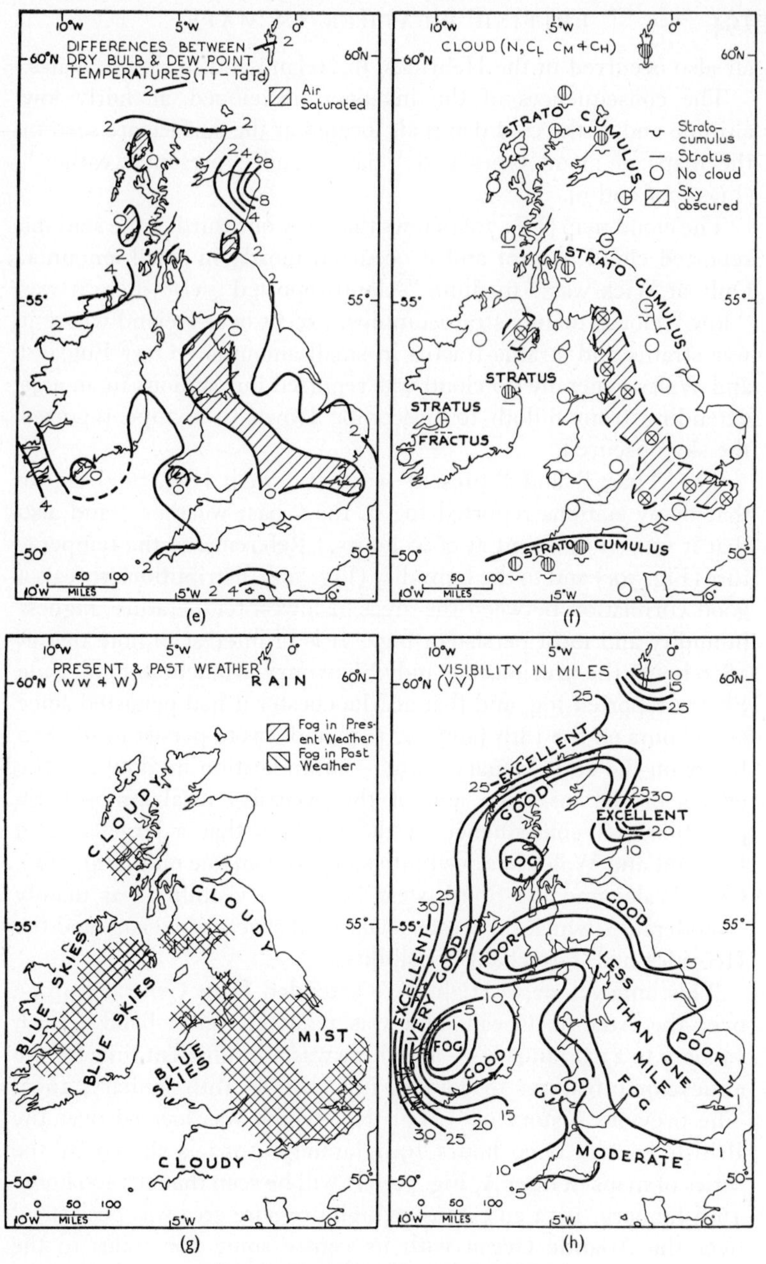

FIG. 70 (*contd.*). — (*e*), (*f*), (*g*), (*h*)

air also occurred in the Hebrides, in Ireland and in South Wales.

The consequences of the inversion developed at fairly low altitude and of the cold damp air located at the surface are seen in the maps of cloud types and " past " and " present weather " (Figs. 70*f* and *g*).

The cloud map (Fig. 70*f*) shows that only one third of the stations reported cloud present and it occurred mostly in small amounts. Only at Wick was " medium " cloud reported ; elsewhere it was " low " cloud, mainly stratocumulus, except over Ireland where it was stratus and stratus-fractus in small amounts. Over England and Wales generally no cloud was reported but stations in an area extending from Silloth to Boscombe Down to Lympe reported the sky obscured.

The " past " and " present weather " map (Fig. 70*g*) shows that many stations reported fog in the " past weather " and also that it was still present at 0600 hours. Reference to the temperature (Fig. 70*c*) and to the humidity (Fig. 70*e*) distributions reveals a good correlation between the areas of lowest temperature, highest humidity and most persistent fog. It is of interest to note that at 1800 hours the previous day only Shawbury, Manchester and Sule Skerry reported fog, and that at Manchester it had persisted since 0600 hours on the 18th January, 1953 and was to persist until 1800 hours on the 20th January, 1953 — an indication no doubt of the effects of the inversion and of the excessive local atmospheric pollution. A consequence of the fog was that a large area in England and Wales had visibilities of less than one mile (Fig. 70*h*). Over Wales and the South-west Peninsula visibility was mainly " moderate " whilst the western coastal districts of Ireland and the Hebrides had " excellent " visibility.

This anticyclone, " High H ", extended from Central Europe over the Atlantic Ocean, and was relatively short-lived — 18th January to 23rd January — and there was not sufficient time for the anticyclonic features to develop fully by the 19th January, 1953. The previous history of " High H " which was located over the British Isles at 0600 hours 19th January, 1953 is shown by the series of maps in inset A, Fig. 70. It will be seen that at 1200 hours 16th January, 1953 an extensive high pressure area was positioned over the Atlantic Ocean with its centre some 500 miles to the south-east of Newfoundland (40° N. 50° W.). The area of highest pressure was enclosed by the isobar for 1,028 millibars. Subsequently, movement was to the north-east and the system intensified so that pressure at the centre was 1,036 millibars at 1200 hours 18th January, 1953. The movement of "High H" was in the order of 2,500 miles in 3 days.

Cloudy Anticyclone: Winter

4th March, 1953, 0600 hours G.M.T.

Pressure was high over the British Isles (inset map C, Fig. 71), the highest pressure being at Pembroke Dock (1,038·3 millibars); over the greater part of England and Wales, except for the east coast and Ireland, pressure was higher than 1,036 millibars. Except in the extreme north of Scotland the isobars were widely spaced and circular in pattern, forming the north-west quadrant of an anticyclone "High E" which covered France, Southern Germany and Switzerland. Inset Map A, Fig. 71 shows stages in the past history of "High E" which was located over the British Isles at 0600 hours 4th March, 1953. It will be seen that this anticyclone approached the British Isles from the east, for at 1200 hours 1st March, 1953, it was centred over northern Germany with a pressure of 1,040 millibars at the centre. Subsequent movement was to the west and pressure at the centre decreased to 1,036 millibars. The total movement in 3½ days was about 1,000 miles though it may be noted that between 1200 hours 3rd March and 0600 hours 4th March (inset C, Fig. 71) the centre was stationary.

The inversion, due to subsidence, a conspicuous feature of anticyclones in general[1], is very well marked on the temperature/height graph constructed for 1500 hours at Liverpool (inset B, Fig. 71). The inversion extends from 975 millibars (1,580 feet) to 926 millibars (2,700 feet) with a temperature of 31° F. at the base, and 52° F. at the top, of the inversion layer. An extreme inversion of this kind would constitute a very effective "lid" confining any convection to the lower layers of the atmosphere. The very dry atmosphere, typical of layers above inversions, is also well illustrated on the graph: the relative humidity at the surface at Liverpool (1500 hours) was 85%, and at 1,000 millibars it was 82%, but at 950 millibars the relative humidity was as low as 2% and at 900 millibars it was even lower than 2%.

[1] See pp. 19–21.

The range of temperature over the British Isles was from 22° F. at Dishforth and Boscombe Down to 46° F. at Benbecula in North-west Scotland, where conditions were generally warmer (Fig. 71*a*). The coldest areas were located in Southern Ireland and in England within an area bounded by a line Dishforth — Ross-on-Wye — Calshot — Lympe — Felixstowe. Within this area temperatures were below 32° F. Here, isothermal distribution was somewhat complex, the stations at Dyce and Boscombe Down forming centres of low temperature (22° F.) around which isotherms were concentric. Noteworthy is the influence of the Irish Sea which effectively separates the two low temperature areas over England from the one over Ireland. Note also the purely local effect of distance from the sea when Calshot (30° F.) is compared with the neighbouring station of Boscombe Down (22° F.). It appears that discontinuities in the temperature distribution were localised, small scale and often coincident with coastlines, and therefore do not suggest the presence of fronts at this time. Temperatures were well below the average minimum for days in March as shown by the following Table.

Station	*Temperature* 0600 *hours* 4*th March*, 1953 °F.	*Average minimum temperature, March* °F.
Tynemouth	35	37·9
Spurn Head	33	37·6
Ross-on-Wye	26	36·8
Holyhead	35	39·9
St. Anne's Head	31	40·4
Plymouth	33	40·2

Averages for 1921–1950

The pattern of the isopleths of dew point temperature (Fig. 71*b*) is essentially the same as that already described for dry bulb temperatures. There are again two areas of low values — one over Southern Ireland (30° F.) and two over England centred about Dishforth (20° F.) and Boscombe Down (22° F.). Over Ireland, England and Wales (except Cornwall) the air had to cool to 32° F. and below before condensation could take place ; over the greater part of Scotland there is a gradual gradation westwards and north-

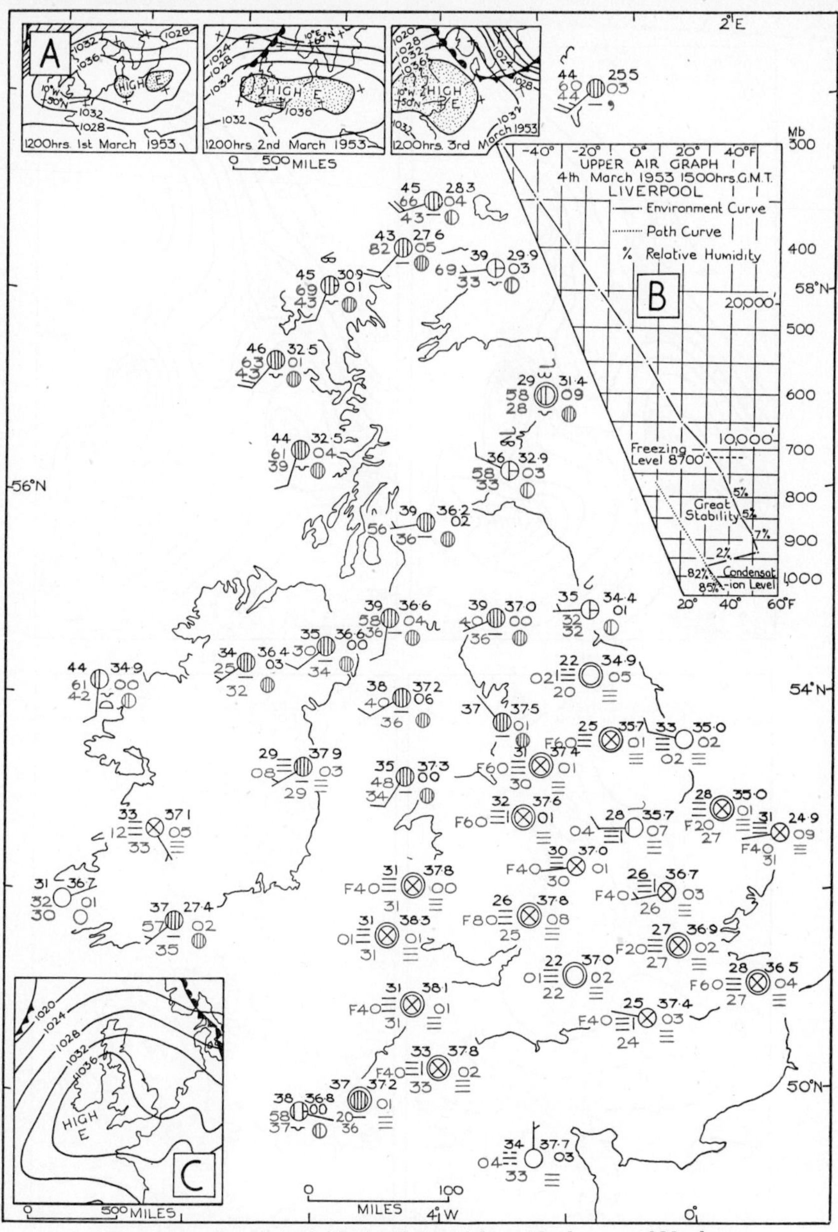

Maps redrawn from the Daily Weather Reports of the 1st March 1953, 2nd March 1953, 3rd March 1953 and 4th March 1953 by permission of the Director-General, Meteorological Office, London. Copyright H.M. Stationery Office.

FIG. 71. — Selected Data for 4th March 1953 : 0600 hrs. G.M.T.
The Cloudy Anticyclone — Winter
Inset A — Previous Synoptic Situations
Inset B — Upper Air Graph
Inset C — Isobars : 0600 hrs. G.M.T. 4th March 1953

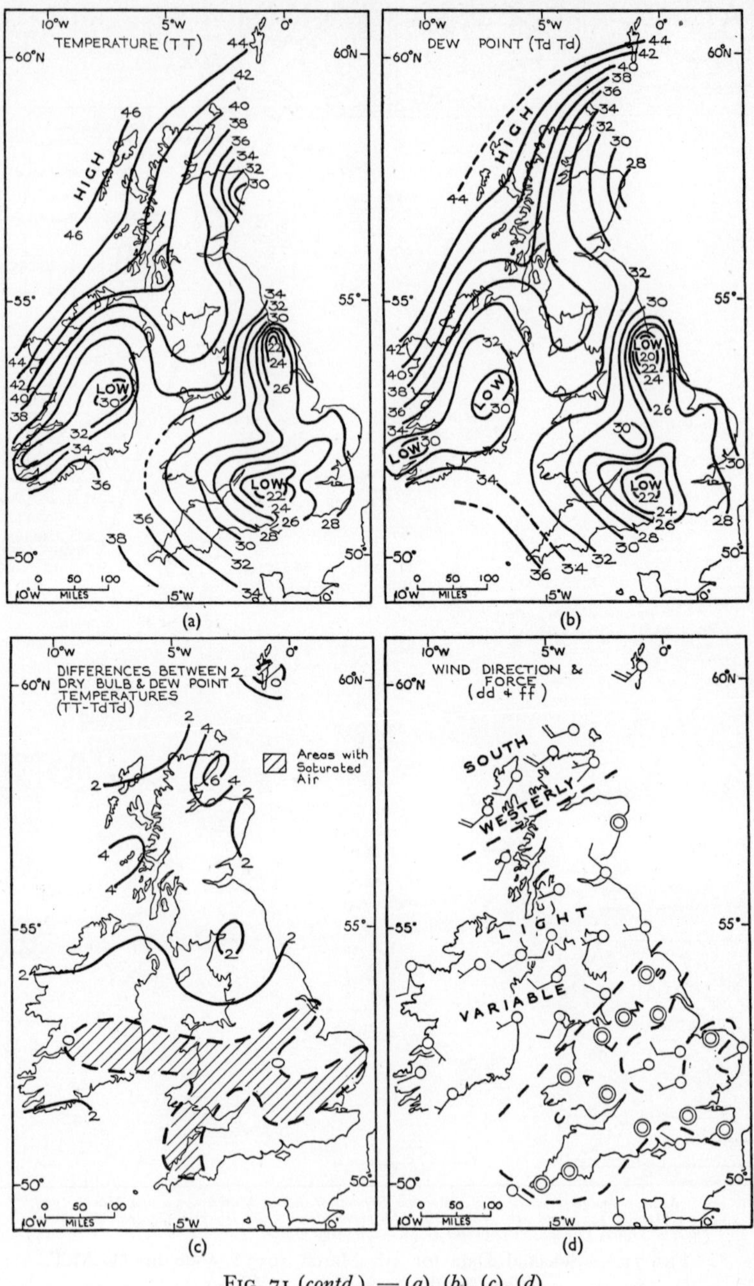

FIG. 71 (*contd.*). — (*a*), (*b*), (*c*), (*d*)

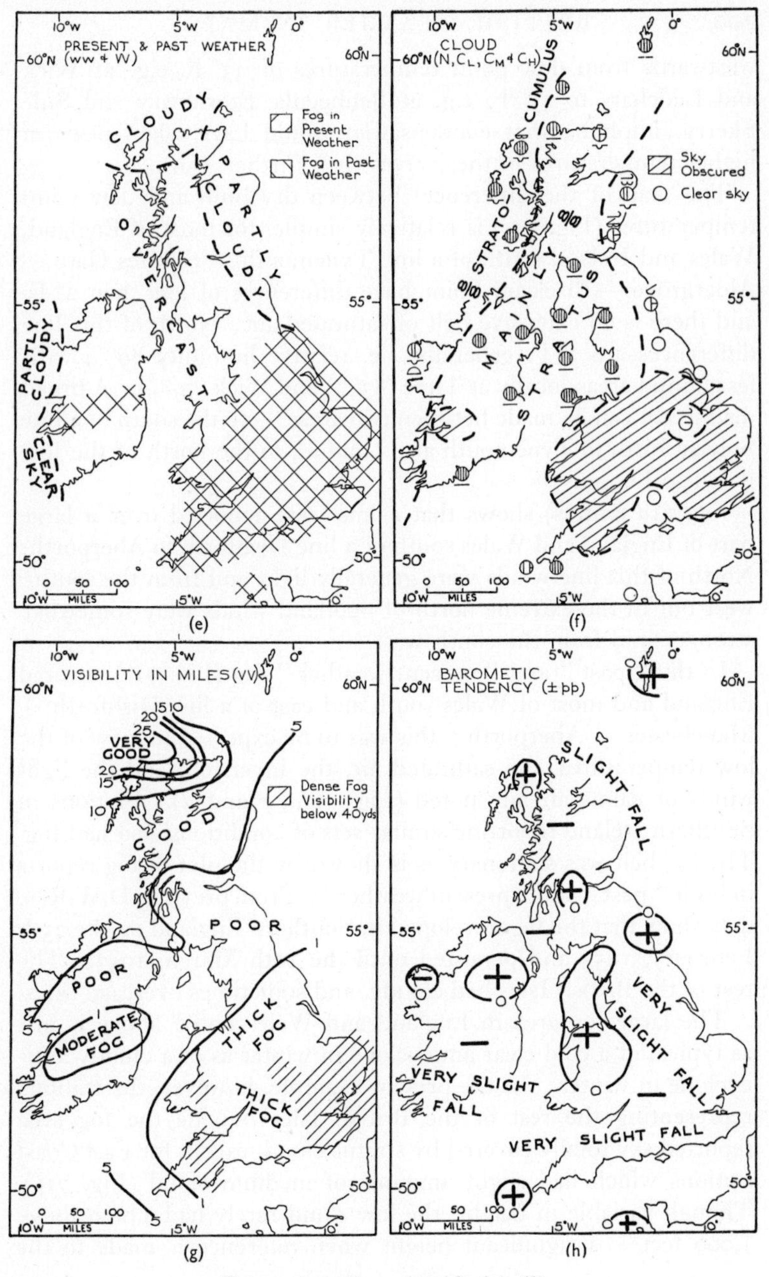

FIG. 71 (*contd.*). — (*e*), (*f*), (*g*), (*h*)

westwards from dew point temperatures of 33° F. e.g. at Wick and Leuchars to 43° F. e.g. at Benbecula, Stornoway and Sule Skerry, implying that condensation would have taken place at higher temperatures in these areas than further south.

The map of the difference[1] between dry bulb and dew point temperatures (Fig. 71*c*) is relatively simple, for most of England, Wales and Ireland south of a line Tynemouth — Squires Gate — Aldergrove — Blacksod Point have differences of less than 2° F. and there is an extensive belt of saturated air. North of this line differences are 3° F. generally, i.e. relative humidity 89%, with less humid areas locally at Tiree (83%) and Wick (79%). A broad distinction can be made between two areas — to the south of a line Solway Firth to Tynemouth air is humid, to the north of the line it is less humid.

Fig. 71*d* (winds) shows that calms were reported over a large part of England and Wales south of a line Dishforth to Aberporth. North of this line winds were generally light and from the south-west but in the extreme north of Scotland winds were somewhat stronger and from the south-west.

In the " past " and " present weather " fog (Fig. 71*e*) covered England and most of Wales south and east of a line Dishforth — Manchester — Aberporth ; this was to be expected in view of the low temperatures, the saturated air, the inversion, and the light winds or calms already noted (Figs. 71*a*, *c* and *d*). Stations in Southern Ireland reporting similar sets of conditions also had fog. The fog belt was stationary as is shown by the plot of fog reports in both " past " and " present weather ". From previous D.W.R.'s, data show that the fog developed in Southern England on the 25th February, 1953 and persisted until the 10th March, 1953. The rest of the British Isles had cloudy, and sometimes overcast, skies.

The large fog area in England and Wales noted above is just as typical of a cold clear anticyclone in winter as of a cloudy anticyclone in winter. In the present example, however, the stations representing the rest of the British Isles outside the fog area reported sky totally covered by stratus cloud, except for East Coast stations which had slight amounts of medium cloud (Fig. 71*f*). Though variable in height, the low cloud rarely had a base above 1,000 feet — a significant height when reference is made to the

[2] See Fig. 44, p. 100.

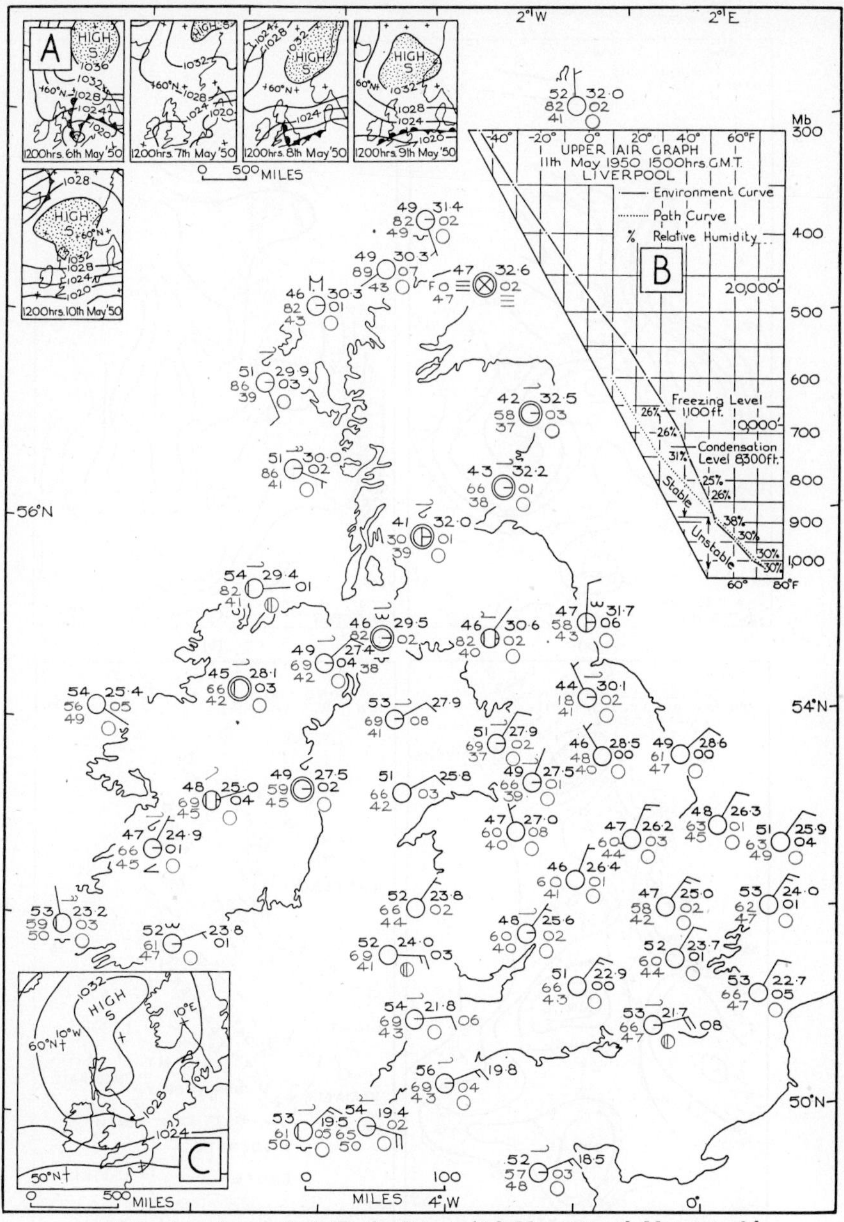

Maps redrawn from the Daily Weather Reports of 6th May 1950, 7th May 1950, 8th May 1950, 10th May 1950 and 11th May 1950 by permission of the Director-General, Meteorological Office, London. Copyright H.M. Stationery Office

FIG. 72. — Selected Data for 11th May 1950 : 0600 hrs. G.M.T.
The Clear Anticyclone-Summer
Inset A — Previous Synoptic Situations
Inset B — Upper Air Graph
Inset C — Isobars : 0600 hrs. 11th May 1950

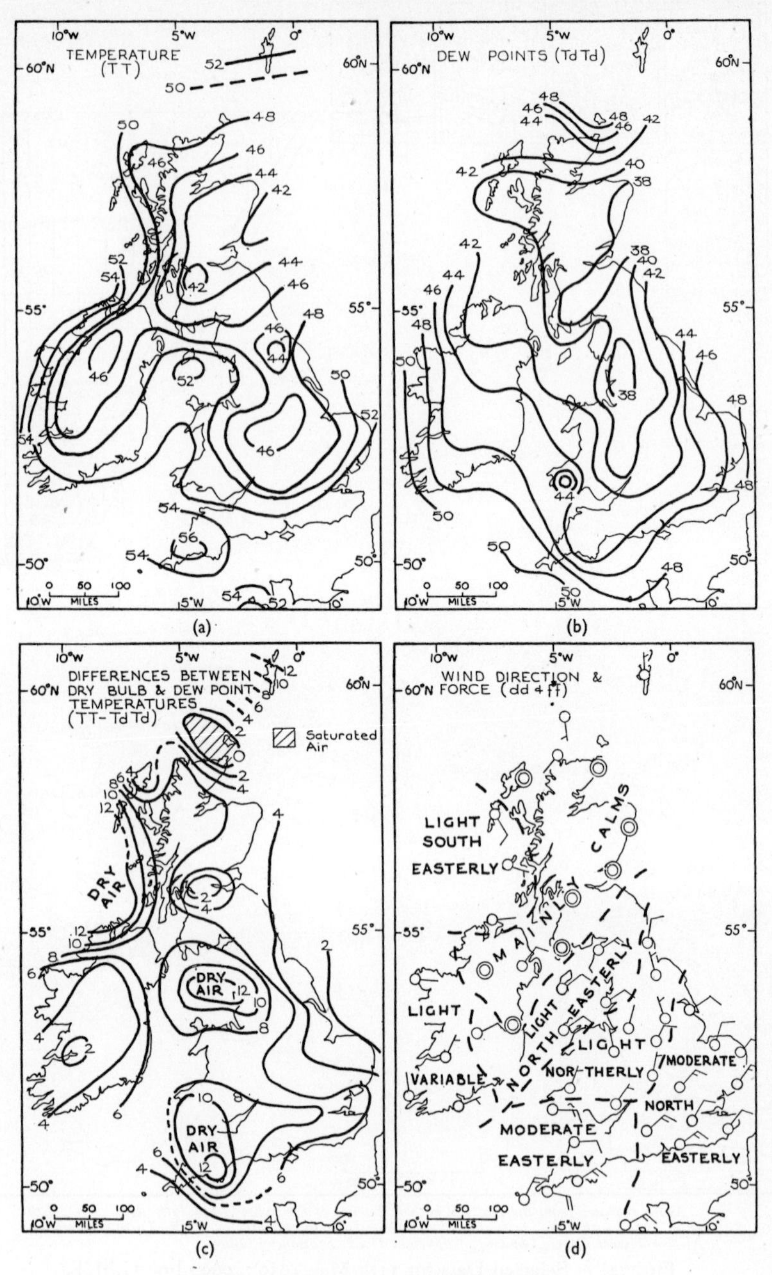

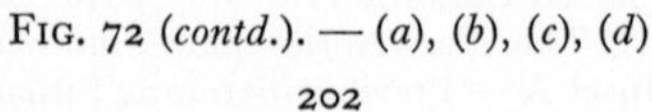
FIG. 72 (*contd.*). — (*a*), (*b*), (*c*), (*d*)

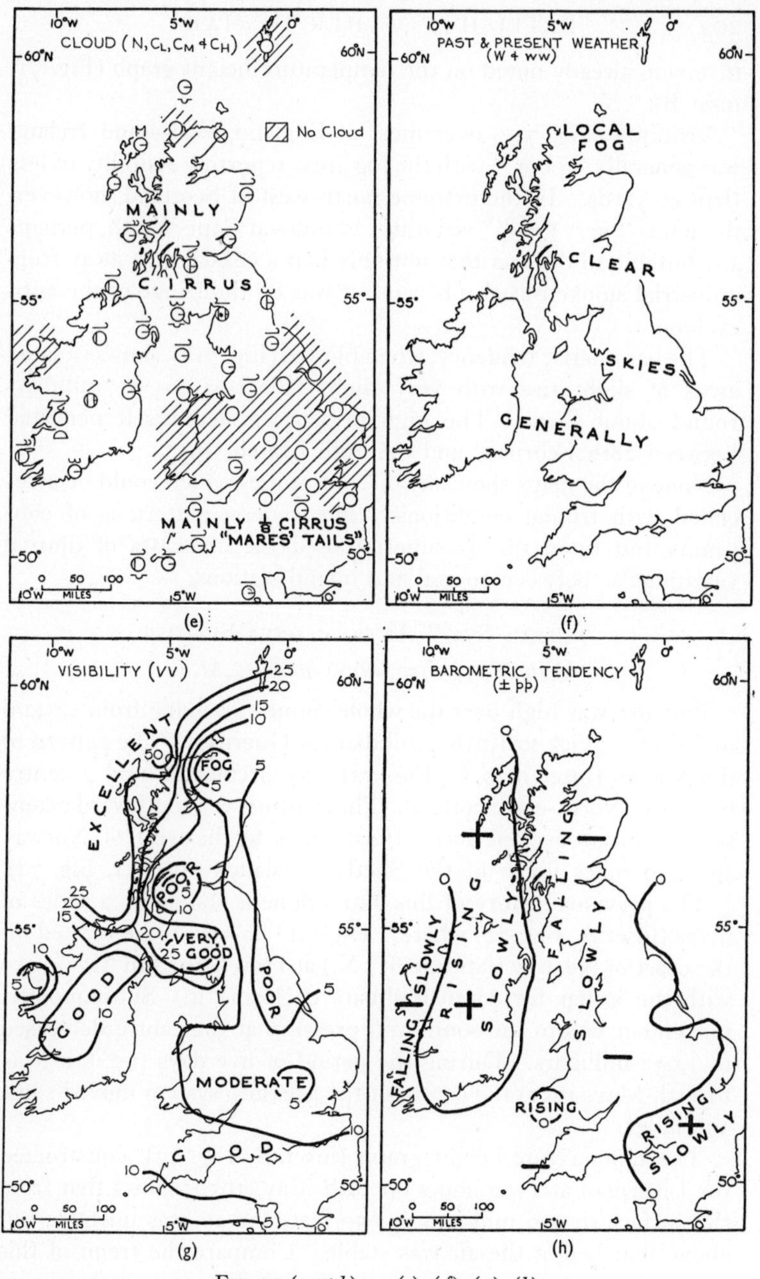

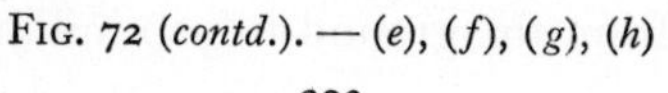
FIG. 72 (*contd.*). — (*e*), (*f*), (*g*), (*h*)

inversion already noted on the temperature/height graph (Fig. 71, inset B).

Visibility (Fig. 71*g*) over most of England, Wales and Ireland was generally " poor " with the fog areas reporting visibility of less than 40 yards. In the extreme north-west of Scotland, however, there was " very good " visibility, 25 miles at Cape Wrath, perhaps attributable to the fact that not only is it a coastal area away from industrial smoke but also because it was on the fringe of the anticyclone.

The barometric tendency, when plotted (Fig. 71*h*), shows isolated areas of slight rise with very slight falls (·04 to ·01 millibars round about them. The high pressure system itself persisted between 28th February and the 16th March, 1953.

None of the maps show any discontinuities which could be associated with frontal conditions. The general pattern is of continuity but upon this is superimposed the contrasts of diurnal variations as between coastal and inland stations.

" Clear Sky " Anticyclone: Summer

11th May, 1950, 0600 hours G.M.T.

Pressure was high over the whole country, ranging from 1,032·6 millibars at Wick to 1,018·5 millibars at Guernsey. The pattern of the isobars (inset map C, Fig. 72) was circular around a centre lying over North-east Scotland. This centre was a southward extension of an anticyclone located 200 miles to the west of Norway and 100 miles north of the Shetland Islands (inset A, Fig. 72).

The previous history of this anticyclone is shown by a series of maps (inset A, Fig. 72) where " High S " is seen to be located off the coast of Norway (latitude 65° N.) at 1200 hours 6th May, 1950 with the isobar for 1,036 millibars enclosing it. Subsequently, movement was to the south and pressure at the centre decreased to 1,032 millibars. During the period of five days (i.e. 6th May to 11th May, 1950) the centre of the pressure system moved some 500 miles.

The temperature/height graph (inset B, Fig. 72), constructed for Liverpool at 1500 hours on 11th May, 1950, shows that from the surface to 900 millibars (3,650 feet) the air was unstable but above that height the air was stable. Compare the trend of this upper air graph from the ground to 900 millibars with the theoretical one (Fig. 13) which illustrates the effects of heating during the course of the day upon the lower layers of the atmosphere. The condensation level was high at 9,000 feet and the freezing level was at 12,000 feet. The air was extremely dry as evidenced at Liverpool where at 1500 hours the relative humidity was 30% at the ground surface. This dry atmosphere was maintained at least as far as 12,000 feet (inset B Fig. 72).

The horizontal temperature distribution (Fig. 72*a*) is one of arcuate isotherms about a centre of low temperatures in North-east Scotland ; the lowest temperature being recorded at Dyce (42° F.) and the highest temperature at Plymouth (56° F.). Local areas of low temperature (Leeming 44° F.) and local centres of high temperature (Ronaldsway 53° F.) complicate the pattern but even so there appear to be no marked zones of steep temperature gradient except those associated with contrasts between coastal and inland stations ; for example, Castle Archdale 45° F., Blacksod Point 54° F. ; Cranfield 47° F., Felixstowe 53° F. This is to be expected under the cloudless conditions reported in the " past weather ". Radiation at night from the land is much greater than from the sea, and consequently, coastal stations, especially those in the South-west Peninsula and Western Ireland reported relatively warm conditions for the time of year. Inland stations however, reported temperatures nearer to the average for the time of year as can be seen by reference to the Table below.

Station	*Temperature at* 0600 *hours* 11*th May*, 1950	*Temperature Monthly average* *Minimum*	*Mean daily*
Coastal	°F	°F	°F
Malin Head	54	45·0*	49·6*
Valentia	53	46·5*	52·2*
Blacksod Point	54	45·8*	50·9*
Scilly	53	48·1	52·7
Felixstowe	53	46·0	52·4
Tiree	51	44·7	49·9
Inland			
Manchester	49	45·2	52·9
Elmdon (Birmingham)	46	44·5	52·2

* Average for 1881–1915 ; other averages for 1921–50.

The pattern of the isopleths of dew point temperature (Fig. 72*b*) is essentially the same as that just described, for about an elongated area of low dew point centred at Dyce (37° F.) the isopleths form arcs of circles whose values increase generally to the south and west to maxima of 50° F. at Valentia, Scilly and Lizard.

Attention has already been drawn to the low relative humidity at Liverpool at 1500 hours. The relatively large differences[1] between dry bulb and dew point temperatures shown on Fig. 72*c* also illustrate the point. The pattern is somewhat complex with several areas forming a north to south belt in which differences are about 12° F. extending from Tiree, across the Irish Sea to the Severn Estuary and the South-west Peninsula. Within this area relative humidity was 63–64%. Areas of high relative humidity were small and localised, for example Valentia 93%, Wick 100%, Renfrew 93%. In general the relative humidity over the rest of the British Isles was 80–86%. It will be noted that in most areas generally, the air would have to be cooled to at least 60° F. for condensation to occur.

The winds (Fig. 72*d*) were mainly light from the north-east except in North-east and Central Scotland where there were calms. A regional subdivision of this wind map gives a pattern of great complexity but the broad trend is quite clear. It is to be expected that the calms would be located in North-east Scotland which is the centre of highest pressure, and that the weak clockwise circulation of winds round a high pressure centre would give the British Isles, located to the south of the centre, relatively light easterly winds. It is interesting to note that at Liverpool at 1500 hours the upper air ascent showed the easterly winds to be maintained to over 54,000 feet above the ground.

As can be expected in a " clear sky " anticyclone most of Wales, Central and Eastern England reported no cloud at all (Fig. 72*e*). Elsewhere, one eighth to two eighths cloud were reported and they were all cirrus types created by the intermixing at high levels (+30,000 feet) of the air entering the anticyclone with the air already inside it (Fig. 69). One station, Wick, reported the sky obscured, and from the " past " and " present weather " reports it will be seen that fog had developed there (Fig. 72*f*). Note also that this area was the only one where the air was saturated (Fig.

[1] See Fig. 44. p. 100

72*c*). The plot of the "past" and "present weather" is relatively insignificant, for all stations except Wick reported clear skies (Fig. 72*f*).

Visibility (Fig. 72*g*), as might be expected, was good, especially in the Hebrides where Cape Wrath reported 50 miles. Though not shown on the upper air graph for Liverpool, at 1500 hours other stations in the British Isles (Lerwick, Stornoway, Leuchars, Aldergrove, Downham Market, Camborne and Valentia) reported an inversion about 900 millibars (*c.* 3,000 feet), and it is most likely that this caused the poor visibility over the Midlands and Central Scotland for smoke and dust would be trapped beneath such an inversion.

Changes in pressure (Fig. 72*h*) were very slight indeed. Over England, Wales and Scotland generally, pressure was falling slightly; over Ireland and South-east England it was rising slowly.

The anticyclone was maintained from 6th May to 16th May, 1950. The system had first appeared off the coast of Norway and moved slowly southward and at the same time it increased in horizontal extent (inset A, Fig. 72). It was a relatively stable synoptic situation though the period of relatively clear skies was itself variable both in time and place.

Cloudy Anticyclone: Summer

15th May, 1952, 0600 hours G.M.T.

Inset A (Fig. 73) shows the past history of this anticyclone "High L" which was located over the British Isles on 15th May, 1952 at 0600 hours. It will be seen that on the 11th May, 1952 the anticyclone, enclosed by the isobar for 1,024 millibars, was located off the west coast of Portugal. Subsequent movement was to the north-east. By the 13th May it covered quite an extensive area over the Bay of Biscay and Western France but after that date it moved to cover the south of the British Isles. The high pressure decreased in intensity to 1,022 millibars and the system had moved 900 miles in 4 days.

Pressure was generally high over the whole of the British Isles (1,021–1,022 millibars). From the centre of highest pressure over Central England (Cranfield, 1,022·2 millibars; Ross-on-Wye

1,022·9 millibars) there was a gradual decrease in all directions and the isobars were widely spaced and had a circular pattern (inset map C, Fig. 73). The general weather situation was that an anticyclone, centred over Northern France and Belgium, extended north-westwards to cover the British Isles.

A temperature/height graph has been constructed for Liverpool at 1500 hours 15th May, 1952 (inset B, Fig. 73). It will be seen that the surface temperature was 65° F., the condensation level was at *c.* 4,000 feet and the freezing level at *c.* 12,000 feet, which are data very similar to those reported at Liverpool when the "clear sky" anticyclone of summer[1] was considered, though the relative humidity of 70% was very much higher than it was on that occasion.

Subsidence[2] in an anticyclone normally has two consequences:

(*a*) An inversion, which is evidenced in the present example between 958 millibars (56° F.) and 934 millibars (61° F.), i.e. 1,800 feet to 2,400 feet approx.

(*b*) Relatively dry air, immediately above the inversion, which is identified in this example by relative humidities of 57% at 900 millibars and 850 millibars, and by 50% at 800, 750 and 700 millibars, and by 30% at 600 millibars.

The pattern of the isotherms (Fig. 73*a*) is generally simple being arcuate about a centre of high temperature in South-east and Central England. Temperatures ranged from 50°–57° F. over the British Isles; Lerwick (44° F.) was exceptional due to frontal influences (inset map C, Fig. 73). The greater part of England and Wales (except Devon and Cornwall) had temperatures of 54°–57° F.; Ireland reported temperatures of 51°–54° F. and Scotland 50°–52° F., except Renfrew (55° F.) and Wick (55° F.). These regional differences, however, were essentially of local significance and data mapped reveal no extensive areas of steep temperature gradient. Between the Orkneys and the Shetland Islands the rather steep gradient was due to frontal influences whilst in Southern England inland stations recorded higher temperatures than coastal stations, for example, London Airport 56° F., Lympe 52° F., producing a minor temperature discontinuity. On the whole temperatures were high for the time of day and time of year

[1] See pp. 204–5.
[2] See pp. 19–21.

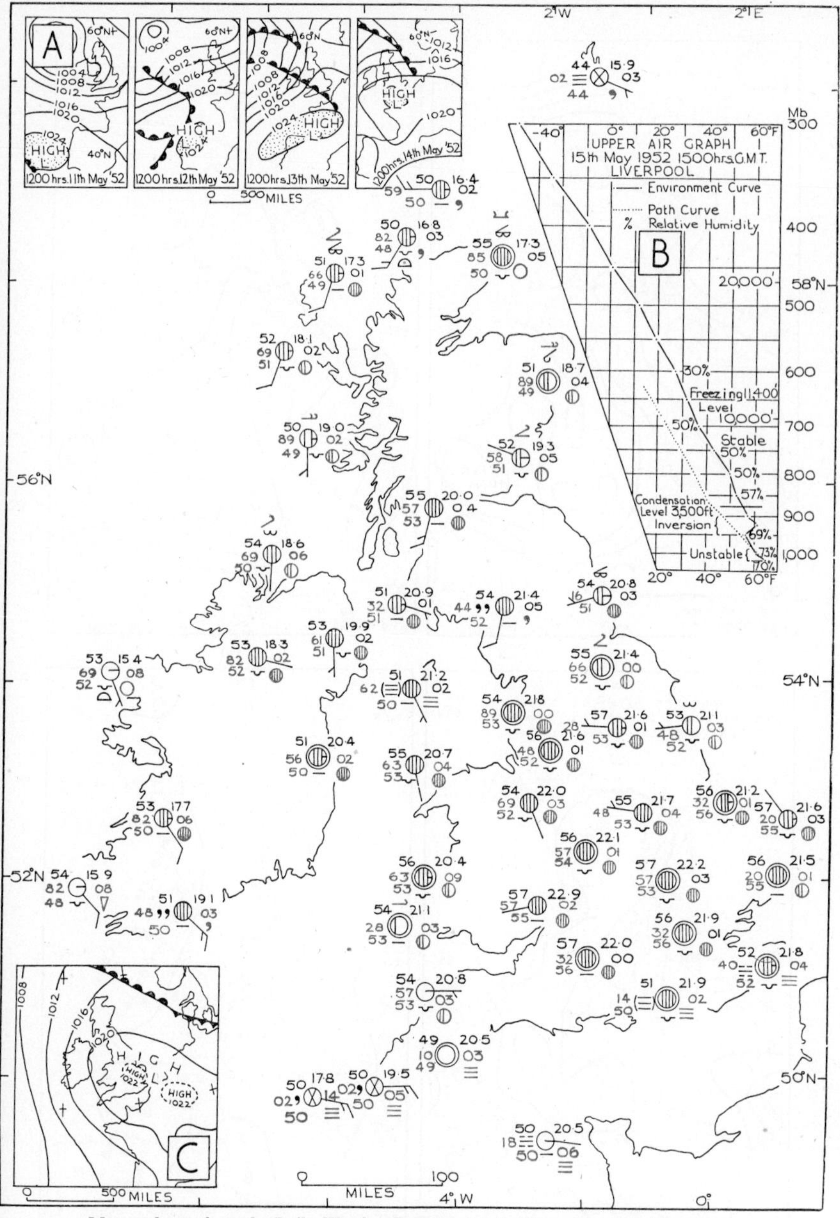

Maps redrawn from the Daily Weather Reports of 11th May 1952, 12th May 1952, 13th May 1952, 14th May 1952 and 15th May 1952 by permission of the Director-General, Meteorological Office, London. Copyright H.M. Stationery Office

FIG. 73. — Selected Data for 15th May 1952 : 0600 hrs. G.M.T.
The Cloudy Anticyclone — Summer
Inset A — Previous Synoptic Situations
Inset B — Upper Air Graph
Inset C — Isobars : 0600 hrs. G.M.T. 15th May 1952

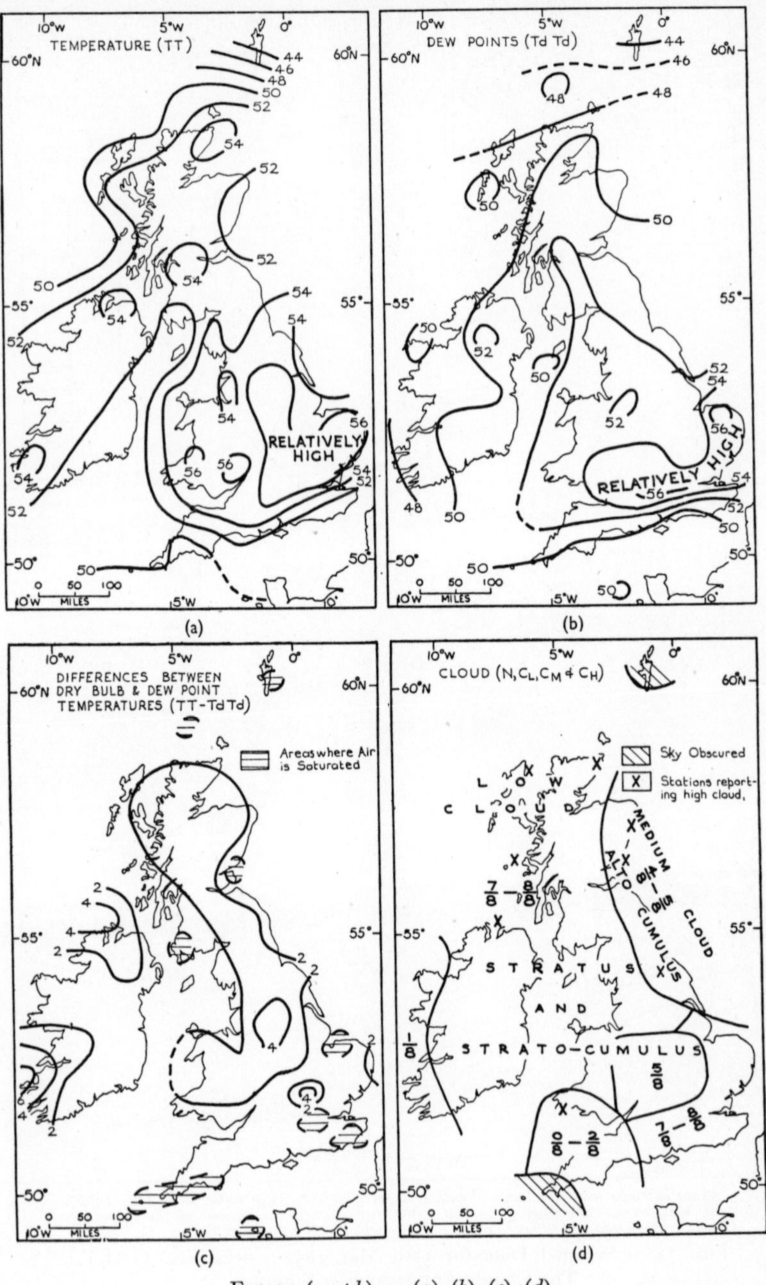

FIG. 73 (*contd.*). — (*a*), (*b*), (*c*), (*d*)

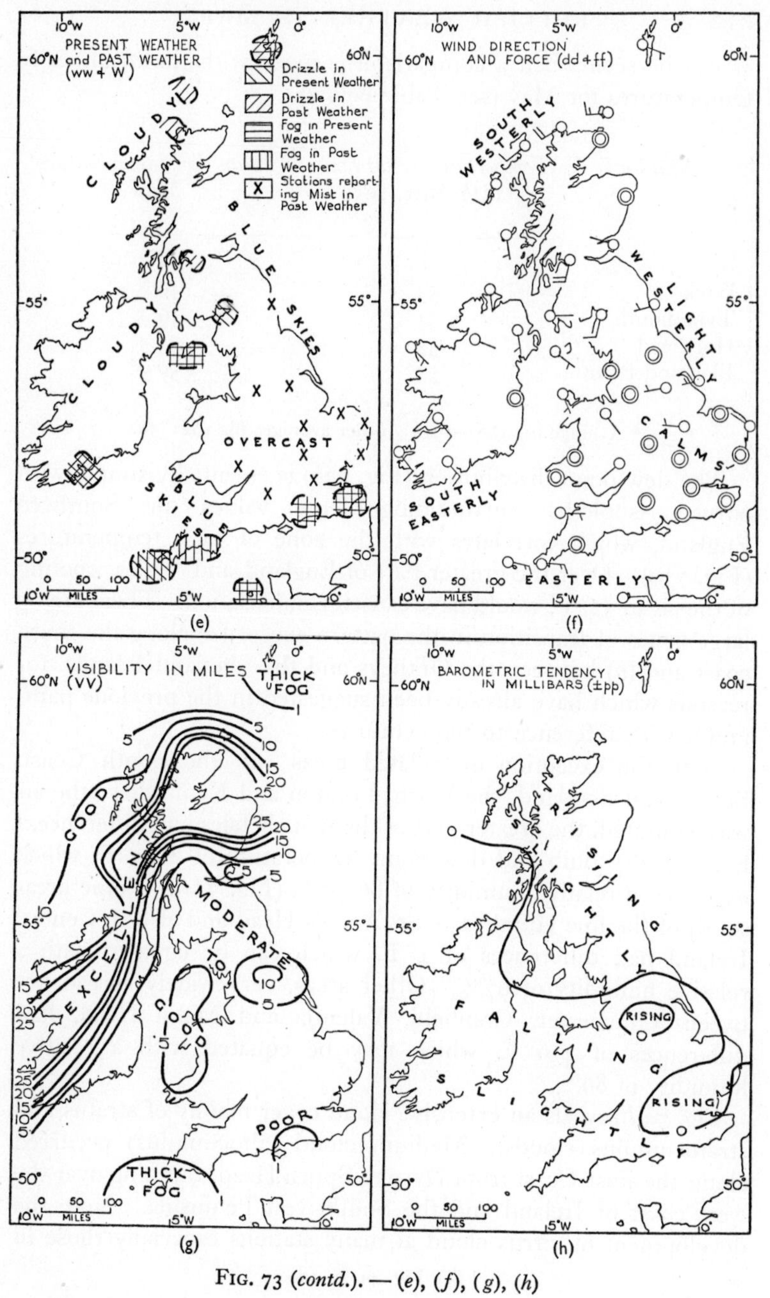

FIG. 73 (*contd.*). — (*e*), (*f*), (*g*), (*h*)

as can be seen when a comparison is made with the mean daily temperatures for May (see Table below).

Station	*Temperature* 0600 *hours* 15*th May*, 1952	*Mean daily temperature May*
	°F.	°F
Wick	55	46·6
Tynemouth	54	49·2
Holyhead	55	51·3
Blacksod Point	53	50·9*

* Average for 1881–1915 ; other averages for 1921–50.

The dew point distribution (Fig. 73*b*) is essentially simple with curved isopleths surrounding high values in Southern England, which correlates with the zone of high temperatures (Fig. 73*a*). Over the greater part of England and Wales, cooling of the air to 52° F. would have caused condensation. There are no large zones of transition in the pattern except (*a*) along the south coast and (*b*) between the Orkneys and the Shetland Islands, for reasons which have already been suggested in the previous paragraph with reference to temperatures.

With the exception of isolated areas e.g. the South Coast, South-west Scotland, the Wash, London and Kent where the air was saturated, the greater part of the British Isles had differences[1] between dry bulb and dew point temperature of 2°–4° F. which expresses a relative humidity of 86–97% (Fig. 73*c*). Some areas south of the line Humber — St. Anne's Head and also in Central Ireland had differences of 1° F. which can be equated with a relative humidity of 97%. Other areas, very widely spread between Manchester, Cranfield, Valentia and Malin Head, had differences of 4–6° F. which may be equated with a relative humidity of 86%.

Fig. 73*d* reveals an extensive cloud cover mainly of stratus and stratocumulus clouds. Medium cloud (altocumulus) occurred along the East Coast from Dyce to Spurn Head, thinning over the west coast of Ireland and the South-west Peninsula. Note the development of cirrus cloud at many stations especially those in

[1] See Fig. 44, p. 100.

North Scotland. The "low" cloud layers are undoubtedly associated with the inversion previously described [1] and in view of their persistence (Fig. 73*e*) they may also help to account for the relatively high temperatures recorded.

Also associated with the inversion is the occurrence of mist at many stations (Fig. 73*e* — as there is no symbol specifically for "mist" in the past weather, those stations reporting "mist" are marked with a cross) expecially those south of a line Tynemouth to the Severn Estuary. In South-east England the high humidities already noted undoubtedly gave rise to the fog which was reported in the "past" and "present weather". In coastal Devon and Cornwall, similar high humidities can be associated with drizzle. Generally, there were overcast skies but the smaller cloud amounts over the East Coast north of the Wash must have given rise to blue skies.

The wind force, when plotted (Fig. 73*f*), shows a typically weak and indeterminate anticyclonic circulation about an area of calms centred over the Midlands, and extending over Kent where the fog persisted. Meanwhile, the easterly winds blowing down the Channel brought drizzle to coastal areas of the South-west Peninsula.

Visibility (Fig. 73*g*) shows an interrupted belt of "excellent" visibility extending over Ireland and Western Scotland. Over much of North and Central England, Wales and Scotland visibility was "moderate" to "good" but the mist and fog areas of Southern England had "poor" visibility.

The barometric tendency (Fig. 73*h*) shows slight rises to the north and east of a line from Benbecula to London. South and west of this line pressure was falling slightly. This would appear to indicate the persistence of the high pressure system.

It will be apparent that the anticyclone considered above was a cloudy one — though the cloud cleared from most localities by 1800 hours due to heating at the ground during the course of the day — and that the cloud and the poorness of the visibility were closely associated with the inversion of temperature consequent upon the subsidence of air within the high pressure area.

[1] See p. 208.

Chapter 6

OTHER SYNOPTIC TYPES

In addition to the two major synoptic types, namely the depression and the anticyclone, several subsidiary types may also be differentiated. These are the *secondary depression*, the *trough of low pressure*, the *wedge* or *ridge of high pressure* and finally, the *col.*[1]

The Secondary Depression

A *secondary* depression, as the name implies, develops usually within the system of a "*primary*" or "parent depression", especially a large, occluded one which is becoming inactive in the general circulation. A secondary depression, or, more simply, a secondary, may develop in a number of ways, five of which may be noted. *Firstly*, (Fig. 74*a*) on a trailing cold front on the edge of an existing primary depression a small area of low pressure may

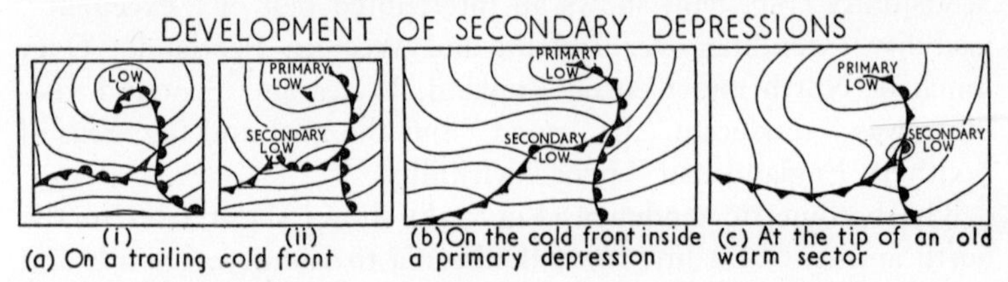

FIG. 74. — The Development of a Secondary Depression
(*a*) i. and (*a*) ii. On a Trailing Cold Front
(*b*) On the Cold Front inside a Primary Depression
(*c*) At the tip of an old Warm Sector
Adapted from Sutcliffe R.C. (1946)

develop around which a small circulation is evolved, warmer air moving tongue-like over the cold air which undercuts from behind. Thus a warm-sector secondary depression is formed which often becomes progressively more vigorous and rotates anticlockwise (in the Northern Hemisphere) round the primary depression.

[1] See Fig. 5, p. 6 and Fig. 27, p. 41

Should the secondary become as vigorous as the primary, the two depressions may spin anticlockwise round each other. The primary is usually declining, however, when the secondary is forming, and ultimately becomes so inactive and small that the secondary ultimately assumes the primary rôle. It is quite usual for a secondary of this type to become very intense. *Secondly*, (Fig. 74*b*) a secondary may originate at a point along the cold front itself and well within the structure of a depression. A kink only in the isobars (Fig. 74), and not closed isobars, will usually indicate it. As a rule, such a secondary is relatively weak and moves along the cold front towards the centre of the original depression where it is eventually assimilated. *Thirdly*, (Fig. 74*c*) a secondary may occasionally develop where an occluded front at the ground divides into remains of the warm front and the cold front. This process involves a lowering of pressure at the point where the fronts meet at the ground, and the re-assertion of the old warm sector as the new warm sector of the secondary depression. This produces a complex situation which, however, is only of rare occurrence in the British Isles. *Fourthly*, surface heating due to excessive insolation may cause a local fall in pressure. A large scale illustration of this is the monsoonal " low " over Asia in summer. On a much smaller scale, a shallow secondary may perhaps form over Central or South-east England, for example on a hot summer's afternoon; such secondaries are termed *thermal lows*. Associated weather is

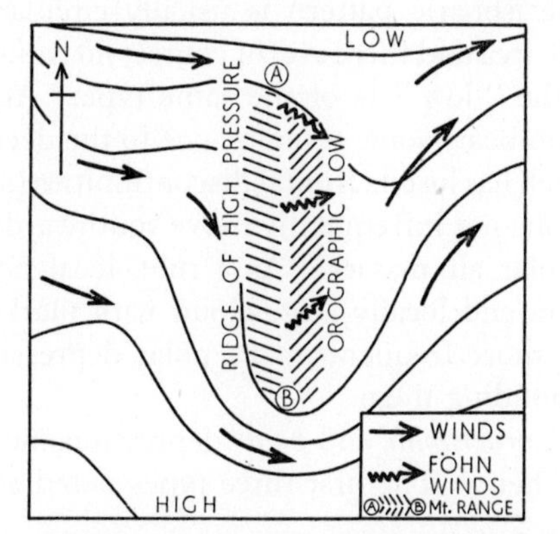

FIG. 75. — The Development of an Orographic Depression
Note : The continuous curving lines are isobars.
Adapted from Sutcliffe R.C. (1946)

usually fine and warm with occasional tendencies to local thunder especially when the pressure gradients are very weak. Only on rare occasions, does a primary thermal depression develop over the British Isles, an area which is so extensively penetrated by seas, channels and estuaries which retard heating up in the summer months. *Fifthly*, an "*orographic*" depression (Fig. 75), again usually of "secondary" rather than "primary" significance, in the British Isles area, may develop on the leeward side of a mountain range when air is moving at right angles across it. Air, rather than ascending over the mountain range, tends to sweep round the ends of it, particularly the right end (facing down-wind), in the Northern Hemisphere, due to the earth's rotation.[1] Any air that completes the ascent of the mountain range descends as *föhn* winds in the sheltered lee of the range. Air on the wind-ward side of the range tends to be at a higher pressure than air on the leeward side resulting in a ridge of high pressure on the wind-ward side and a shallow orographic depression on the leeward side. With the depression itself, weather may be relatively warm and fine due to the effects of the *föhn* winds. Near the mountain range orographic cloud and rain often develop. Eastern Scotland is a typical area where orographic depressions may develop.

It is appropriate to note also in this section the *Polar air depression*, or simply the *Polar depression* (Fig. 76). This type of "low" develops entirely within Polar air where local instability is pronounced. The isobaric pattern is usually circular and covers a relatively small area and there are, of course, no fronts present since all the air in the "low" is of the same type. At this stage the polar depression bears some resemblance to the decayed, occluded depression which has lost its frontal discontinuities (see pp. 174–81). Polar depressions not infrequently move southwards to the British Isles within Polar air masses. As a rule, local heavy but intermittent showers and locally large cloud with marked vertical development are more frequent in the polar depression than in the Polar air surrounding them.

The *thermal*, *orographic* and *polar* depressions need not concern us any further here. The first three types noted above, provided

[1] This is explained in terms of Buys Ballot's law which expounds the deflection of surface winds to the *right* in the *Northern* Hemisphere, and to the *left* in the *Southern* Hemisphere, provided the observer is facing down-wind.

FIG. 76. — The Development of a Polar Depression "P": 16th February 1957 to 20th February 1957

Note: An infilling trough of low pressure extended across the British Isles from an area of low pressure over Denmark, southern

they attain adequate vigour, acquire and develop the succession of characteristics already described in detail in Chapter 4 with reference to depressions in general. Indeed, the example analysed to illustrate the partial occlusion (12th November, 1954) was in fact a secondary, and not a primary, depression. Suffice it, therefore, just to give an example of a secondary depression on a selected Daily Weather Report (Fig. 77), and to add that it is very difficult to generalise about the weather sequences in secondaries, except to say that weather normally deteriorates at their approach, is bad at their passage and improves with their departure. They bring much low cloud, rain and wind and, over land in summer, thunderstorms. This description applies in a general way to the smaller, immature type of secondary. As the cold and warm fronts become more clearly developed, the weather sequences display more resemblances to those described for such fronts (see pp. 106 and 120).

The Trough of Low Pressure

A trough of low pressure in an isobaric pattern corresponds to valley or re-entrant on a relief map (see Fig. 5, p. 6). It is normally an extension from a parent centre of low pressure and often contains a front which may be of the cold or warm or occluded type. The trailing cold front behind a depression is a very common example of a frontal trough, with its V-shaped isobars usually angling sharply at the front, accompanied by marked backing and veering of winds before and after the front respectively. The complete details of such a situation have been described earlier under the section on fronts (Chapter 4); indeed the warm

---

Norway and the adjacent portion of the North Sea on the 16th–17th February (see (1), (2), (3) above). Early on the 18th February (4), however, a small shallow centre of low pressure, low " P ", had been clearly identified west of Ireland. This low developed within Polar Maritime air moving southwards from Iceland and the sea areas to the north of Iceland. By 0600 hrs. on the 19th February (5) Polar Depression " P " was off Southwest Ireland, though still small and shallow. By midnight on the 19th–20th February (6) Low " P " was centred over Brittany and covered a larger area. An Occluded front system associated with Low " T " (5) which had moved into the Bay of Biscay area by 0000 hrs. on the 20th February, eventually became connected with low " P " by 0600 hrs. on the 20th February. Prior to this event Low " P " had no frontal system and was a Polar Depression developed entirely within Polar air.

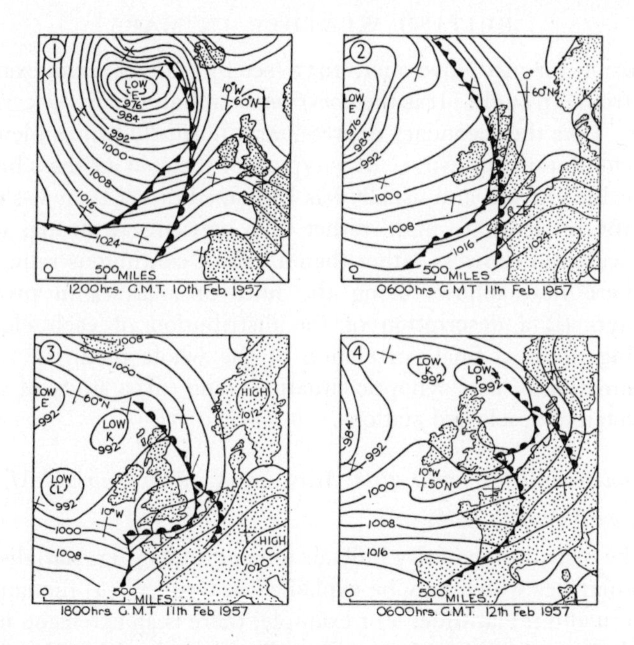

Maps redrawn from the Daily Weather Reports for 10th February 1957, 11th February 1957 and 12th February 1957 by permission of the Director-General, Meteorological Office, London. Copyright H.M. Stationery Office.

FIG. 77. — Synoptic Situations showing the Development of a Secondary Depression: 10th–12th February 1957

Note: At 1200 hours 10th February 1957 (see (1) above) an occluding depression, Low *E*, was centred some 500 miles to the southwest of Ireland, and its frontal system was moving eastwards towards the British Isles. By 0600 hours on the 11th February (see (2) above) Low *E* had moved very slightly but it was beginning to fill in and its barometric gradient was becoming less steep. The occluded frontal system lay north-south across the British Isles and only a narrow and diminishing warm sector remained over South-west Wales and South-west England. However, along the trailing cold front some 350 miles off Cornwall, a secondary depression was beginning to form. By 1800 hours on the 11th February (see (3) above), this secondary was quite well developed and was centred only about 100 miles off the coast of Cornwall. Its frontal and isobaric patterns indicate that it was much more active at that time than the primary depression, Low *E*, whose relatively flat central pressure field had acquired two subsidiary shallow centres in Low *L* and Low *K*. By 1600 hours on the 12th February (see 4 above), the secondary had moved northeastwards with the primary, moving slightly anticlockwise round it in the process.

occlusion for 7th November, 1955 (see pp. 146–54) is an example of a frontal trough. It is the *non-frontal* trough which concerns us here. Like the secondary depression, it normally brings plenty of low cloud, rain and wind. It is typical of the cold air mass behind an occluded front and usually has U-shaped rather than V-shaped isobars, moderate to light, rather than particularly strong, winds and scattered showers rather than a belt of continuous rain.

There now follows along the lines of analyses in previous chapters (i) a description of the distribution of each element leading up to a final correlation of the whole picture; (ii) an examination of past synoptic situations, and (iii) a study of upper air details for selected stations.

Non-frontal Trough : 16th May, 1955, 0600 hours G.M.T.

Surface Synoptic Data

The distribution of dry bulb air temperatures (Fig. 78*a*) displays irregularities which may be explained in terms of (*a*) the land-sea pattern and (*b*) latitude. For example, there is an extension northwards (40°–42° F.) over Cardigan Bay and the Irish Sea of the warmer conditions (44°–46° F.) prevalent over the south of England. In contrast, Southern Ireland (36° F.) and Northern England (36°–38° F.) have rather cooler conditions. The most extensive area of low temperatures (36° F.) lies north-south through the eastern half of Scotland but in the far north (e.g. Sule Skerry 41° F.) maritime factors are in evidence again. Discontinuities, then, tend to follow the coasts and appear to have local, rather than frontal, significance. In general terms, temperatures over the British Isles at 6 a.m. on 16th May, 1955 were substantially below the average mean minimum for May (36°–46° F. as compared with 42°–48° F.).[1] This suggests that relatively cold air, probably Polar, was in occupation at this time over the British Isles.

The dew point distribution is less complex (Fig. 78*b*). Relatively high values (42° F.) over the south of England decrease regularly northwards to a line Valentia-Aberporth-Spurn Head at 34° F. North of this line dew points are generally uniform at about 34°–35° decreasing only a degree or two in extreme North-east England and the Western Isles. This pattern appears to suggest

[1] Op. cit., p. 112, footnote 2.

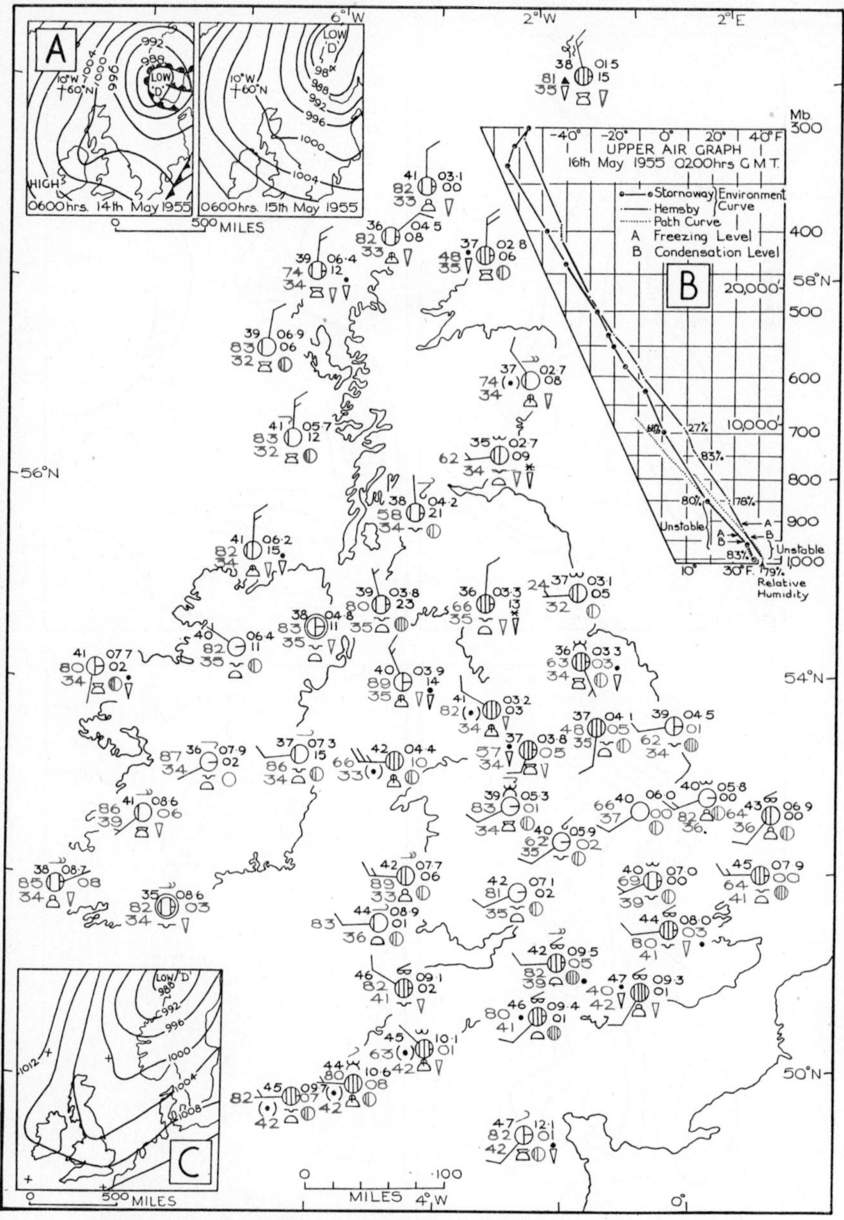

Maps redrawn from the Daily Weather Reports for the 14th May 1955, 15th May 1955 and 16th May 1955 by permission of the Director-General, Meteorological Office, London. Copyright H.M. Stationery Office.

FIG. 78. — Selected Data for 16th May 1955 : 0600 hrs. G.M.T.
The Non-Frontal Trough
Inset A — Previous synoptic situations
Inset B — Upper Air Graphs
Inset C — Isobars : 0600 hrs. G.M.T. 16th May 1955

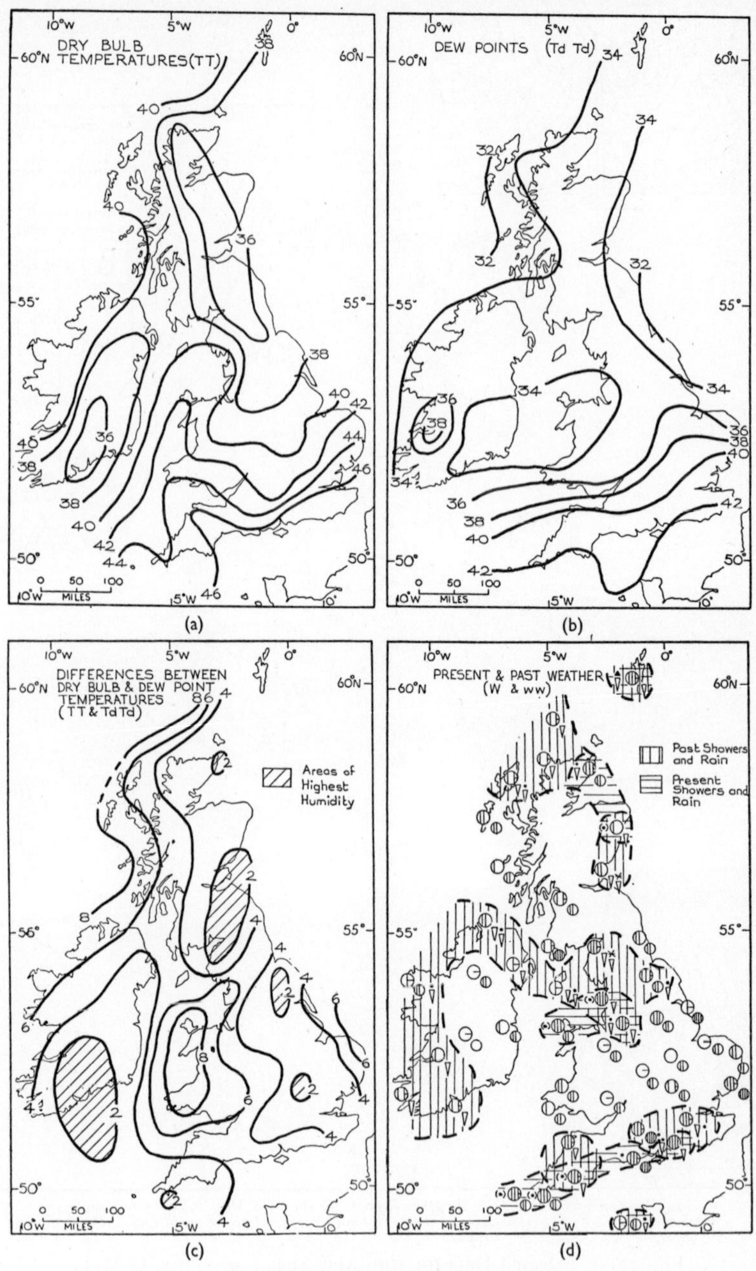

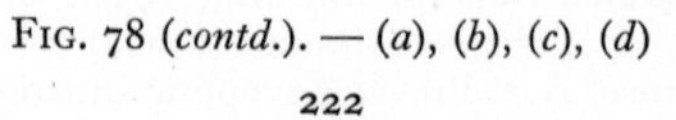
FIG. 78 (*contd.*). — (*a*), (*b*), (*c*), (*d*)

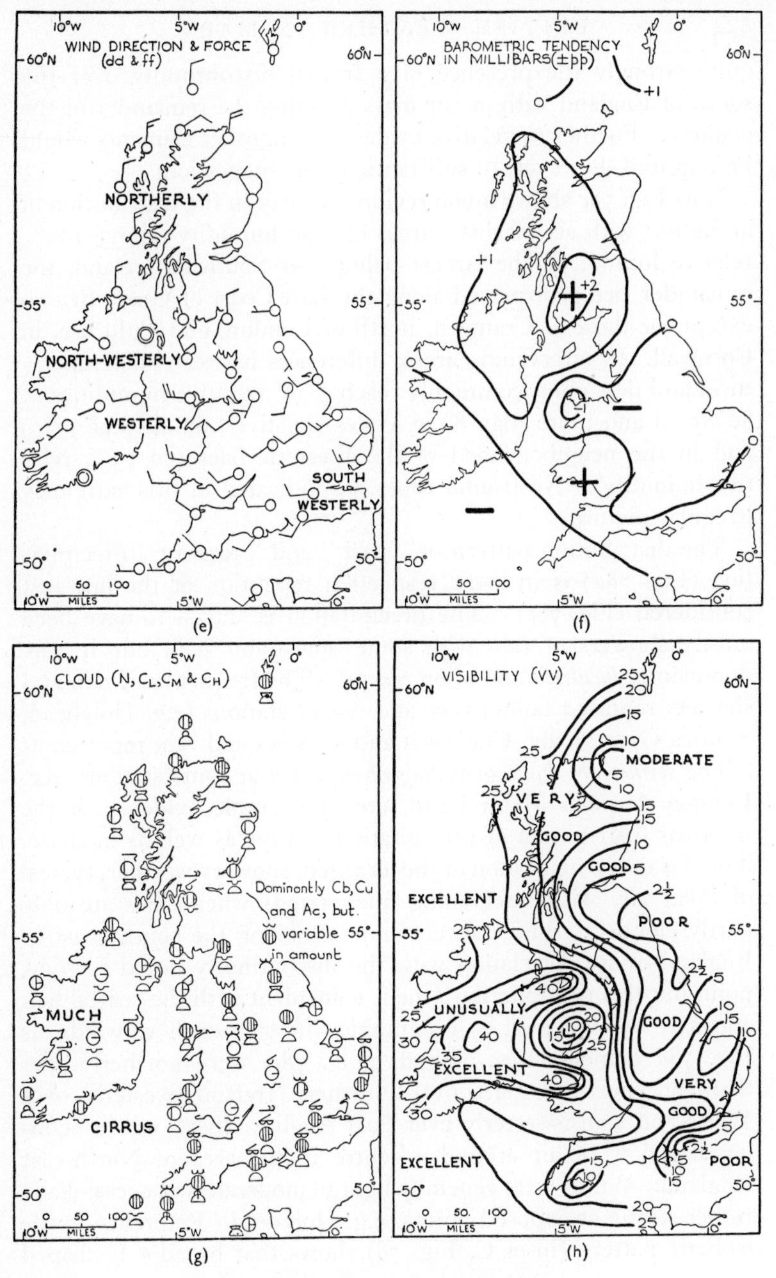

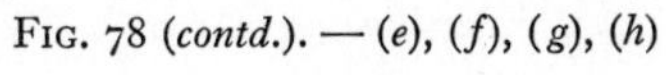
FIG. 78 (*contd.*). — (*e*), (*f*), (*g*), (*h*)

quite strongly the presence of a frontal discontinuity over the south of England with an air mass covering the remainder of the country. Further correlative evidence from other elements would be required, however, to substantiate this suggestion.

Now Fig. 78*c* shows much regional variety in the distribution of humidity[1] with six localised areas of high humidity (all 93–100% relative humidity), the largest being over Southern Ireland, the remainder being dispersed along the East Coast of Great Britain except for those at Cranwell, north of London, and Culdrose, in Cornwall. In intervening areas, differences between air temperatures and dew point commonly reach 4°–6° (relative humidities of 80–85%) and more than 8° in Wales (relative humidity of 73%) and in the neighbourhood of the Western Isles (70–73% relative humidity). No frontal zones are indicated in this extremely irregular picture.

The distribution pattern of " past " and " present " precipitation (Fig. 78*d*) is in some respects a repetition of the one just considered (Fig. 78*c*). The precipitation is shown to have been mostly showers of rain with some snow and hail, but it was dominantly *localised* and often *coastal*. The frequency of rain and showers reported falling *near* and not *at* stations (e.g. Holyhead, Squires Gate, Scilly, Culdrose) and showers and rain reported as falling *within the hour preceding observation* at some stations (e.g. London Airport, Malin Head, etc.) are ample evidence of the irregular distribution of precipitation in time as well as in space. There is every suggestion of the localised, showery weather, typical of Polar air, with intervening fine periods when skies are only partly clouded. The showers and rain along the south coast of England invite correlation with the discontinuity noted for dew point but this precipitation zone is coincident with the coastal belt and may be explained by orographic lifting of onshore winds, as Fig. 78*d* demonstrates. Winds (Fig. 78*e*) were northerly over Scotland, north-westerly over Northern Ireland, westerly over Wales and south-westerly over East Anglia; there was a semicircular flow of air around a centre in the area of North-east England. Winds were generally light to moderate and occasionally rather strong at exposed points, e.g. Holyhead. Reference to the isobaric pattern (inset C, Fig. 78) shows that broadly U-shaped

[1] See Fig. 44, p. 100.

isobars formed a shallow trough of low pressure (1,002–1,006 millibars) extending southwards over Great Britain from a centre of low pressure off the Norwegian coast. Winds tended to blow slightly across the isobars inwards and anticlockwise to the axis of the trough. The smoothness of the curves of the isobars across the axis of the trough supports the idea that no fronts were present.

The barometer (Fig. 78*f*) was falling slightly over Central and Eastern England and North Wales and also South-west Ireland and Cornwall. Over the remainder of Ireland, Scotland, Northern England, South Wales and the South coast of England, the barometer was rising slightly. No clear discontinuities are shown here. Perhaps the main conclusion to be derived is that the trough appears to have been moving very slowly eastwards and was ultimately to be replaced by another low pressure area coming in from the southwest. The cloud distribution (Fig. 78*g*) shows an abundance of cirrus cloud, some of it "mares' tails", in Southern Ireland, South Wales and South-west England, suggesting perhaps the approach of the warm front of this low pressure area. Otherwise large cumulus and cumulonimbus clouds dominated in most districts of the British Isles, accompanied locally by altocumulus. Cloud amounts varied locally but completely overcast skies were infrequent. This pattern is strongly suggestive of Polar-Maritime air (P3 or P1) with variable convective cloud often associated with local and short-lived instability showers, especially at coastal stations with onshore winds. (Fig. 78*d*).

Visibility (Fig. 78*h*) was uncommonly " excellent " over Ireland, " good " to " very good " over Great Britain and only locally " moderate " to " poor " in a few places. This again suggests Polar-Maritime air.

Past-Synoptic Situations

Fig. 78 (inset A) shows this trough to have persisted in present position since at least 12th to the 14th May. Polar-Maritime air was flowing round an old occluded " low " centred off the Norwegian coast. Another " low " lies across the South Western Approaches.

Upper Air Data

Upper air details (inset B, Fig. 78) for Hemsby and Stornoway (2.0 a.m. 16th May, 1955) show the absence of inversions up to about 23,000 feet. The isothermal layer[1] about 24,000 feet (400 millibars) and the inversion at 29,000 feet to 32,000 feet (330 millibars to 300 millibars) may possibly be associated with the approaching warm front some 700 miles away to the south-west. Otherwise, Polar air, unstable at some levels and only just stable at other levels, is indicated, in which local heating (e.g. due to increasing insolation during the day) or orographic uplift would cause vertical cloud and short, heavy showers.

In conclusion then, Polar air was in occupation over the British Isles at 0600 hours on 16th May, 1955 and the isobaric pattern confirms the existence of a trough of low pressure, with no frontal discontinuities present. Associated weather was showery, cool (for time of day and year) with variable cloud amounts and exceptionally good visibility except in showers.

The Wedge or Ridge of High Pressure

As the name implies, a *wedge* or *ridge* (sometimes a " tongue ") of high pressure is an extension outwards from a parent anticyclone. It corresponds to a " spur " on a relief map. The isobars are usually U-shaped, but sometimes tend to be V-shaped. In winter the spread of " continental weather " (e.g. in February 1956) over the British Isles is due to the extension of the European " high " westwards usually in the form of a ridge. A southward migration of Polar air behind depressions may result in the formation of a southward-thrusting ridge of high pressure over Britain.[2] Or again, the Azores " high " may be extended northwards, more frequently in summer, although the example analysed below shows that this development is possible in winter also. It is customary for ridges of high pressure to punctuate a series of depressions coming from the Atlantic. The weather associated with ridges is normally akin to that of the parent anticyclone but usually of much shorter duration, viz. calms or light to moderate winds of variable direction but flowing slightly outwards from, and clockwise (in the Northern Hemisphere) round, the axis of the ridge, i.e. the line of highest pressure along the ridge. The weather is *either* fine, clear and sunny with blue or variable skies *or* fine but cloudy, the former being more frequent than the latter as a rule. The follow-

[1] See p. 132.
[2] See Fig. 68, p. 183, footnote 1.

ing analysis of data relating to a ridge of high pressure which was developed over the British Isles at 6.0 a.m. on the 19th January, 1952, includes consideration of (i) horizontal distributions of surface weather conditions (ii) past synoptic situations (iii) conditions in the upper air at selected stations.

The Wedge or Ridge of High Pressure : 19th January, 1952, 0600 hours G.M.T.

Surface Synoptic Data

The distribution of surface air temperatures (Fig. 79*a*) is generally irregular with centres of low values over land areas, e.g. Central Ireland and Central England (32° F.) and progressively higher values towards coastal areas, e.g. 42° F. at Scilly, 36° F. at Valentia, 40° F. at Blacksod Point, 40° F. at Sule Skerry and 35° F. at Gorleston. Note, however, that the sea areas of the Orkney and Shetland Islands are exceptional suggesting the effects of cold Polar air in those areas. Such discontinuities as exist are small-scale and usually follow the coasts, e.g. around Ireland, indicating the effects of greater cooling at night over land than over the sea.

The dew point distribution (Fig. 79*b*) shows a smaller range of values but in many areas a pattern similar to the temperature distribution with the higher values located at coastal stations and lower ones at stations inland. Values attain 38° F. in North-west Ireland causing a marked gradation to values of 28° F. near Dublin.

The distribution of humidities[1] (Fig. 79*c*) shows only one area with relative humidities higher than 95% and up to 100%, i.e. in Western Ireland. From this maximum, relative humidities decrease generally to about 92–93% in Scotland, 70–85% over much of England and Wales, and a minimum of 57% at Scilly. Air therefore is generally relatively dry (except in Western Ireland) anticipating the later evidence of relatively little cloud and hardly any precipitation (Figs. 79*d* and *g*) in many parts of the British Isles. In Fig. 79*d* a well defined belt of consistently cloudless skies in both " past " and " present weather " extends from Central Scotland to the south coast of England. It is flanked by areas with variable cloud and a few showers, some of snow, at

[1] See Fig. 44, p. 100.

coastal stations, e.g. Gorleston, Spurn Head, Tynemouth, Aberporth and Dyce. Only in North-west Ireland were consistently overcast conditions reported, e.g. Blacksod Point and Malin Head. This was the area of highest humidities (95–100% relative humidities) noted on Fig. 79*c*. There is no evidence at all of precipitation belts such as could be associated with presence of fronts.

Fig. 79*e* shows how " light " to " moderate " winds blow slightly outwards and clockwise from a centre of calms over Ireland and the Western Isles (cf. Castle Archdale, Benbecula and Midleton). Over Great Britain a generally northerly or north westerly air stream has been established, varying in strength from " light " to " moderate ". This pattern of relatively weak circulation may be associated with high pressure conditions.

The barometric tendency map (Fig. 79*f*) shows a slight general rise throughout the British Isles of 1–2 millibars, except over Western Ireland where a slight fall is in evidence. There is certainly no suggestion of the presence of fronts.

Fig. 79*g*, showing the cloud details merely confirms Fig. 79*d*, (" past " and " present weather "). A cloudless zone lying north-south over Great Britain is flanked by variable amounts of strato-cumulus and cumulus of low and medium altitude which must be designated " fair weather cumulus ". This is the type of cloud which forms in Polar air and increases in amount about the middle of the day, as insolation reaches a maximum, causing temporary local instability.[1] Towards evening, surface cooling induces stability in the lower layers of the atmosphere and cloud amounts decrease again.

Visibilities (Fig. 79*h*) are generally " moderate " to " very good " and locally " excellent ", all suggesting Polar air. Finally, the isobars reveal a ridge of high pressure (up to 1,030 millibars) extending northwards across Ireland towards Stornoway. As inset C on Fig. 79 shows, the ridge is attached to an anticyclone centred off Spain and connects with another anticyclone centred over Greenland. The relatively low pressure over Europe was cut off from a complex area of low pressure centred west and south-west of Iceland, which judging by the isallobars (Fig. 79*f*) was about to replace the ridge lying across the British Isles.

[1] See p. 55.

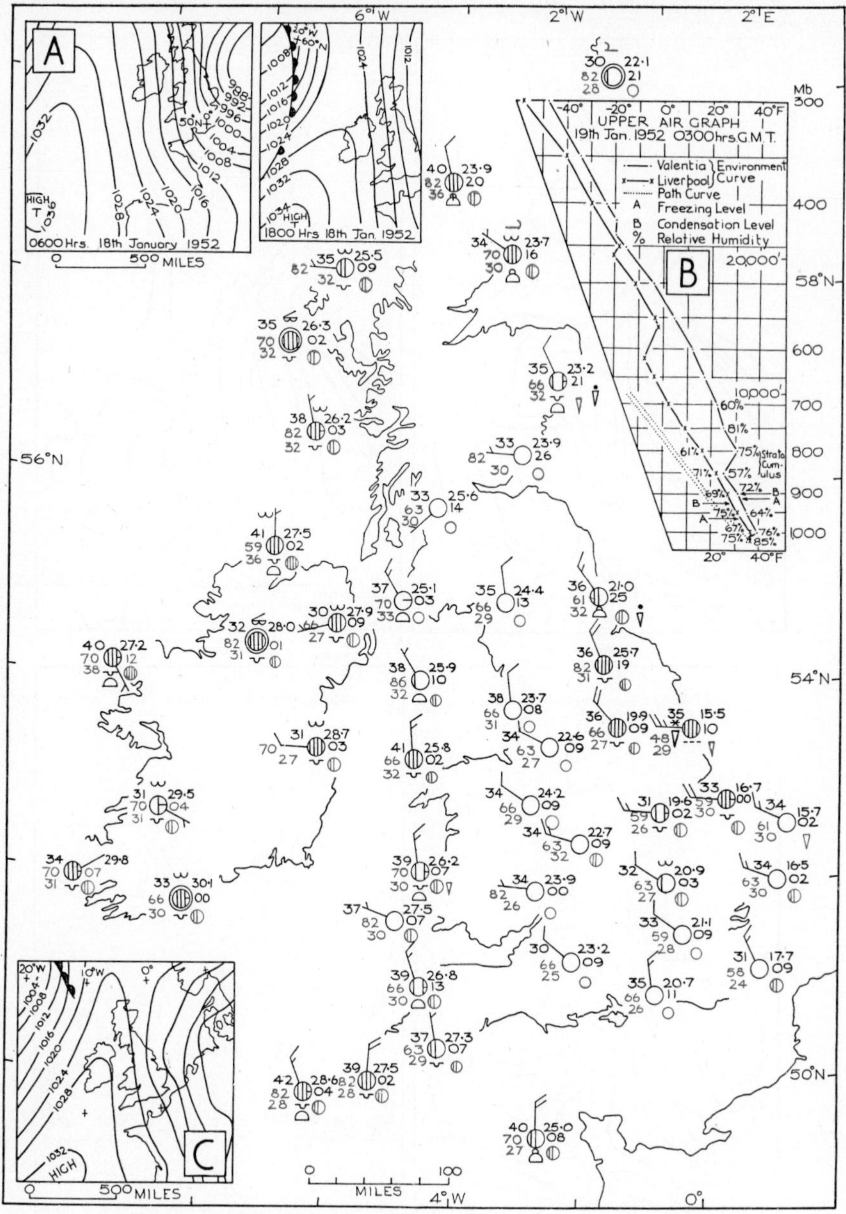

Maps redrawn from the Daily Weather Reports of the 18th January 1952 and the 19th January 1952 by permission of the Director-General, Meteorological Office, London. Copyright H.M. Stationery Office.

FIG. 79. — Selected Data for 19th January 1952 : 0600 hrs. G.M.T.
The Ridge or Wedge of High Pressure
Inset A — Previous Synoptic Situations
Inset B — Upper Air Graphs
Inset C — Isobars : 0600 hrs. G.M.T. 19th January 1952

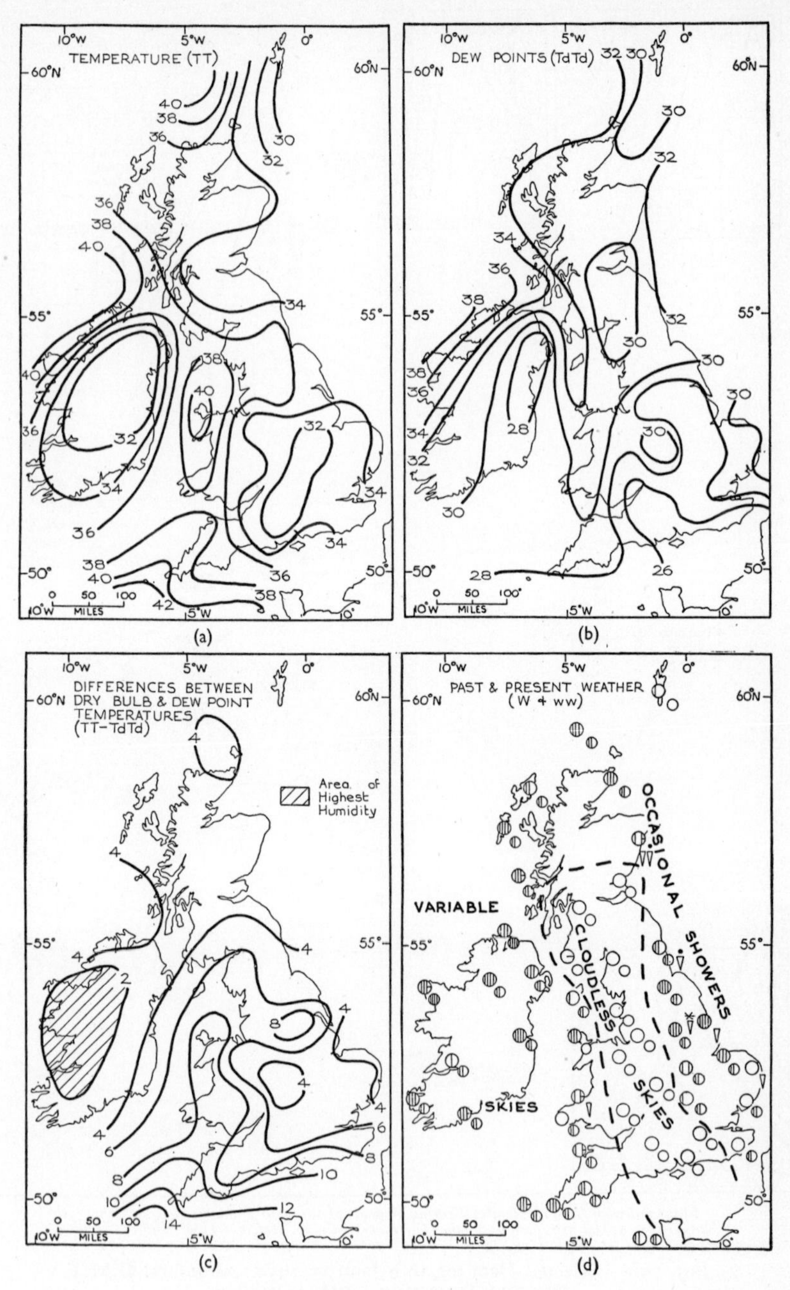

FIG. 79 (*contd.*). — (*a*), (*b*), (*c*), (*d*)

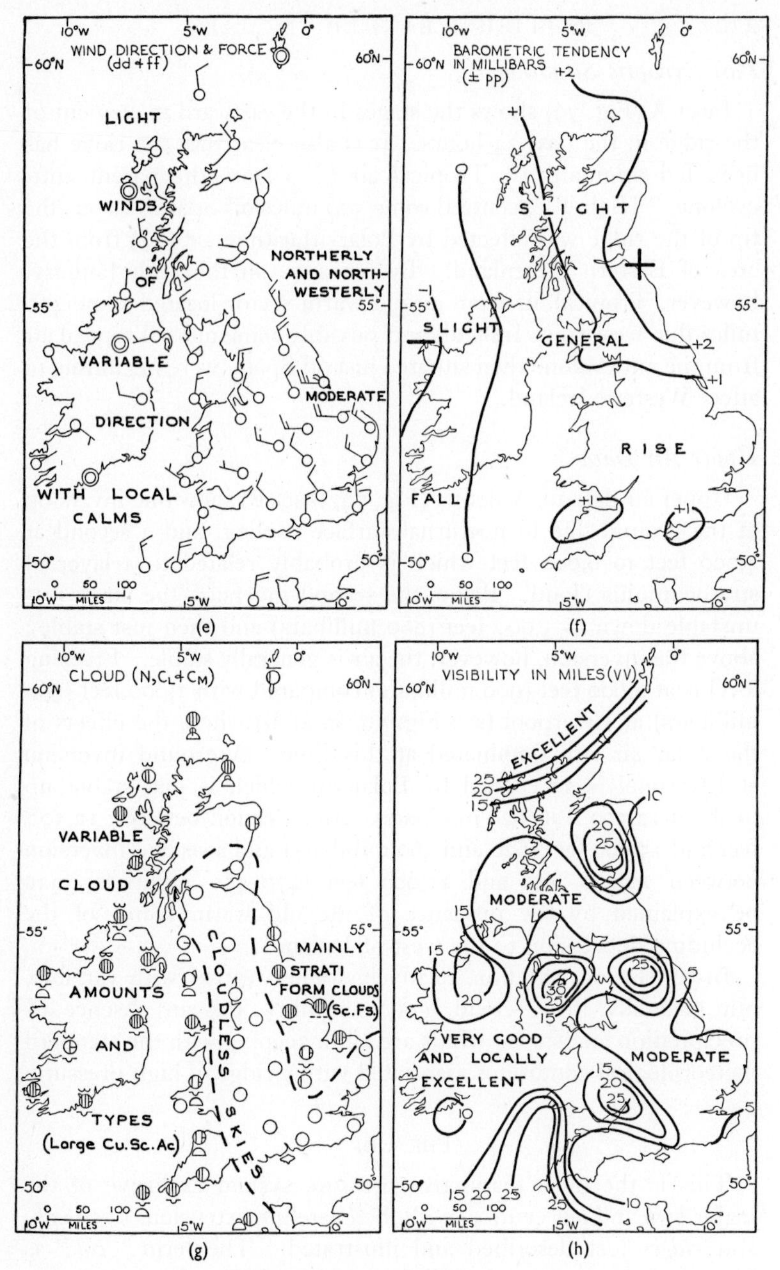

FIG. 79 (*contd.*). — (*e*), (*f*), (*g*), (*h*)

Past Synoptic Situations

Inset A (Fig. 79) shows the stages in the eastward movement of the ridge in the past 24 hours. It is also clear that the ridge has been fed originally by Tropical air (T2) from the parent anticyclone, " High T ", centred some 500 miles off Spain. Later, the tip of the ridge was affected by Polar-Maritime air (P2) from the area of Eastern Greenland. By 6.0 a.m. on the 19th January, however, Tropical air from an old warm sector located some 400 miles due west from Ireland, and possibly some more Tropical air from the anticyclone then situated just off Spain, were beginning to affect Western Ireland.

Upper Air Data

Upper air data for Valentia (Fig. 79, inset B) show one inversion at the ground due to nocturnal surface cooling, and a second at 4,000 feet to 6,000 feet which is probably related to a layer of stratocumulus cloud. Below the second inversion the air is just unstable down to 3,000 feet (880 millibars) and then just stable; above the inversion, however, the air is generally stable. Freezing level is at 2,600 feet (900 millibars) compared with 1,000 feet (960 millibars) at Liverpool (see Fig. 79, inset B) where the effects of the Polar air still dominated at this time. A ground inversion at Liverpool is succeeded by Polar air which is just stable up to about 12,500 feet (620 millibars). An inversion between 12,500 feet and 15,200 feet (620 and 560 millibars) and a second inversion between 20,000 feet and 21,000 feet (470–450 millibars) may be explained by the influence of the old warm sector of the occluding depression to the west of Iceland.

In conclusion, the fine, relatively stable weather with variable, but generally little, cloud, good visibility and an absence of precipitation and strong winds are all in keeping with the standard meteorological conditions associated with a ridge of high pressure.

The Col

This is the most distinctive pressure system exclusive of the major *high* and *low* centres, with their satellite extensions of *troughs* and *ridges* just described and illustrated. The term " *col* " is borrowed direct from the relief map and refers to the neutral area which may develop between two centres of high pressure and two centres of low pressure. Specific isobars defining the col do not cross it but double back forming a U or V shape, sometimes narrow and sometimes open, round the depressions and anticyclones fringing the col. The fundamental law governing the pattern and value of isopleths of any kind at a col has been previously explained (see pp. 6 and 41 and Fig. 27). The accompanying diagram (Fig. 80) applies this more directly to isobars.

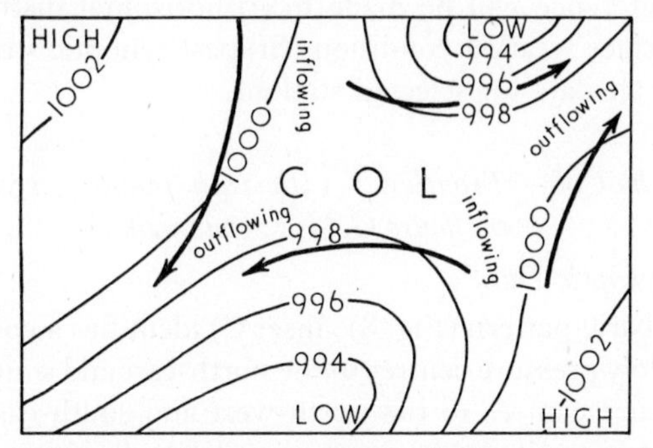

FIG. 80. — Diagram of a Col. Arrows indicate the major wind directions about the col

Note that cols are usually elongated rather than square, with winds flowing inwards at two corners and outwards at the other two corners. Winds flow towards the col in certain places and away from it at others but the centre of the col is often indicated by calms. Inevitably then, the col is an area of intermixture of different weather systems and different air masses. It is therefore impossible to generalise about weather experienced in cols except to note that the isobaric pattern is standard, with relatively wide spacing of the isobars indicating a relatively even or flat pressure field with its associated calms and light winds of indeterminate direction. Falling atmospheric pressure at a col induces the development of a front with accompanying cloudy, rainy weather ; ultimately such a col may develop into a trough. More frequently, pressure is rising in a col, or at least steady, and fronts are absent ; eventually, pressure may rise so that the col may resemble a long, narrow ridge of high pressure with associated fine weather. In summer, cols may have altocumulus cloud which tends to rise in turrets to form " *altocumulus castellatus* ". This type of cloud is an indication of instability in the upper atmosphere which may ultimately find expression in thunderstorms. Because such storms develop independently of day time heating they can occur at night. In autumn and winter, cols are often dominated by low cloud and fog, provided winds are sufficiently light and the air is adequately moist. In summary, almost any kind of weather may develop in a col except strong winds. The example to be analysed is a *frontless col* of the *winter* variety.

Usual reference will be made to (i) horizontal distributions of ground surface weather conditions (ii) past synoptic situations and (iii) upper air data for selected stations.

The Col — Frontless : 13th–14th January, 1956, 0000 *hours G.M.T.* (*midnight*).

Surface Synoptic Data

The isobaric pattern (Fig. 81, inset C) identifies a col over Scotland with low pressure centres to the north-east and south-west and high pressure centres to the north-west and south-east. Isobars are characteristically widely spaced and Fig. 81, inset A together with the isallobars (Fig. 81*f*) demonstrate the persistence of the col over the past 24 hours or more with the barometer tending to rise a little in the areas of low pressure to the north-east and south-west of the British Isles.

Temperatures (Fig. 81*a*) were conspicuously low throughout the col, remaining generally constant at about freezing point in a NW.–SE. zone extending from the Outer Hebrides to the Wash. A general rise in temperature south-westwards to 46°–48° F. over Southern Ireland and Cornwall, was combined with orthodox development of minima overland (e.g. 36° F. in Central Ireland) and maxima over the sea (e.g. 40°–42° F. over the Irish Sea). The uniformity of temperature over Scotland in the col stands out in an isothermal distribution dominated by local variations.

The pattern of dew points (Fig. 81*b*) reflects that of temperature just considered, a NE.–SW. gradation again being in evidence and within it a tendency for dew points to increase coastwards from minima at inland stations. In Fig. 81*c* a long, rather narrow belt of high relative humidities [1] (95–100%) extends from East Anglia to

[1] See Fig. 44, p. 100.

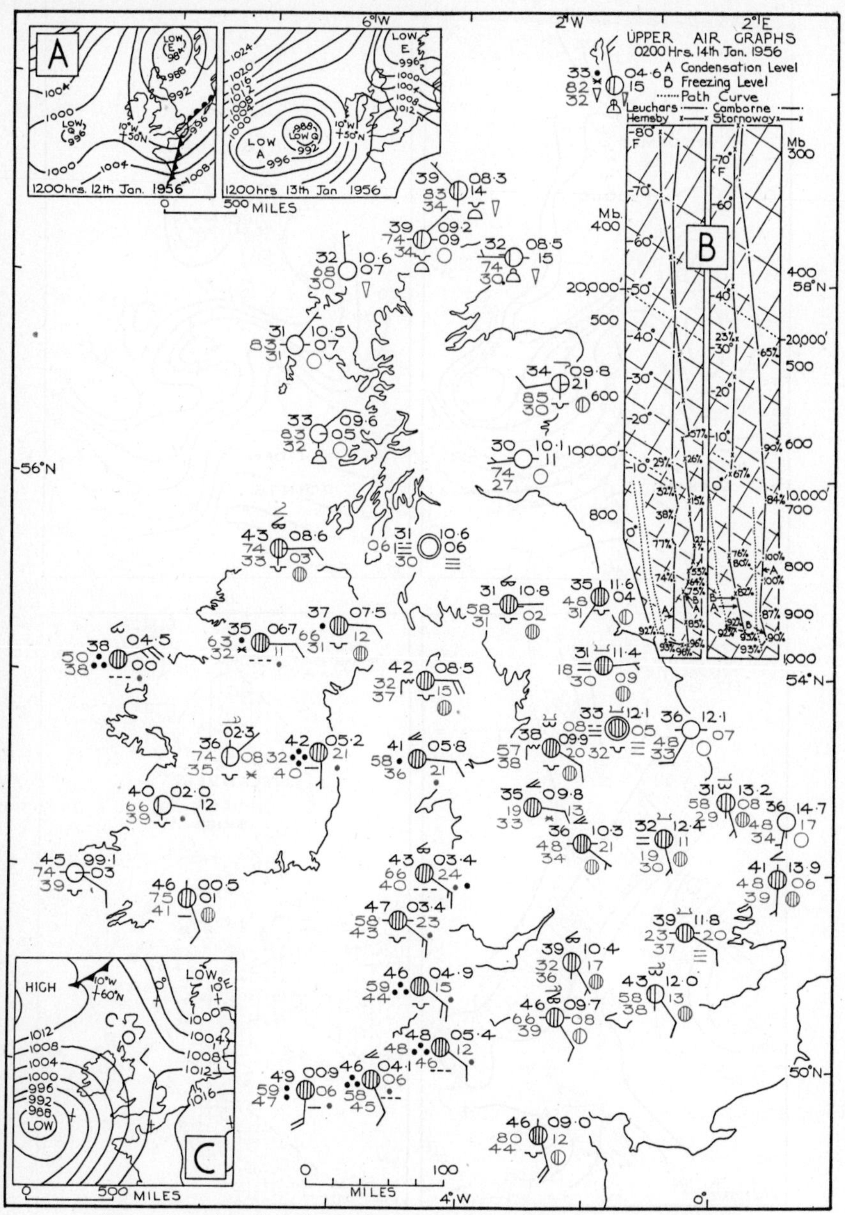

Maps redrawn from the Daily Weather Reports of the 12th January 1956, 13th January 1956 and 14th January 1956 by permission of the Director-General, Meteorological Office, London. Copyright H.M. Stationery Office.

FIG. 81. — Selected Data for 13–14th January 1956: 0000 hrs. G.M.T. (midnight)

The Col — Frontless

Inset A — Previous Synoptic Situations

Inset B — Upper Air Graphs

Note: The orientation of the upper air graphs is due to the

[over

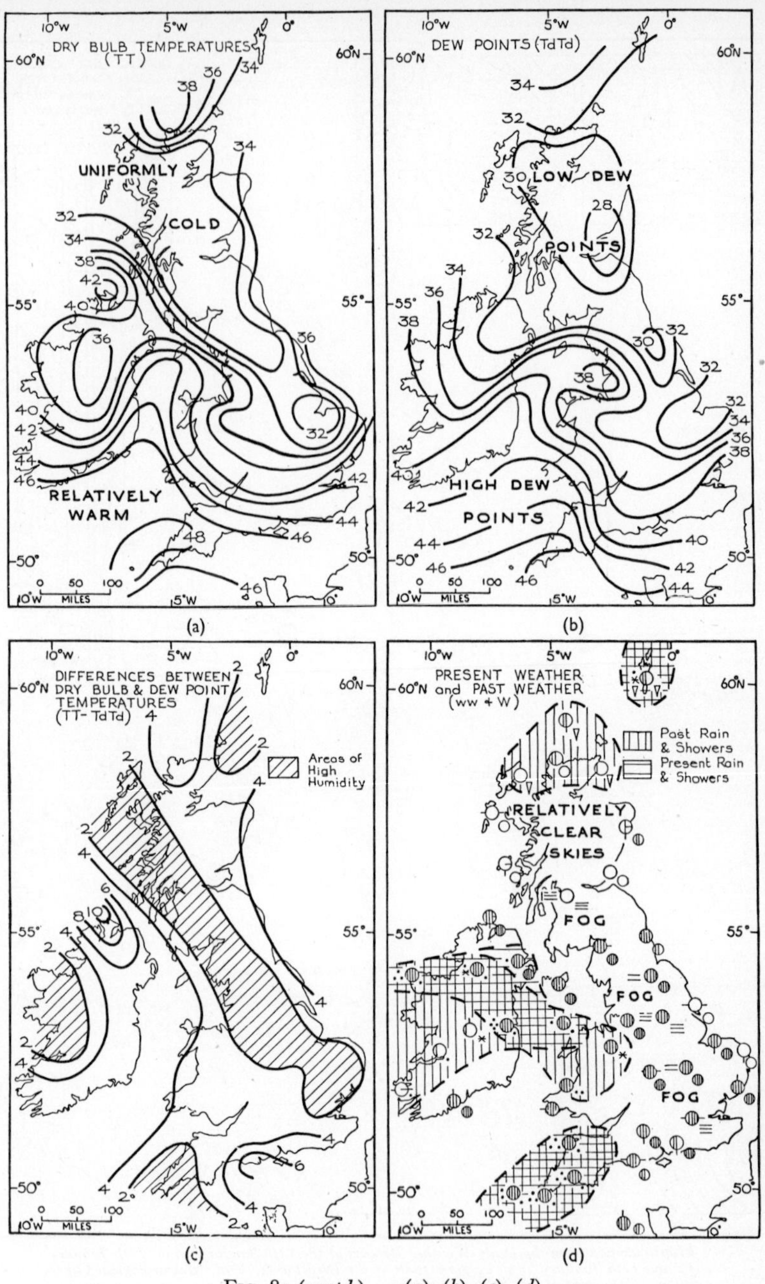

FIG. 81 (*contd.*). — (*a*), (*b*), (*c*), (*d*)

Note contd:

limitations of space and for the sake of clarity. The graphs for stations Leuchars and Hemsby, and for Camborne and Stornoway, respectively, have been drawn separately, and the temperature axis of the graph is inclined instead of being horizontal as in other similar types of diagram.

Inset C — Isobars : 00 00 h rs. G.M.T. 13–14th January 1956

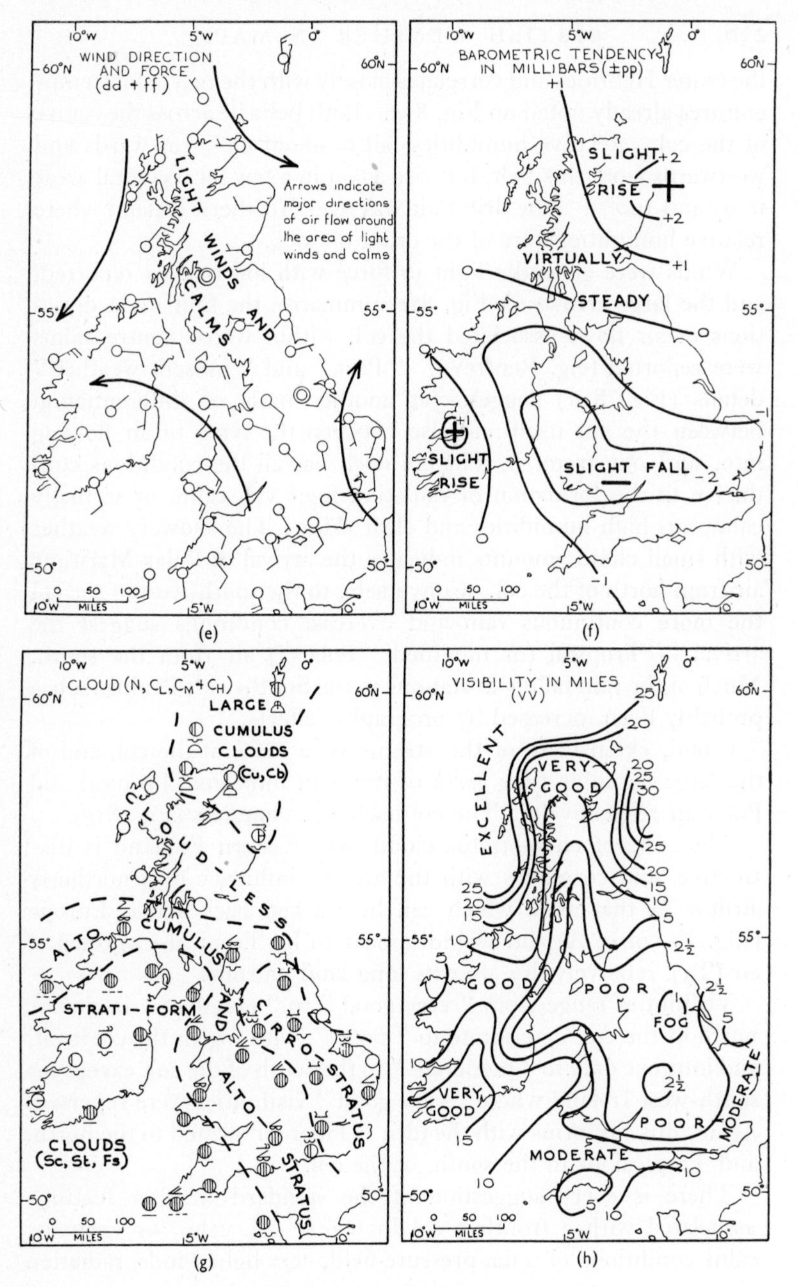

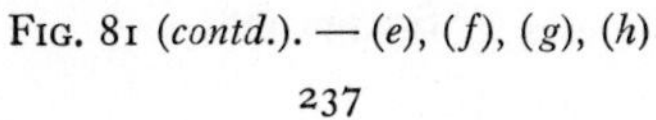
FIG. 81 (*contd.*). — (*e*), (*f*), (*g*), (*h*)

the Outer Hebrides and correlates closely with the belt of low temperatures already noted on Fig. 81*a*. Both belts lie across the centre of the col. Relative humidities fall to about 85% eastwards and westwards from this belt, but rise again in a few local coastal areas to 95 and 100%. The driest air was over Northern Ireland where relative humidities were of the order of 70%.

Winds were generally light in force with local calms reported, and the large arrows on Fig. 81*e* summarise the four main directions of air flows associated the col, within whose centre calms were reported (e.g. Renfrew). " Past " and " present weather " details (Fig. 81*d*) suggest yet another basis of differentiation between the col itself and also between the types of air flowing into, and out from, it. The col itself has all the conditions conducive to the formation of radiation fog,[1] viz. calm, or virtually calm, air, high humidities and clear skies. The showery weather with small cloud amounts indicates the arrival of Polar-Maritime air from north of the col. Conversely, to the south-west of the col the more continuous rain and overcast conditions suggest the arrival of Tropical (or modified " Polar ") air from the south. Much of the rain falling at stations in the South-west Peninsula has probably been increased by orographic effects.

Cloud, extensively of the stratus type *south* of the col, and of the large cumulus type *north* of it, again indicated Tropical and Polar air respectively. The col itself was cloudless (Fig. 81*g*).

The zone of cirro-stratus cloud over Eastern England is distinctive, and correlates with the area of influence of a northerly airflow in that area, which can be tracked back across Europe (Fig. 81, inset A) and would appear to be Tropical-Continental air (T3), relatively dry after its long land journey.

Visibilities range from " very good " to " excellent " in the air north of the col, deteriorate to " poor ", with fog in the col itself, and improve only to " moderate " to the south of the col, except for south-west Ireland where " very good " visibilities were reported. Again, this conforms with the idea of Polar air located to the north, and Tropical air to the south, of the col.

There is every suggestion of the standard weather features associated with a frontless col in winter viz. calm, or virtually, calm conditions of a flat pressure field, very light winds, radiation

[1] See pp. 188.

fog formation under conditions of little cloud and high humidity. Also flanking the col there is every evidence of contrasts in types of air mass involved in the adjacent circulations. The steady and slightly rising barometer and the slight infilling of the two flanking areas of low pressure are evidence of stability and continuity in the col itself which however was moving very slowly north-eastwards.

Past Synoptic Situations

Inset A, Fig. 81 shows how "Low Q" (996 millibars) had developed by 1200 hours on 12th January, 1956, some 400 miles south-west of Ireland. "Low E" (984 millibars) was situated between Scotland and Norway and its secondary, "Low P" (992 millibars), was situated over Kent. Pressure was relatively high (1,006 millibars) near Iceland. By 1200 hours on the 13th January, 1956 (one day later), Low Q had deepened to 998 millibars and Low E had filled in to 996 millibars. Further, Low P had moved north-eastwards and had been replaced by anticyclonic conditions (1,016 millibars) over Western Europe and South-east England. Pressure near Iceland had become even higher at 1,024 millibars. Thus was created between the two high pressure centres to the north-west and south-east, and the two low pressure centres to the south-west and north-east, the col which has been examined as it was at 0000 hours (midnight) on the 12th–13th of January, 1956.

Upper Air Data

In inset B, Fig. 81 upper air data have been plotted for Leuchars (0200 hours), Hemsby (0200 hours), Camborne (0240 hours) and Stornoway (0200 hours) on the 14th January, 1956. The weather situation since 0000 hours on the 14th January, 1956, analysed above, had changed but little by 0200–0300 hours on the same date, so upper air data for these four stations may be reasonably referred to the situation at 0000 hours shown on Fig. 81, p. 235. Note, first of all, the marked inversions of temperature at the ground reported at all four stations. The effects of rapid cooling of the ground surface under clear, and virtually calm, conditions is shown especially well at Hemsby, Leuchars and Stornoway. At Camborne, however, skies were overcast and in all probability rain was falling ;

an isothermal layer[1] is shown extending from the ground surface up to 975 millibars.

The four stations selected reveal contrasts in upper air conditions inside the col (Leuchars), north of the col (Stornoway), south-east of the col (Hemsby) and south-west of the col (Camborne). Inside the col at Leuchars cold, very stable air is indicated on the graph; above 8,000 feet (750 millibars) at about which height a minor cloud layer may have developed (it was definitely reported at 0600 hours) air is very dry (29% relative humidity). At Stornoway on the northern edge of the col, cold air, inevitably Polar (P1), was reported; it was only just stable and certainly less dry in its lower layers than the air at Leuchars. In contrast, warmer air was reported at Camborne and Hemsby. At Camborne reference to inset A, Fig. 81 suggests that air arriving over the South-west Peninsula was associated with Low Q and has come from relatively southerly latitudes (40° S.). It gives every appearance of warmed Maritime air (P7); upper air data at Camborne show high temperatures and high humidities (84–100% relative humidity range between 1,000 millibars and 630 millibars, i.e. 0 feet and 12,000 feet) and conditions of slight instability in some lower layers but general stability above 800 millibars (6,000 feet). Now at Hemsby similarly warm air is shown but above 750 millibars (8,000 feet), where there was in all probability a cloud layer, the air is very dry indeed, e.g. 22%, 15% relative humidity. Air is generally quite stable. Reference to inset A, Fig. 81 suggests this may be classified as Tropical-Continental air which has come across France from the Western Mediterranean area (T3).

Thus the presence and intermixture of several types of air about the col in question has been demonstrated.

[1] See p. 132, footnote 1.

Appendix I

OTHER EXAMPLES

Note : Except where marked *, †, or ‡ the examples are for 0600 hours G.M.T.

* signifies 1200 hours G.M.T.
† signifies 1800 hours G.M.T.
‡ signifies 0000 hours G.M.T.

Polar-Maritime Direct P1 and P2

27/6/54	13/1/55	8/6/56	11/4/57
25/10/54	6/2/55	5/10/56	5/5/57
	11/2/55	25/10/56	17/5/57
	19/5/55		24/6/57

Polar-Maritime P3–P7 (inclusive)

26/4/50	9/7/53	17/1/54	17/12/56	9/1/57*
		19/9/54		26/1/57*
		28/11/54		15/2/57*
				20/3/57*
				10/5/57

Polar-Continental A1 and A2

23/12/50	28/3/52	27/1/54	3/1/55	11/2/56	14/1/57
	29/3/52		18/2/55	22/2/56	7/4/57
			23/2/55	11/3/56	15/6/57
			11/3/55		

Tropical-Maritime T1 and T2

5/8/53	13/10/56	4/1/57†
12/10/53	3/12/56	16/3/57

Tropical-Continental T3 and T4

5/7/52	18/12/53	13/3/54	22/9/56

Warm Front

30/9/50 29/11/51 16/12/52 15/1/53 21/2/54 12/12/56 4/1/57*
18/11/50 15/10/54 7/1/57*
25/1/57*
4/2/57*
18/4/57
27/6/57‡

Cold Front

5/11/49 5/9/50‡ 17/1/51 2/9/54 10/1/55 9/1/57‡
13/12/49 6/10/54‡ 18/3/57‡
18/4/57†

Mature Warm-Sector Depression

26/2/51 30/3/53 25/3/55
19/5/53

Occluding Depression

8/2/51 2/8/54 7/2/55 4/1/57‡
30/12/51 31/1/57*
23/2/57*
8/3/57*
9/3/57*

Warm Occlusion

7/2/54 29/1/57
10/2/54 30/1/57
17/2/54 11/2/57
13/2/57
24/2/57

Cold Occlusion

6/9/54 23/11/54

Bent-Back Occlusion

24/3/55

Frontless, Decayed Depression

2/8/50 31/12/56

Anticyclone Winter (Clear)

6/3/50 2/2/53 18/4/55 10/1/57†
8/3/50 3/2/53
5/3/53

Anticyclone Winter (Cloudy)

23/2/52 15/3/53
8/10/53

Anticyclone Summer (Clear)

12/5/50 2/6/54 20/5/57†
2/7/50 7/5/54 2/7/57
31/7/54

Anticyclone Summer (Cloudy)

16/6/49 27/10/50 14/7/51 18/5/53 2/6/54 23/6/56
7/5/54

Secondary

26/4/50
11/7/50 15/5/57

Trough

26/2/51 11/5/52 10/5/55 12/1/56 16/2/57†

Ridge

24/6/53 18/1/55 10/2/57*
24/4/57‡
20/6/57

Col

16/5/55 21/2/57
1/7/57

Appendix 2

A SELECTION OF SYMBOLS USED ON WEATHER MAPS

(Taken from M.O. 515, Instructions for the Preparation of Weather Maps, 1954, H.M.S.O. Tables III and IV, by permission of the Director-General, Meteorological Office, London. Copyright H.M. Stationery Office.)

PRESENT WEATHER (ww)

PRECIPITATION

Drizzle

- , slight intermittent.
- , , slight continuous.
- ,/, moderate intermittent.
- ,‘, moderate continuous.
- ,/,/, thick intermittent.
- ,‘,, thick continuous.

Showers

- •/▽ slight rain.
- •/▽ moderate or heavy rain.
- •/•/▽ violent rain.
- •/*/▽ slight rain and snow.
- •/*/▽ moderate or heavy rain and snow.
- */▽ slight snow.
- */▽ moderate or heavy snow.

Rain

- • slight intermittent.
- • • slight continuous.
- •/• moderate intermittent
- •˙• moderate continuous.
- •/•/• heavy intermittent.
- •˙•/• heavy continuous.
- •/* rain or drizzle and snow, slight (sleet).
- */•/* rain or drizzle and snow, moderate or heavy (sleet)

Fall of Snowflakes

- * slight intermittent.
- * * slight continuous.
- */* moderate intermittent.
- *˙* moderate continuous.
- */*/* heavy intermittent.
- *˙*/* heavy continuous.

Fog

(≡) distant.

patches

sky discernable } becoming thinner during preceding hour.
sky not discernable

sky discernable } no appreciable change during preceding hour.
sky not discernable

sky discernable } becoming thicker during preceding hour.
sky not discernable

mist.

shallow fog in patches.

PHENOMENA DURING THE HOUR PRECEDING OBSERVATION
(plotted to the right of the past weather symbol in black (w))

drizzle.

rain.

snow.

rain and snow.

showers of rain.

showers of snow.

showers of hail.

≡ fog.

thunderstorm.

CLOUD AMOUNT (N)

Cloudless.

$\frac{1}{8}$th of sky covered.

$\frac{2}{8}$ths of sky covered.

$\frac{3}{8}$ths of sky covered.

$\frac{4}{8}$ths of sky covered.

$\frac{5}{8}$ths of sky covered.

$\frac{6}{8}$ths of sky covered.

$\frac{7}{8}$ths of sky covered.

Sky entirely clouded: overcast.

Sky obscured, or cloud amount cannot be estimated.

PAST WEATHER (W)

○ Cloud covering half or less of sky throughout the appropriate period : i.e. little or no cloud.

◐ Cloud covering more than half of sky during part of appropriate period, and covering one half or less during part of the period : i.e. much cloud but not overcast.

● Cloud covering more than half of sky throughout appropriate period : i.e. very cloudy or overcast.

Sandstorm, duststorm or drifting snow.

≡ Fog or thick haze.

, Drizzle.

• Rain.

* Snow or rain and snow mixed (sleet).

▽ Shower(s).

Thunderstorm(s) with or without precipitation.

CLOUD TYPES

Form of Low Cloud (C_L)

Ragged *cumulus* other than bad weather, i.e. "*fair weather cumulus* ", or cumulus with *little vertical development* and seemingly flattened (indicating atmospheric stability), or both.

Cumulus of *moderate or strong vertical development*, generally with protuberances in the form of domes or towers, either accompanied or not by the other cumulus or by stratocumulus, all having their bases at the same level.

Cumulonimbus (*well but not fully developed*) the summits of which, at least partially, lack sharp outlines, but are neither clearly fibrous neither cirriform nor in the form of an anvil ; cumulus, stratocumulus or stratus may be present.

Stratocumulus formed by the spreading out of cumulus : cumulus may also be present.

Stratocumulus not proceeding from the spreading out of cumulus.

— *Stratus* in a more or less continuous sheet or layer, or in ragged shreds, or both, but no stratus fractus of bad weather.

--- *Stratus fractus* of bad weather (scud) or cumulus fractus of bad weather (pannus), or both ; usually below altostratus or nimbostratus. By " bad weather " is meant the conditions which generally exist before, during or after precipitation.

Cumulus and stratocumulus, other than those formed from the spreading out of cumulus ; the base of cumulus is at different level from that of stratocumulus.

Cumulonimbus (fully developed), the upper part of which is clearly fibrous (cirriform), often in the form of an anvil ; either accompanied or not by cumulus, stratocumulus, stratus or pannus.

Form of Medium Cloud (C_M)

Altostratus (*thin*,) the greatest part of which is semi-transparent ; through this part the sun or moon may be weakly visible as through ground glass.

Altostratus (*thick*), the greatest part of which is sufficiently dense to hide the sun (or moon), or *nimbostratus*.

ω *Altocumulus* (*thin*), the greatest part of which is semi-transparent, other than crenelated or in cumuliform tufts ; the various elements of the cloud change but slowly and are all at a single level.

Patches of semi-transparent *altocumulus* (often in the form of almonds or fishes) which are at one or more levels ; the elements of this cloud are continuously changing of aspect.

(*Thin*) Semi-transparent *altocumulus in bands* or *altocumulus in one more or less continuous layer* progressively invading the sky ; these altocumulus clouds generally thicken as a whole. The layer may be opaque or double with a second sheet.

Altocumulus proceeding from the spreading out of cumulus.

Any one of the following cases :

(*a*) *Altocumulus* in two or more layers, usually opaque in places and not progressively invading the sky.

(*b*) Opaque layer of *altocumulus* not progressively invading the sky.

(*c*) *Altocumulus* co-existing with *altostratus* or *nimbostratus* or with *both.*

Altocumulus (*castellatus*), i.e. with sprouts in the form of small towers or battlements, or altocumulus having the aspect of cumuliform tufts.

Altocumulus, generally at several layers in a chaotic sky ; dense cirrus is usually present.

FORM OF HIGH CLOUD (C_H)

Cirrus in the form of filaments, strands or hooks, not progressively invading the sky (often called "*mares' tails*").

Dense cirrus in patches or entangled sheaves which usually do not increase and sometimes seem to be the remains of the upper part of cumulonimbus ; or *cirrus with sproutings* in the form of towers or battlements or having the aspect of cumuliform tufts.

Cirrus, often in the form of an anvil, either the remains of the *upper parts of cumulonimbus or parts of distant cumulonimbus*, the cumuliform portions of which cannot be seen.

Cirrus in the form of *hooks or of filaments*, or both, progressively invading the sky ; they generally become denser as a whole.

Cirrus, often in bands converging towards one or two points of the horizon, *and cirrostratus* or *cirrostratus only* ; in either case they are progressively invading the sky, and generally growing denser as a whole, but the continuous veil *does not reach 45° above the horizon.*

Cirrus, often in bands converging towards one or two points of the horizon, and *cirrostratus* or *cirrostratus only* ; in either case they are progressively invading the sky, and generally growing denser as a whole, but the continuous veil *exceeds 45° above the horizon* without the sky being totally covered.

Veil of cirrostratus completely covering the sky.

Cirrostratus not progressively invading the sky and not completely covering the sky.

Cirrocumulus alone or *cirrocumulus* accompanied by *cirrus* or *cirrostratus*, or both, but cirrocumulus is the predominant cirriform cloud.

CLOUD FORMS AND ABBREVIATIONS

Low Cloud

- *Cumulus* = Cu.
- *Cumulonimbus* = Cb.
- *Stratus* = St.
- *Stratocumulus* = Sc.
- *Nimbostratus* = Ns.
- *Stratus-Fractus* = Fs.

Medium Cloud.

- *Altocumulus* = Ac.
- *Altostratus* = As.

High Cloud

- *Cirrus* = Ci.
- *Cirrocumulus* = Cc.
- *Cirrostratus* = Cs.

Bibliography

Abercromby, R. 1883. *Principles of Forecasting by means of Weather Charts.*
Admiralty Weather Manual, W 9. 1938. H.M.S.O. (Reprinted 1953.)
Air Ministry. *Elementary Meteorology for Aircrew.* 1954. A.P. 3307.
Belasco, J. E. 1952. "Characteristics of Air Masses over the British Isles." Air Ministry. *Meteorological Office Geophysical Memoir* 87. M.O. 530*b*. H.M.S.O.
Bergeron, T. 1928. *Geophys. Publikasjoner. Norske. Videnskaps. Akad.*, Oslo, Vol. V, No. 6.
Bilham, E. G. 1938. *The Climate of the British Isles.* Macmillan.
Bjerknes, J. & Solberg, H. 1922. "Life Cycle of Cyclones and the Polar Front Theory of Atmospheric Circulation." *Geofysiske Publikationer*, Vol. 3, No. 1.
Brunt, D. and Douglas, C. K. M. e.g. 1928. "The Modification of the Strophic Balance for Changing Pressure Distribution and its Effect on Rainfall." *Mem. Roy. Met. Soc.*, VIII, No. 22.
Meethan, A. R. 1955. "Know your Fog." *Weather*, Vol. 10, pp. 103–5.
Meteorological Office Publications :
Averages of Temperature for Great Britain and Northern Ireland, 1921–50. 1953. M.O. 571, H.M.S.O.
Book of Normals of Meteorological Elements for the British Isles for Periods Ending 1915. 1919. M.O. 236, H.M.S.O.
Climatological Atlas for the British Isles, 1952. M.O. 488, H.M.S.O.
Cloud Forms (International Classification), 6th Edition, 1949, H.M.S.O.
Hygrometric Tables. 1940. 4th Edition. M.O. 265, H.M.S.O.
Instructions for Meteorological Telegraphy. 1943. M.O. 191/1, H.M.S.O.
Instructions for the Preparation of Weather Maps. 1954. 2nd Edition. M.O. 515, H.M.S.O.
Meteorological Observers Handbook. 1954. M.O. 191, H.M.S.O.
The Meteorological Glossary. 1939. 3rd Edition. M.O. 225ii (A.P. 897), H.M.S.O.
The Weather Map. 1939. 3rd Edition. M.O. 225i, H.M.S.O. (Reprinted 1950).
Weather Map. An Introduction to Weather Forecasting. 1956. 4th Edition. M.O. 595, H.M.S.O.
Miller, A. A. 1953. *Climatology.* (8th Edition.) Methuen, London.

Miller, A. A. "Air Mass Climatology." *Geography*, Vol. XXXVIII, Pt. 2, 1953, p. 61.

Petterssen, S. 1940. *Weather Analysis and Forecasting*, (1st Edition). McGraw-Hill.

Petterssen, S. 1956. *Weather Analysis and Forecasting*, (2nd Edition). Vols. I & II. McGraw-Hill.

Pick, W. H. 1938. *A Short Course on Elementary Meteorology*. M.O. 247, H.M.S.O.

Shaw, N. & Lempfert, R, G. K. 1906. *The Life History of Surface Air Currents*. M.O. 174.

Strahler, A. N. 1951. *Physical Geography*. John Wiley & Sons Inc., New York.

Sutcliffe, R. C. 1948. *Meteorology for Aviators*. M.O. 432 (A.P. 1699), H.M.S.O.

Other Reading

Abercrombie, R. & Goldie, A. R. 1934. *Weather*. London.

Brunt, D. 1942. *Weather Study*. Nelson, London. (Reprinted 1956.)

Brunt, D. 1939. *Physical and Dynamical Meteorology*. Cambridge.

Douglas, A. C. 1943. *Cloud Reading for Pilots*. Murray, London.

Grant, H. D. 1944. *Cloud and Weather Atlas*. New York.

Hare, K. 1953. *The Restless Atmosphere*. Hutchinson.

Horrocks, N. K. 1956. *Physical Geography and Climatology*. Chapter X. Longmans.

Haurwitz, B. & Austin, J. M. 1944. *Climatology*. New York.

Kendrew, W. G. 1949. *Climatology*. Oxford.

Kimble, G. 1952. *The Weather* (Pelican Books).

Ludlam, F. H. & Scorer, R. S. 1954. *Further Outlook*. Allan Wingate, London.

Ludlam, F. H. & Scorer, R. S. 1957. *Cloud Study ; a Pictorial Guide*. Murray, London.

Manley, G. 1952. *Climate and the British Scene*. Collins.

Penman, H. L. 1955. *Humidity*. Institute of Physics, London.

Shaw, N. 1940. *Forecasting Weather*. London.

Shaw, N. 1940. *The Drama of the Weather*. Cambridge.

Trewartha, G. T. 1945. *An Introduction to Climate and Weather*. New York. (3rd Edition 1954.)

INDEX

Note. Roman figures refer to page numbers ; italics refer to figure numbers

PRINTED IN GREAT BRITAIN BY ROBERT MACLEHOSE AND CO. LTD
THE UNIVERSITY PRESS, GLASGOW